MODERN
VERY HIGH PRESSURE
TECHNIQUES

ENGLAND:	BUTTERWORTH & CO. (PUBLISHERS) LTD. LONDON: 88 Kingsway, W.C.2.
AFRICA:	BUTTERWORTH & CO. (AFRICA) LTD. DURBAN: 33/35 Beach Grove
AUSTRALIA:	BUTTERWORTH & CO. (AUSTRALIA) LTD. SYDNEY: 6-8 O'Connell Street MELBOURNE: 473 Bourke Street BRISBANE: 240 Queen Street
CANADA:	BUTTERWORTH & CO. (CANADA) LTD. TORONTO: 1367 Danforth Avenue, 6
NEW ZEALAND:	BUTTERWORTH & CO. (NEW ZEALAND) LTD. WELLINGTON: 49/51 Ballance Street AUCKLAND: 35 High Street
U.S.A.:	BUTTERWORTH INC. WASHINGTON, D.C.: 7235 Wisconsin Avenue, 14

MODERN

VERY HIGH PRESSURE

TECHNIQUES

Edited by

R. H. WENTORF, JR., PH. D.

Research Associate
General Electric Research Laboratory
Schenectady, New York, U.S.A.

LONDON
BUTTERWORTHS
1962

Suggested U.D.C. No.: 66·083·2·001·5

Suggested additional U.D.C. No.: 621–186·5

Printed in Great Britain by Love & Malcomson Ltd., Brighton Road, Redhill, Surrey

PREFACE

THE purpose of this volume is to bring together under one cover some descriptions and discussions of the main forms of apparatus which have been developed for very high pressure work in various laboratories throughout the world. The boundary between 'very high pressure' and plain 'high pressure' is not well defined, but is usually regarded as lying near 20 kilobars or 20,000 atmospheres. Below this pressure, fairly straightforward experimental techniques are adequate, but above it, in the very high pressure region, special techniques become necessary for both the generation and utilization of pressure, and a wide variety of apparatus has been created in order to perform experiments in this region.

In this book the main emphasis is on apparatus, but some experimental results have been included in order to illustrate the uses and potentials of each particular technique. It is possible that this volume will be the first of a series which in the future will deal relatively less with the apparatus and relatively more with experimental results.

The great diversity of methods now used in very high pressure work makes a detailed, comprehensive treatment of this field rather difficult for a single author. Furthermore, in a field as vigorous and expanding as this one, a single view may not prove to be as helpful as a number of different viewpoints, each with its own characteristic flavour, each written by an expert and originator in a section of the field.

For this reason the book has taken the form of a collection of papers on related topics. As might be expected, a slight overlapping of subject matter has occurred here and there; this is the natural result of each author developing his subject in what he regarded as the best way. The resulting treatment of the field is probably not exhaustive, for the book would otherwise be too bulky. The aims have been to acquaint a newcomer to the field with the main streams of work, and to provide a fairly up to date set of key references to the high pressure literature.

The editor wishes to express his gratitude to the contributors to this volume for their thorough treatment of their topics, which they, as individuals, understand so completely. The excellence which the reader will find is the result of their labours, both in the laboratory and at the writing-desk.

INTRODUCTION

I. Historical Comments

DURING the last ten years, increasing numbers of persons have begun work in the field of very high pressure. Earlier, before this period of increased activity, Professor P. W. Bridgman of Harvard University and a few others worked virtually alone in this field. Definite impetus for increased activity in very high pressure research has come largely from the successful synthesis in a few laboratories in the early 1950's of several minerals of special geologic or economic importance. Included in these were diamond, certain garnets, kyanite, and jadeite. Consequently it became apparent that very high pressure research had been relatively neglected in relation to its importance, and within a few years many laboratories took up very high pressure research work, not only in order to synthesize materials which might be prepared only at high pressures, but also in order to study the behaviour of matter while it is subjected to high pressures.

II. General Literature References

A book such as this would be incomplete and less useful in its role of helping to provide keys to the literature if it did not mention the other currently available works in the field of high pressure.

The best known of these, a classic in the field, is P. W. Bridgman's 'The Physics of High Pressure', published in 1949 by G. Bell and Sons, London. Every worker interested in high pressure will welcome the forthcoming collection of all of Professor Bridgman's papers on high pressure; this will be published soon by Harvard Press.

During June, 1960, a symposium on high pressures was held at Lake George, N.Y. The many rich and diverse papers presented at this symposium were published in 1961 by John Wiley and Sons, New York, under the title 'Progress in Very High Pressure Research'.

Other recent texts of note include 'High Pressure Technology', by E. W. Comings, published by McGraw-Hill, New York, in 1956, and 'Physico-Chemical Effects of Pressure', by S. P. Hamann, published by Butterworths, London, in 1957.

A significant number of Russian workers have made contributions to the field of very high pressures during the past few years. Judging from the work which they have published so far, it appears that the types of apparatus used by them are not essentially different from those described in this book, although probably many of them were created independently.

III. Pressure Measurement

Nearly all very high pressure work has been reported in terms of three units of pressure: kilogrammes per square centimetre (kg/cm^2), bars (or kilobars, kb), or atmospheres. Each of these units of pressure is described in terms of the others in Appendix A. Recently there has been a tendency to express the results of high pressure work in terms of bars or kilobars, and it is hoped that this trend towards convenience will continue.

All those who work in the field of very high pressures know well the difficulties of ascertaining exactly what pressures exist in their experiments. Difficulties arise in the reckoning of forces and areas as higher pressures are reached because of the distortion of the materials of construction and because of friction between the moving parts and in the compressed materials. Pressures of up to 25 kilobars, in the vicinity of which bismuth metal exhibits several different structures, may be determined to within less than 1 per cent by refined free piston gauges. For pressures above 25 kilobars, the best procedure, pending further developments, is to use as a basis of calibration or reference certain sharp volume, phase, or electrical resistance transitions which occur in certain substances at convenient temperatures, usually 25°C. In the future, after the pressures at which these transitions take place have been satisfactorily determined, the work which employed these transitions as pressure reference points may easily be put on a firm basis with respect to the absolute values of the pressures involved. The problems of pressure calibrations are treated in greater detail in Chapters 1 and 2.

The most convenient and popular of these reference transitions are listed in Appendix B, together with the approximate pressures at which they occur. Most of the phenomena below 100 kilobars were discovered by P. W. Bridgman; many of the phenomena above 100 kilobars were first noted by H. G. Drickamer and his colleagues. The experimental aspects of the study of the transitions above 100 kilobars are thoroughly discussed in Chapter 2.

Recently there has been a downward revision of some of the old electrical resistance transitions between 30 and 80 kb. These were originally determined by Bridgman in a simple anvil apparatus which, it has developed, was unfortunately subject to unusual pressure distributions at higher pressures. Thus the electrical resistance transition in barium, which was earlier reported to occur at 77 kb, is now believed to be the same physical event as the volume transition at 58–60 kb. This assignment is based upon the work of Drickamer *et al.* described in Chapter 2 as well as upon simultaneous measurements of the volume and resistance of barium in the General Electric Research Laboratory. In similar fashion, a wealth of evidence from various laboratories, when taken together, has reduced the electrical resistance transition pressure in thallium from 43·5 kb to about 37 kb, and the pressure of the resistance maximum in caesium from 53 kb to about 42 kb. The pressures of the transitions in bismuth near 25 kb remain quite firm, having been determined with great care by Bridgman in 1940 and again by Kennedy and LaMori in 1960.

Readers should bear these revisions of the pressure reference scale in mind when reading papers published between 1952 and 1960.

At extremes of temperature the accurate determination of pressure becomes even more difficult than at 25°C because of the various effects of temperature upon compressibility, rigidity, viscosity, and phase transitions. The reader is referred to Chapters 5 and 8, and Chapter 10 for a more complete discussion of these problems at high and low temperatures, respectively.

IV. A Look Ahead

At the present time the maximum pressures attainable in the laboratory are of the order of 5,000 kilobars in dynamic (shock wave) experiments, and somewhat over 400 kilobars in small, statically loaded specimens. High as these pressures may seem, and difficult as they are to achieve, they are yet relatively low compared with the pressures existing inside most stars, and they are only moderately effective in altering the electronic clouds surrounding most atoms. An increase in the dynamic pressure range is primarily dependent upon the use of more energetic explosives; atomic fission or fusion explosions set the ultimate limit. An increase in the static pressure range is dependent upon the use of stronger confining materials, e.g. diamond, and upon a better understanding of the physical behaviour of materials at high pressures so that their properties may be used advantageously. So far little use has been made of strong magnetic fields, and one may expect some advances in this direction.

A consideration of the internal pressures of various substances indicates that any new materials which may be prepared at high pressures and brought back to room pressure will be strong and hard. Since the number of elements having atoms small enough to participate in such structures is limited, the number of such new, recoverable very high pressure materials would also seem to be limited.

Nevertheless, the lure of the unknown and the prospect of forcibly altering the electronic environments of atoms will prove to be sufficiently attractive to sustain progress to ever higher pressures and ever greater understanding and we may look forward to much fascinating work in the years to come.

July, 1961   Robert H. Wentorf, Jr.

CONTENTS

CONTENTS

CONTENTS

CONTENTS

GENERAL PRINCIPLES OF HIGH PRESSURE APPARATUS DESIGN

F. P. BUNDY

General Electric Research Laboratory, Schenectady, N.Y.

I. Introduction

IN THIS chapter only apparatus capable of pressures over 25 kilobars will be considered. Since at these pressures practically all materials are solids at room temperature, the containment of gases and liquids need not be discussed, at least in terms of seals and fittings. Such subjects have been adequately dealt with in other publications by experienced workers in the field, such as Bridgman[1], Comings[2], and Hamann[3]. The intention is to concentrate on apparatus in which samples of materials can be subjected to very high pressures and temperatures for periods of time much longer than required for thermal equilibrium. Since all substances are compressible, the pressure of a sample of material can be increased in a static equilibrium manner only by enclosing it in some kind of pressure-resisting chamber and then decreasing its volume. In a practical apparatus this means that at least one wall of the chamber must be movable, and that the joints between the parts that move relative to each other must be sealed so that none of the contents of the chamber can leak out. Then, the pressures attainable are limited only by the amount of compression of the sample or by the breaking of the wall structure.

All construction materials have a limited range of stresses in which they behave elastically and a larger range of stresses in which they yield plastically without actually breaking. *Table 1* lists some nominal properties of typical die steels and several grades of cemented carbide. In actual high pressure apparatus applications, the rigidity modulus of the construction materials is also an important factor, as demonstrated by the fact that in certain parts 55A Carboloy cemented carbide performs much better than hard steel even though the ultimate strength of 55A is slightly less, and its proportional limit considerably less, than steel.

II. Thick-Walled Cylinders

Experience with high pressure apparatus designs has shown clearly that geometry and stress distribution are fully as important as the nominal strength of the materials used. For example, in thick-walled cylinders in which the outside diameter is several times the inside diameter, application of pressure to the inside wall produces greater hoop tension stress at the inner wall than at the outer wall. Thus the plastic flow stress is reached at the inner wall first, and as the bore pressure increases the outer wall sustains a greater and greater burden until it fails. The maximum confining strength of a thick-walled cylinder may be attained by prestressing the wall material such that at zero pressure loading the inner parts are under high hoop compression and the outer parts are under high hoop tension, and when the full pressure load

Table 1. Properties of Steel and Cemented Carbides

Material	Tension 10³ psi		Compression 10³ psi		Young's Mod. 10⁶ psi	Density g/cc	Coef. therm. exp.	Hardness R_A
	Ult.	Prop. lim.	Ult.	Prop. lim.				
Best die steels	350	260	600	260	32	8·2 to 8·6	7·1 × 10⁶	82.0
55A Carboloy*	210	80	610	80	80	14·2	3·4	88·2
44A Carboloy	—	—	648	210	100	14·9	2·8	91·0
883 Carboloy	—	—	615	286	105	14·9	2·8	92·0
999 Carboloy	—	—	815	—	110	15·2	—	92·6

* Trademark of the General Electric Company.

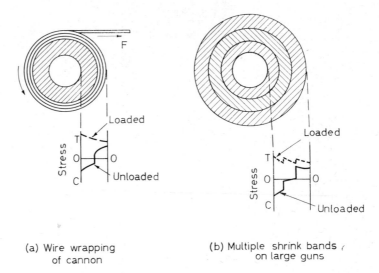

(a) Wire wrapping of cannon

(b) Multiple shrink bands on large guns

Figure 1. Prestressing of walls of cylindrical vessels by wire wrapping or shrink-fitting of rings

is applied all parts of the wall rise to a hoop tension just short of the proportional limit (or yield point).

Historically this was first done on guns by wrapping them with high-strength piano wire under tension so that the inner layer of the gun barrel was under compression and the wire winding under tension, as shown in Figure 1(a). Then upon firing, the gas pressure load caused the stress in the inner layer to rise from compression to tension and that of the wire to higher tension, all within the elastic limits so that the gun suffered no permanent dilation.

A second way, which is the one most used in pressure vessel construction today, is to make the cylindrical wall of two or more concentric layers, the dimensions being such that the inner layers must be forcibly shrunk into the outer layers to produce an initial stress distribution like that shown in *Figure 1(b)*.

A third method of prestressing thick-walled cylinders, called 'autofrettage', is illustrated in *Figure 2*. Here, the virgin unstressed cylinder is

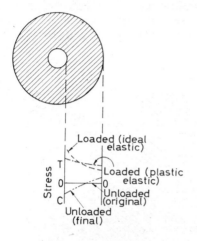

Figure 2. Prestressing a thick-walled pressure vessel by 'autofrettage' (Michels)

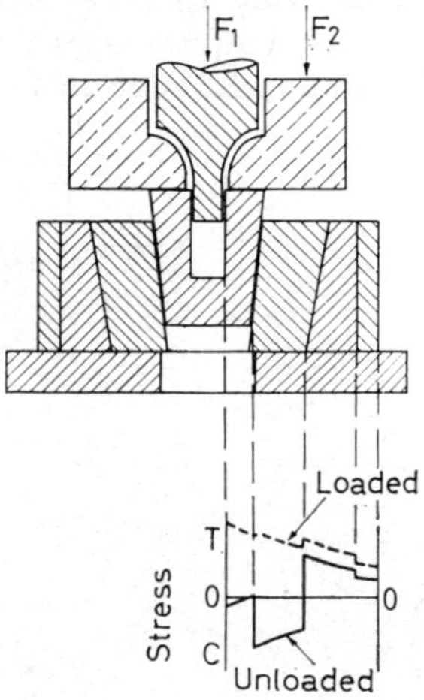

Figure 3. Progressive internal and external loading of pressure cylinder (Bridgman)

deliberately subjected to internal pressure great enough to cause plastic flow of the wall material just to the outermost parts. At this condition the hoop stress distribution in the walls is as shown for 'plastic–elastic' as compared to the theoretical 'ideal elastic'. Then when the bore pressure is removed the stress distribution reduces to 'unloaded final' with the inner parts under hoop compression and the outer parts under hoop tension. The vessel may then be subjected to bore pressures nearly as great as that of the original autofrettaging without exceeding elastic limits.

A fourth example of this principle of proper distribution of hoop stress with radius is an ingenious one by Bridgman[4], shown in *Figure 3*. In this case the innermost cylinder of the vessel is initially unstressed, while the outer two 'binding rings' have been forced together to give the hoop compression–tension distribution shown. The pressure chamber is then filled with the sample and the latter compressed by application of force F_1 to the piston. Simultaneous application of force F_2 to the inner part of the pressure vessel drives it into the outer binding ring set. The forces F_1 and F_2 are brought up together in such a ratio that the inner cylindrical vessel never exceeds its tensile strength. Bridgman reported[4] that steel vessels of this type could be

3

operated dozens of cycles to 50 kilobars without failure. The piston was the weakest part of this apparatus.

The radial supporting effect of the outer binding ring assemblies may be enhanced by increasing the sectional area of the outer rings. Examples of this will be shown later when higher pressure apparatuses are described.

III. High Pressure Pistons

The ultimate axial loading of cylindrical pistons of the best steel or cemented carbide is about 50 kilobars, or 750,000 psi (see *Table 1*). Failure is by shear when the side walls bulge under the terrific axial loading. There are two general ways of preventing this failure. The most direct is to subject the cylindrical wall to inward radial compression by a binding ring or by a hydrostatic medium under pressure. A second way is to replace the cylinder with a truncated cone so that the stress drops rapidly with axial distance

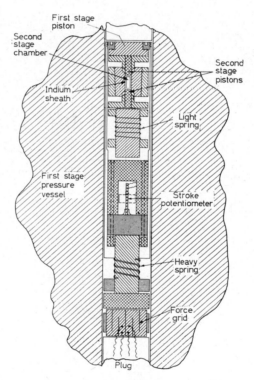

Figure 4. Assembly in Bridgman's two-stage $\Delta V/V_0$ apparatus

from the face. Both of these treatments present obvious difficulties regarding movement of the piston into the cylinder. Thus the close-fitting piston-cylinder concept must be abandoned or modified. Both paths, i.e. abandonment and modification, have been followed and successful apparatuses of both kinds, capable of pressures exceeding 100 kilobars, have been developed by various workers. Some typical examples will be presented later in this chapter.

Before abandoning the piston-and-cylinder concept, one other principle can be invoked, that of cascading; that is, putting one pressure vessel within another so that each stage of pressure vessel has to sustain only the pressure difference between it and the next outer vessel. An immediately obvious characteristic, and difficulty, of this system is that the size of the innermost, highest pressure chamber gets rapidly smaller with the number of stages. To date, the practical limit for useful work has been two stages. Bridgman did some excellent work on the compressibilities of materials up to 100 kilobars[5,6] using a two-stage apparatus illustrated in *Figure 4*. In the drawing only the bore of the first stage is shown, the first stage being of the general type shown in *Figure 3*. The second stage is a cylinder with moving pistons in each end, located at the top of the assembly. The other parts contained within the first stage are a slide-wire potentiometer to indicate accurately the stroke of the second stage pistons, and a force grid which indicates electrically the force transmitted to the second stage pistons. In the second stage structure the inner cylinder and both pistons are made of cemented tungsten carbide, and both pistons and cylinder were backed by shrunk-on steel backing rings. The short parts of the carbide pistons not supported by steel are supported by the hydraulic pressure of the fluid in the first stage chamber.

IV. Multiple Piston Apparatus

If the idea of a cylindrical part of a pressure vessel is abandoned entirely, the pressure vessel walls must be the faces of an array of truncated conical or pyramidal pistons. If the arrays are symmetrical in space, they may be described as 'spherical'.

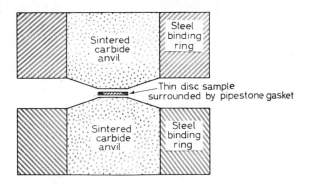

Figure 5. Bridgman flat face supported anvils

(i) Flat Face Anvils

The simplest possible device of this kind was developed and used by Bridgman[7], and is illustrated in *Figure 5*. The pressurized region is bounded by the flat faces of opposed, truncated pistons and by a thin, crushable gasket which is pinched between the rims of the piston faces. The gasket material used by Bridgman was pipestone, a reddish pyrophyllite type of natural stone. Other kinds of stone or certain metals may also be used for gaskets. The hard steel or cemented carbide pistons are surrounded by strong steel rings under high hoop tension so that the pistons are prestrained to a smaller diameter and greater length. When axial force is applied to push the pistons against the sample, the strain distribution becomes reversed so that a large loading and stress range is possible without breakage occurring. In most practical designs the loaded face area is about a tenth of the cross-sectional area of the body of the piston. Bridgman refers to this design concept as the 'principle of massive support'. Apparatus of this kind works easily up to 100 kilobars, and with some difficulties up to about 200 kilobars. Some have claimed pressures as high as 400 kilobars, on the basis of force/area values, but the actual area of contact under such high loading is subject to question.

Flat face anvil apparatus has been used mainly for room temperature work. Several investigators have used it for tests up to 600°C by heating the entire apparatus. Some higher temperature work has been done by inserting tiny, thin resistance heating elements in the thin sample between the anvil faces, but the temperatures attainable are strongly limited by the high thermal conduction of the anvils. Higher, but very transient, temperatures have been reached by flash-heating the sample with spot welding current equipment.

(ii) Tetrahedral Apparatus

The next most simple 'spherical' multi-piston apparatus is the tetrahedral one developed by Hall[8]. This consists essentially of four piston elements with blunt, three-sided, pyramidal ends and equilateral triangular faces which bound a tetrahedral volume (*Figure 6*). Means are provided for

Figure 6. Nest of tetrahedral pistons in Hall apparatus

subjecting each piston to thrust inward along its axis against the material to be pressurized, such as the hydraulic rams shown in *Figure 7*. The 'sample' is enclosed in a pyrophyllite stone tetrahedron (called the 'sample holder') which is about 10 per cent larger in edge dimensions than the piston faces (*Figure 8*). Thus when the piston faces engage the faces of the pyrophyllite 'sample holder', small gaps separate the flanks of neighbouring pistons and allow room for piston movement to compress the charge. As the pistons squeeze in on the enclosed material some of the pyrophyllite extrudes into the thin gaps between piston flanks to form a gasket structure which absorbs a small fraction of the thrust load. This automatically-formed 'flash-gasket' may be seen in *Figure 9*. The sample of material to be studied is generally

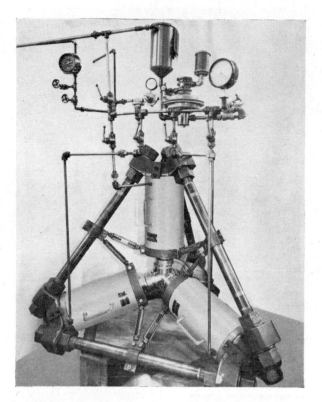

Figure 7. Tetrahedral hydraulic ram assembly in Hall apparatus

cylindrical in form and is placed with the axis of the cylinder between opposite edges of the tetrahedral sample holder, as shown in *Figure 8*. Electrical contact to the pistons is generally provided by strips of metal which lie across notches in the edges of the sample holder, as shown. This type of apparatus has been used successfully to pressures of about 100 kilobars and to temperatures limited only by the melting or reaction of the pyrophyllite material surrounding the heated core.

A modification of the original Hall tetrahedral apparatus, made at the U.S. National Bureau of Standards[9], is shown in *Figure 9*. This arrangement requires only one hydraulic ram, or press, which pushes downward on the top piston of the array shown in *Figure 10*. The counter-thrust is on the nest ring which supports the bottom three piston elements. The apex cone angle of the inner face of the nest ring is made 37° to match the normal tetrahedral angle plus the angle of sliding friction between steel and teflon. This allows a uniform inward movement of the pistons on the sample when thrust is applied to the top piston. The thin teflon sheets separating the bottom pistons from the nest ring provide electrical insulation as well as lubrication.

7

This apparatus has also been operated successfully up to the 100 kilobar level and sample core temperatures up to about 2,000°C.

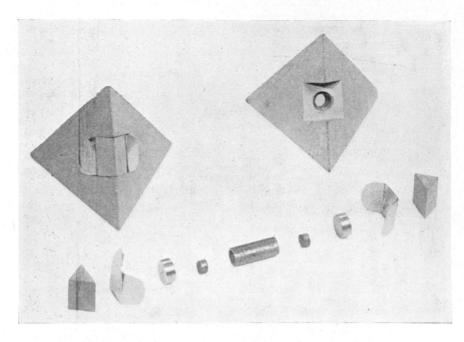

Figure 8. Pyrophyllite sample holder and parts for tetrahedral apparatus

Figure 9. NBS version of tetrahedral apparatus showing bottom three pistons in the nest ring

Figure 10. NBS tetrahedral apparatus showing all four pistons in place in the nest ring

(iii) Cubic Apparatus

The next member of the multiple piston family is the six-piston set. Here the six piston faces define a cubical pressurized volume. Each piston end is a truncated square pyramid with 90° apex angle. As in the case of the tetrahedral apparatus, the sample holder is made larger than the edge length of the piston faces in order to allow a gap between piston flanks for inward piston motion. Several variations of this cube apparatus have been developed and used. Some of these will be described.

Probably the first one was designed and built by von Platen (see Chapter 6) and used by the Swedish group at ASEA to make artificial diamonds[10]. This apparatus is shown diagrammatically in *Figure 11*. In this case the

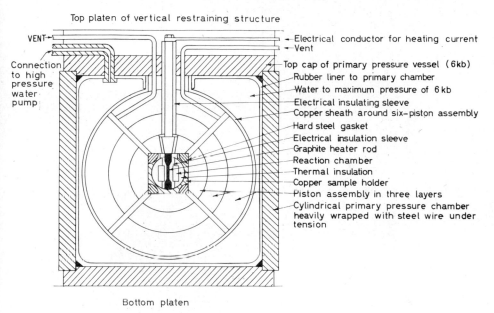

Top platen of vertical restraining structure

VENT →
Connection to high pressure water pump

— Electrical conductor for heating current
← Vent
— Top cap of primary pressure vessel (6kb)
— Rubber liner to primary chamber
— Water to maximum pressure of 6 kb
— Electrical insulating sleeve
— Copper sheath around six–piston assembly
— Hard steel gasket
— Electrical insulation sleeve
— Graphite heater rod
— Reaction chamber
— Thermal insulation
— Copper sample holder
— Piston assembly in three layers
— Cylindrical primary pressure chamber heavily wrapped with steel wire under tension

Bottom platen

Figure 11. Diagram of von Platen's cube apparatus

main body of the sample holder was of copper with hard steel bridges at the corners and edges to prevent leakage of the copper into the gaps between the pistons. An insulated electrical lead was brought into the sample holder through one of the piston assemblies. The six spherical segments which served as rams for the piston tips were surrounded by a fluid-tight spherical shell of copper. The gaps between segments at the outside were also bridged by hard steel caps. This entire spherical assembly was contained in a unique wire-wound pressure vessel, or autoclave, which could contain water to a pressure of 6 kilobars. As the face-area ratio of the spherical segment ram-piston assemblies was about 20, the pressure generated in the cube sample at the centre of the sphere could have been as high as 120 kilobars. Partial piston support by material extruding into the gaps between pistons would reduce this theoretical pressure somewhat. This was a large machine in which the pressurized cube was 7·5 cm on an edge, or over 400 cm³ in volume. Both electrical heating and thermite chemical heating of the sample core were used. Temperatures up to the melting point of graphite (greater than 4,000°K) were attained. One of the major difficulties of this machine was loading and unloading the high pressure assembly.

Figure 12 is a photograph of a Russian[11] six-piston cube apparatus. In this case each high pressure piston is backed by a hydraulic ram. It is relatively easy to load and unload the high pressure chamber by withdrawing one or more piston elements completely.

Figure 12. Photograph of Russian cube press apparatus

Griggs[12] has designed and developed a cube apparatus in which the six ram and piston assemblies are all supported by a single cube block of steel. The latter is bored through the face centres in the three principal directions. The hydraulic ram and piston assemblies are held in the main cubical block frame by a bayonet lock arrangement. This arrangement also ensures positive alignment and control of the pistons.

The high pressures group at the U.S. Bureau of Standards[9] has extended the principle of the nest ring of pistons, used in their tetrahedral apparatus, to a two-ring, six-anvil, cube apparatus. In this arrangement the diagonal of the cube sample lies along the common axis of the two nest rings (the axis of the hydraulic press used to pressurize the assembly). Preliminary runs with this machine indicate that it operates quite satisfactorily to pressures of the order of 100 kilobars, like its tetrahedral predecessor.

It is obvious that the multiple piston concept can be extended to even more pistons, such as eight for an octahedral arrangement, twelve for a dodecahedral arrangement, etc., but to the author's knowledge none of these more elaborate systems has been built. The more numerous the pistons, the smaller their apex angle becomes, and the less is the 'massive support' of the highly stressed piston face region. Thus it is questionable from the stress point of view, as well as from consideration of mechanical complication, whether or not more than six-piston (cube) sets are practical.

V. Development of the 'Belt' Apparatus

Returning now to the Bridgman flat face anvil apparatus (*Figure 5*), the steps of development from it to successful conical-piston, reinforced-cylinder

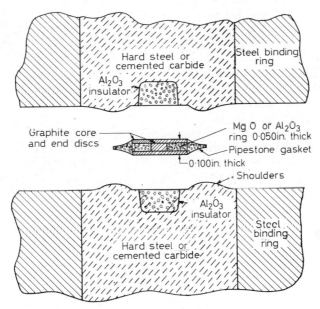

Figure 13. Cupped anvil assembly with thermal-insulation inserts and thicker sample

apparatus will be presented. This development was carried out at the General Electric Research Laboratory.

It has already been pointed out that the very thin sample of the flat face anvil apparatus does not lend itself to reactions at high temperature for prolonged periods of time because of temperature weakening of the anvils. The first step, therefore, was to thicken the centre part of the sample and insert some refractory thermal insulation in the centres of the anvils, as shown in *Figure 13*. The graphite core of the sample was heated by passage of current from the top anvil through the outer rim of the top graphite end disc, through the graphite core, and out through the rim of the bottom graphite disc to the bottom anvil. This apparatus worked quite successfully up to temperatures greater than 2,000°C and pressures up to about 25 kilobars. The pressure attainable was limited by the compression being stopped by the close approach of the shoulders of the opposing anvils. It was found that increasing the initial thickness of the sample and gasket did very little good because upon closing the anvils the excess gasket and sample would simply extrude out until the critical gasket locking thickness was reached.

One way of increasing the compression stroke without increasing the thickness of the gasket, suggested by H. T. Hall, is shown in *Figure 14*. As

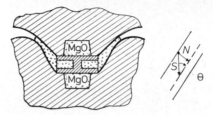

Figure 14. Conical gasket for increased stroke for given gasket thickness

shown by the geometry at the right of the drawing, a compression stroke S decreases the gasket thickness by only $N = S \sin \theta$; thus the main centre part of the sample can be compressed to a higher pressure. Pressures up to about 50 kilobars could be reached.

Experiments with laminated stone-and-metal gaskets in both the flat and conical gasket designs of *Figures 13* and *14* showed that the metal laminations

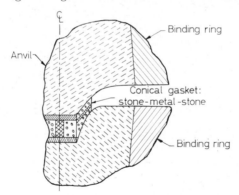

Figure 15. Conical gasket set with laminated stone-and-metal gaskets

gave the gaskets greater toughness and strength and made possible greater compression strokes than with stone alone, and thus the heated core part of the sample could be made thicker, and the attainable pressures higher, toward 60 kilobars. One such design is shown in *Figure 15*.

Another idea, also contributed by Hall, was to make the set double-ended, as shown in *Figure 16*, which automatically doubled the axial length of the heated core part of the sample. In this way, what had been the cupped anvil part of the apparatus, became a rough cylindrical component which had to be reinforced very heavily with prestressed binding rings in order to withstand the bursting pressure of the higly compressed sample. This

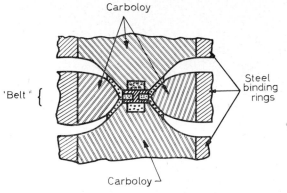

Figure 16. Double-ended anvil apparatus (Hall)

strong binding ring assembly, or belt, was the origin of the name which the apparatus carries to the present day—the 'belt apparatus'[14].

Figure 17 shows the belt apparatus in a more refined state of development. It consists essentially of two opposed, circumferentially supported conical pistons which compress a sample retained in a strongly reinforced cylinder,

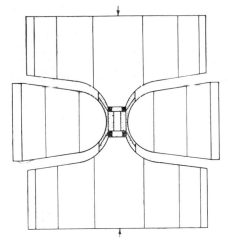

Figure 17. Hall's 'belt apparatus'

with the seal at each end comprised of conical, laminated stone-and-metal gaskets which crush and extrude as the compression stroke proceeds. The cylinder walls are insulated from the hot core by the pyrophyllite stone sample holder and 'flower pot'. The faces of the pistons are protected from the heat of the core by pyrophillite stone pills enclosed in hard steel 'current rings' which engage the rim of each piston. The core is heated by passage of electric current from the top piston, through the top current ring and end disc, through the core (or heater sleeve) of the sample, and out through the bottom end disc, current ring, and piston. The force to push the pistons together is provided by a simple, uniaxial hydraulic press. This apparatus is capable of pressures well over 100 kilobars, and temperatures limited only by melting or chemical reaction of the wall material surrounding the hot core. Most of the General Electric diamond synthesis development was carried out in this apparatus.

Another apparatus developed at the General Electric Research Laboratory, evolved from a combination of the Bridgman flat-face anvil and the simple piston and cylinder apparatus, and elaborated in detail by H. M. Strong, is shown in *Figure 18*. Experiments with short piston and cylinder apparatus showed that the pistons failed from lack of lateral support, while the cylinders (given strong circumferential support) failed from lack of axial support at the mouth region. As the concept of the sandwich gasket developed it became apparent that a thick multiple sandwich gasket might supply both of these support needs simultaneously. The idea was first tried using gaskets made up of flat rings contained between flat shoulders of a

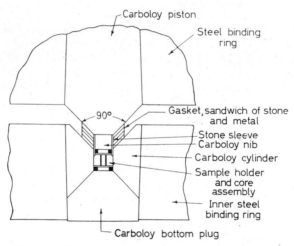

Figure 18. Strong's semi-piston and cylinder apparatus

piston element and flat shoulders of a cylinder element. It soon became clear that this arrangement gave adequate axial support to the cylinder element but not enough lateral support to the piston. The solution was to make this part of the structure conical so as to generate a greater inward thrust. The design shown in *Figure 18*, in which the cone apex angle is 90°, the piston nib L/D ratio a little less than one, and the outside diameter of the gasket assembly about two and a half times the nib diameter, is found to balance all the stresses quite well. Such an apparatus works satisfactorily to the same pressures and temperatures as the 'belt' apparatus, and a considerable amount of diamond synthesis research was done with it. This apparatus could be double-ended, giving a useful sample length of twice that shown. Such a double-ended apparatus would be very similar in appearance, and in stress distribution, to the belt apparatus. It is interesting from the philosophical point of view how nearly the same design was arrived at from two different paths of approach. Both designs satisfy the basic requirements of

14

prestressing, massive backing, large compression stroke with adequate sealing, and no excessively large stress gradients. Both are relatively easy to operate.

VI. Apparatus for Special Applications

A number of workers in the high pressure field have adapted their pressure apparatuses to special kinds of observations, such as for visual or infra-red optical measurements and x-ray diffraction measurements.

Drickamer and colleagues[15] have developed optical pressure apparatus with which they have measured the wavelength shift of absorption bands of various materials to pressures as high as about 200 kilobars. The apparatus is shown in Chapter 2 of this book, which describes the apparatus and work in detail.

Another class of pressure apparatus is that for x-ray diffraction studies of the crystal lattice structure of materials under pressure. In one type, rather standard hydrostatic pressure equipment is used for the 10 kilobar range. In these, the x-ray beam is brought into the pressure chamber through a

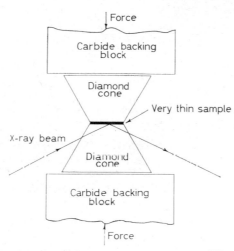

Figure 19. Flat face diamond anvil apparatus for x-ray diffraction work

beryllium window and the diffracted rays are either recorded on a film inside the pressure chamber[16,17], or brought out through a beryllium window to an external film holder[18,19]. In another type, miniature pressure vessels of diamond are used, the x-rays passing directly through the diamond vessel[20]. In one type of diamond apparatus a small hole is drilled through the diamond, perpendicular to an octahedral face, and the sample compressed in this hole between the faces of carbide or hard steel pistons. The incident x-ray beam enters through the diamond along a path perpendicular to the axis of the hole. The diffracted x-rays also go out through the diamond. The entire small pressure chamber is placed at the sample position in a standard x-ray diffraction equipment. This type of pressure apparatus proves to be capable of pressures up to 25 to 30 kilobars at best. A third type of pressure apparatus for x-ray diffraction work[21] is essentially a diamond, Bridgman, flat-face anvil arrangement as shown in *Figure 19*. The assembly shown in the drawing is contained within a clamping tube which is mounted at the sample site of an x-ray spectrometer. It is believed that pressures over 30 kilobars can be achieved with this apparatus.

Diamond 'squeezer' apparatus has also been used for infra-red transmission studies of materials (see Chapter 3). *Figure 20* is a schematic diagram of an apparatus developed at the U.S. National Bureau of Standards[22]. The anvils were made of special Type II diamonds which transmit over 80 per cent of radiation from 1 to 15 microns except for the diamond absorption band at 4 to $5\frac{1}{2}$ microns. The diamond anvils were very carefully figured

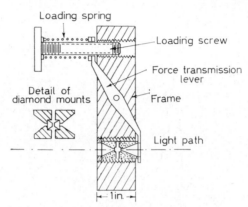

Figure 20. U.S. National Bureau of Standards apparatus for infra-red transmission studies to 30,000 atmospheres

and mounted in their support blocks so that when brought together in the supporting tube the faces met parallel to each other within interferometer accuracy. This requirement was necessary to minimize breakage due to uneven stress distribution, and made it necessary to grind them in matched pairs. Opposing diamond faces were purposely made of different diameters to minimize alignment problems and gain some strength by the massive support principle. The infra-red beam passed through the diamonds on an axis perpendicular to the opposing faces. Calculated (force/area) pressures up to over 100 kilobars were attained with this apparatus with calcite and other carbonates as samples.

VII. Gasket Materials

Gaskets between moving parts of a high pressure chamber ideally provide four functions simultaneously. They must crush or deform to allow compression stroke of the moving parts; they must effectively prevent leakage of pressurized material within the chamber; they should provide graded pressure support to the flanks of the highly stressed parts and thus reduce the stress gradients within those parts; and in many cases they should provide electrical insulation between the pressure chamber parts.

Experience has shown that materials like pyrophyllite stone work quite satisfactorily while other materials like talc, mica, alkali halide salts, metals like copper, lead, iron, etc., do not work at all well. It appears that a good gasket material must have the ability to grip the smooth surfaces of cemented carbide or hard steel parts when pressed firmly against them. The materials that work well in this respect seem to contain a component of fine, hard grit, like quartz or iron oxide. The gripping power of a gasket can generally be enhanced by dusting it with iron oxide rouge, alumina powder, or diamond powder.

Tests also indicate that the shear strength of the bulk gasket material should increase with the compressive stress to which it is subjected. One of the simplest ways of measuring the shear strength of materials under high compressive stress is to insert a torsion block of hard, strong material between the flat faces of an opposed piston apparatus, place thin samples of the material to be tested between each piston face and the block, apply load to the pistons to squeeze the samples between each piston face and the torsion block, and then measure the torque required to rotate the torsion block about the axis of the apparatus, thus shearing the thin samples. The earliest measurements of this type were probably made by Bridgman[23]. Results of such tests by Wentorf for pyrophyllite stone, lead and copper are presented in *Figure 21*. It is clear that poor gasket materials (for high pressure apparatus) like lead and copper show very little increase of shear strength

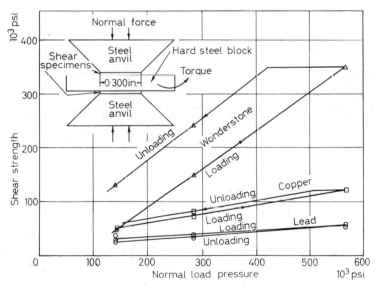

Figure 21. Shear strength of pyrophyllite, lead and copper as a function of compressive loading

with pressure, whereas pyrophillite stone shows a many-fold increase. Some recent work along this line has been done by Hyde[24] and by Cho[25]. From data like those shown in *Figure 21*, a gross coefficient of internal friction can be defined as the ratio of shear strength to compressive stress. On this basis the coefficients for pyrophyllite, copper, and lead from the data shown in *Figure 21* are about 0·61, 0·21, and 0·09, respectively, at about 20 kilobars. *Table 2* lists the coefficient of internal friction found by Hyde[24] at compressive loadings of about 25 kilobars.

The requirements of a gasket yielding to the advance of a piston element and at the same time sealing in the contents of the pressure chamber are in general contradictory because the first calls for easy yielding or compression while the second calls for high coefficient of friction and shear strength. In practice a workable compromise must be found. Experience has shown the successful materials to have internal friction coefficients in the range 0·30 to 0·60, and volume compressibilities of around 15 per cent in 50 kilobars.

Table 2. *Coefficient of Internal Friction of Various Materials at about 25 Kilobars*
(After G. R. Hyde[24])

Ferric oxide powder .. .. 0·71	Aluminium hydroxide powder .. 0·39
Zinc oxide powder .. .. .. 0·58	'Micro-cell' earth powder .. .. 0·37
Pumice stone powder .. .. 0·52	Calcium hydroxide powder .. 0·27
Chromic oxide powder .. .. 0·50	'Permagel' clay powder .. .. 0·18
Pyrophyllite powder .. .. 0·25	Boric acid powder .. .. .. 0·14
Pyrophyllite natural block .. .. 0·47	KCl powder .. .. .. 0·12
'Attasol' clay powder .. .. 0·47	NaCl powder .. .. .. 0·12
Lead dioxide powder .. .. 0·46	Mica sheet .. .. 0·07
Manganese dioxide powder .. 0·46	Boron nitride powder .. .. 0·07
Titanium dioxide powder .. .. 0·45	Graphite powder .. .. .. 0·04
Molybdenum trioxide powder .. 0·42	Molybdenum disulphide .. .. 0·04
Tin oxide powder .. .. .. 0·41	Silver chloride powder .. .. 0·03
Boron carbide powder .. .. 0·40	Indium sheet .. .. .. 0·01

VIII. Pressure Calibration

Pressure calibration of the newer higher pressure apparatuses on an accurate absolute basis is difficult. The primary cause of the difficulty is that friction and pressure in the gasket zones absorb an undetermined amount of the thrust force on the piston elements. Since the over-all force/area ratio is not the true pressure on the piston face, or in the centre of the pressure chamber, other ways of pressure determination must be adopted. The method that has been used most is to insert a substance in the pressure chamber which is known to have an abrupt shift of electrical resistance, or of volume, at a definite pressure and determine the forces at which the known transitions occur. The 'known' transition pressures must have been determined previously in free-piston apparatus, or in apparatus in which the pressure can be calculated accurately from thrust force and area.

Examples of abrupt volume changes found by Bridgman[5,6] in his extensive work on compressibilities of materials are shown in *Figure 22*. These measurements were carried out in two-stage piston and cylinder apparatus in which the force on the second stage piston was known to an accuracy of 1 part in 200, the piston area was known to a fraction of a per cent, and the frictional drag between the pistons and cylinder was only about 5 or 6 per cent (as shown by the force on the piston at a given transition being only 10 to 12 per cent different in the uploading and downloading parts of a cycle). Of the transitions shown in *Figure 22*, the 25 kilobar one for bismuth is the strongest, and the one which has been measured to the greatest accuracy (about ±0·4 per cent). A summary of primary determinations of the pressures at which these volume transitions occur is given in *Table 3*. The most recent, and probably the most accurate volume transition measurements are by

18

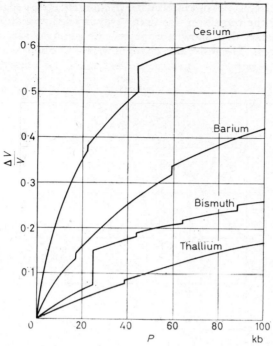

Figure 22. Fractional change of volume with pressure of caesium, barium, bismuth, and thallium

Table 3. Summary of Primary Pressure Calibrations of Abrupt Volume and Resistance Transitions in Bismuth, Thallium, Caesium, and Barium at 25°C (Pressures in kilobars).

Author and method	Bi(1–2)	Tl(2–3)	Cs(2–3)	Ba(2–3)	Bi(5–6) or (6–8)
Bridgman[5,6] 2-stage pist./cyl. $\Delta V/V$ ..	25·2 ±0·6	40·2	44·1	58·6	88·3
Bridgman[7] Flat face anvils $\Delta R/R$ ..	24·9	44	54	78	—
Boyd and England[27] Pist./cyl. $\Delta R/R$	25·2 ±0·4	37·1 ±1·3	—	—	—
Kennedy and LaMori[26] Pist./cyl. $\Delta V/V$	25·4 ±0·1	36·7 ±0·1	41·8 ±1·0	approx. 60	—
Drickamer and Balchan* 2 stage flat face anvils $\Delta R/R$, optical	—	—	—	58–60	88–92
Jura, *et al.** Flat face anvils $\Delta R/R$ ..	23	—	—·	—	82–85
Most probable value ..	25·4	37	42	59	89

* Private communication (1960).

19

Kennedy and LaMori[26], who minimized friction effects by slight rotation of the piston while the transition was under way in the apparatus.

The same metals that show abrupt volume changes also show abrupt resistance changes. The resistance changes were first observed and reported by Bridgman[7] (*Figure 23*). In these measurements he used flat face anvil

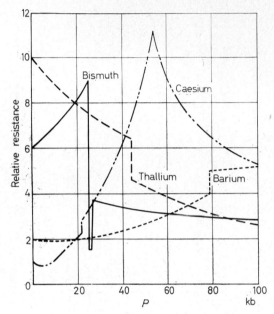

Figure 23. Resistance *v.* pressure of bismuth, thallium, caesium, and barium. From Bridgman[7] (old Bridgman R scale)

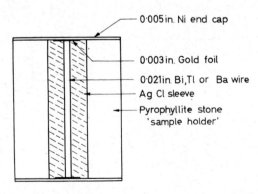

Figure 24. Calibration cell for 'belt' apparatus using wires of bismuth, thallium, or barium

apparatus and, on the basis of place of occurrence of the already known Bi(1–2) transition in terms of force/area for the apparatus, he concluded that the correct pressure was given by the force/area ratio at all higher loadings.

Recent resistance measurements by Drickamer and Balchan in apparatus calibrated as described in reference 15, and by Jura (private communication, 1960), indicate that Bridgman's flat face anvil pressure values were too high. The bottom line of *Table 3* lists the most probable true values of the pressures at which the named transitions occur.

In pressure-calibrating an apparatus that has fairly large gasket loading, such as the 'belt' apparatus, calibration cells like that shown in *Figure 24* are used. The resistance of the wire is recorded as the press load on the apparatus is increased. A typical resistance *v.* press load curve for a barium wire sample is shown in *Figure 25*. The resistance 'step' is not perfectly abrupt

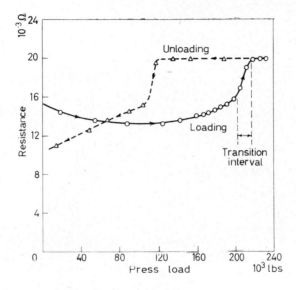

Figure 25. Resistance *v.* press load for a barium calibration sample in a 'belt' apparatus

because, owing undoubtedly to pressure gradients in the cell, the transition pressure is not reached simultaneously at all parts of the barium wire. The reverse transition on downloading does not occur until the press load is about 60 per cent of the value at which it took place on the uploading. This large lag is not due to any appreciable lag in the behaviour of the barium itself, but to reverse friction and differential unloading effects in the gasket and sample. Since all 'working' experiments are made on the uploading cycle, the pressure calibration taken is the uploading one. *Figure 26* shows a typical pressure calibration of a 'belt' apparatus, showing the chamber pressure *v.* press load using the transition pressures listed at the bottom of *Table 3*.

Pressure calibrations are generally carried out at room temperature for convenience, and because the primary calibrations were done at that temperature. When the cores of high pressure cells are heated after they have been brought up to pressure, the core pressure certainly changes. Some factors cause the core pressure to rise while others cause it to decrease. These factors differ from each other in their time and temperature rates. These effects will be discussed in more detail in Chapter 5.

IX. Future Development

It appears that the designs of high pressure apparatus described in this chapter have already been used to the limit of their pressure capability.

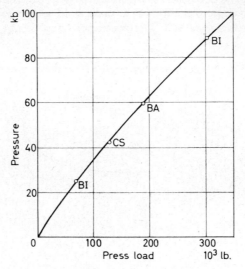

Figure 26. Chamber pressure *v.* press load for a 'belt' apparatus

Straight cylindrical pistons, even though short and made of the strongest available materials, fail at less than 60 kilobars. Straight cylindrical vessels, heavily prestressed and backed by massive binding rings, and subjected to external axial compressive stress, fail at 70 to 80 kilobars. Tapered piston and cylinder apparatus with gaskets providing flank loading and more gentle stress gradients, such as the belt apparatus, fails a little above 100 kilobars. The same is true of multiple tapered piston apparatus, like the tetrahedral or cube systems. Bridgman flat-face anvil apparatus, which is based strongly on the principle of massive support, is probably capable of over 200 kilobars. (Some reports indicate 300 to 400 kilobars, but this will have to be better established.)

Two possibilities for increasing the pressure capability of apparatus still seem open, and both are extravagant of thrust force. The first is to use multistaging or cascading. It has been pointed out earlier in the chapter that this approach requires a very large first-stage chamber if the inner, highest-pressure stage is to have reasonable volume. The linear dimensions need to go down by a factor of about 5 per stage, so the volume goes down by a factor of 125 per stage. Thus, for example, the useful pressurized volume in a three-stage system would be less than 1/15,000th that of the first stage.

The second possibility is to use multi-piston apparatus, such as a six-piston cube array, and include gasket structures between the adjacent flanks of the pistons which, as the pistons close in to compress the cube sample, build up a pressure gradient which supports the flanks of the pistons enough at all points so that the shear strength is never exceeded. These gaskets would have to extend back five to ten face widths from the face edges. The total thrust on each piston would have to be many times that on the face. A stress analysis of the piston readily indicates what the gasket support pressures need to be as a function of the distance out from the piston face, but it is very difficult to build an actual gasket structure which will perform as desired.

In the future, in spite of all the difficulties, there undoubtedly will be developed apparatus capable of long, high temperature runs at well over 200 kilobars.

References

[1]BRIDGMAN, P. W., *The Physics of High Pressure*, 1952 ed., G. Bell & Sons, Ltd, London

[2]COMINGS, E. W., *High Pressure Technology*, McGraw-Hill, New York, 1956

[3]HAMANN, S. D., *Physico-Chemical Effects of Pressure*, Butterworths Scientific Publications, London, 1957

[4]Ref. 1, p. 396–401

[5]BRIDGMAN, P. W., *Proc. Amer. Acad. Arts Sci.*, **74**, 1942, p. 425

[6]BRIDGMAN, P. W., *Proc. Amer. Acad. Arts Sci.*, **76**, 1948, p. 55

[7]BRIDGMAN, P. W., *Proc. Amer. Acad. Arts Sci.*, **81**, 1952, p. 165

[8]HALL, H. T., *Rev. Sci. Instr.*, **29**, 1958, p. 267

[9]LLOYD, E. C., HUTTON, V. O. and JOHNSON, D. P., *Bur. Stand., J. Res., Wash.* **63C**, 1959, p. 59

[10]LIANDER, H. and LUNDBLAD, E., *Arkiv Kemi*, **16**, 1960, p. 139

[11]VERESCHAGIN, L. F., *Progress in Very High Pressure Research*, Proc. of a Conference at Bolton Landing, Lake George, N.Y., June 1960; John Wiley & Sons, New York, 1961

[12]GRIGGS, D. T., Institute of Geophysics, Univ. of California at Los Angeles (private communication)

[13]HUTTON, V. O., et al., *Bur. Stand. J. Res., Wash.* (private communication)

[14]HALL, H. T., *Rev. Sci. Instrum.*, **31**, 1960, p. 125

[15]FITCH, R. A., SLYKHOUSE, T. E. and DRICKAMER, H. G., *J. Opt. Soc. Amer.*, **47**, 1957, p. 1,015; SLYKHOUSE, T. E. and DRICKAMER, H. G., *J. Phys. Chem. Solids*, **7**, 1958, p. 207; BALCHAN, A. S. and DRICKAMER, H. G., *Rev. Sci. Instrum.*, **31**, 1960, p. 511

[16]JACOBS, R. B., *Phys. Rev.*, **54**, 1958, p. 325

[17]JACOBS, R. B., *Phys. Rev.*, **56**, 1939, p. 211

[18]LAWSON, A. W. and RILEY, N. A., *Rev. Sci. Instrum.*, **20**, 1949, p. 763

[19]VERESCHAGIN, L. F., KABALKINA, S. S. and EVODOKIMOVA, V. V., *Akad. Nauk. SSSR, Zhur. Priborii Technika Exper. 1958*, No. 3, 1958, p. 90

[20]JAMIESON, J. C., *J. Geol.*, **65**, 1957, p. 334

[21]JAMIESON, J. C., LAWSON, A. W. and NACHTRIEB, N. D., *Rev. Sci. Instrum.*, **30**, 1959, p. 1,016

[22]WEIR, C. E., LIPPINCOTT, E. R., VAN VALKENBURG, A. and BUNTING, E. N., *Bur. Stand. J. Res., Wash.*, **63A**, 1959, p. 55

[23]BRIDGMAN, P. W., *Phys. Rev.*, **48**, 1935, p. 825

[24]HYDE, G. R., *Friction at Very High Pressure*, M.S. Thesis 1957, Brigham Young University

[25]CHO, Y., *Propagation of High Pressure in The Solid State*, M.A. Thesis 1958, Brigham Young University

[26]KENNEDY, G. C. and LaMORI, P. N., 'Some fixed points on the high pressure scale', *Progress in Very High Pressure Research*, Proc. of Conf. at Lake George, N.Y., 1960; John Wiley & Sons, New York, 1961
[27]BOYD, F. R. and ENGLAND, J. L., *J. Geophys. Res.*, **65,** 1960, p. 741

2

HIGH PRESSURE OPTICAL AND ELECTRICAL MEASUREMENTS*

H. G. DRICKAMER and A. S. BALCHAN

Department of Chemistry and Chemical Engineering
University of Illinois
Urbana, Illinois

THE purpose of this article is to describe equipment developed in the High Pressures Laboratory at the University of Illinois for optical and electrical studies. Optical measurements can be made to 170 kilobars, and electrical measurements to about 500 kilobars. The discussion is divided into three sections: high pressure optical studies, high pressure–high temperature optical studies, and high pressure electrical resistance studies.

I. High Pressure Optical Bomb

(i) General

The high pressure optical apparatus developed in this laboratory[1] consists of two cells, one operable to about 54 kilobars, the second usable to about

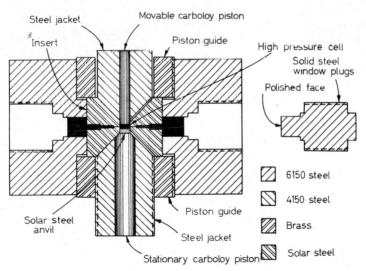

Figure 1. Diagram of Cell I

165 kilobars (see *Figures 1* and *2* and *Table 1*). Both cells use NaCl as a pressure-transmitting 'fluid', as well as NaCl windows. Sodium chloride has

* This work was supported in part by the United States Atomic Energy Commission under Contract AT(11-1)-67, Chemical Engineering Project 5.

relatively low shear strength and acts as a reasonably hydrostatic medium for optical purposes. This is best illustrated by data for the shift in the peak energy of the F centre in alkali halides[2]. The data using the NaCl medium exactly reproduce the results of Jacobs[3] obtained using a true fluid to 7

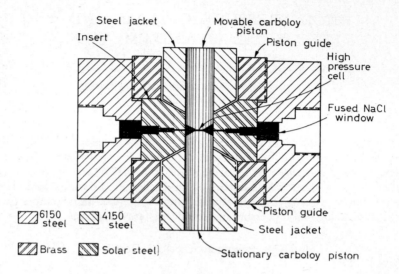

Figure 2. Diagram of Cell II

kilobars. It should be noted that in this range the ratio of shear to hydro-static force is at its worst.

The optical range of the cells is 0·250 microns to about 10 microns, although it is difficult to get sufficient light at wavelengths beyond 5 microns. It is generally possible to achieve better optics with the $\frac{1}{8}$ in. (54 kilobars) cell than with the higher pressure cell.

The cells have a number of features in common, in addition to several distinctive aspects. The centre of the cell consists of an insert of very hard steel. (In our earlier work this was always Carpenter Solar steel hardened to 58–60 Rockwell C. This is quite satisfactory in most ways, but tends to crack when being hardened. More recently, Crucible Labelle HT tool steel hardened to 54–55 R.C. has been used with considerable success. Doubt-lessly other steels such as Bethlehem Omega would also be usable.) Outside of the insert is a jacket of AISI 6150 or 4340 steel hardened to 44–46 R.C. The pistons are made from grade 883 carboloy and jacketed with AISI 4140 steel hardened to 40–42 R.C. Brass piston guides are threaded into the jacket. In each cell there is one stationary and one moving piston. The length of bearing area of the moving piston on the insert is limited to about $\frac{1}{16}$ in. to minimize friction.

The windows in both cells are similar in design although different in dimensions (see *Table 1*). They consist of a series of holes in the insert, telescoped to allow for a converging beam of light. These holes are lined up with the 0·250 in. diameter holes in the jacket. (The insert is a 0·002–0·003 in. press fit in the jacket.) Before filling the windows, it is essential that they be scoured clean of all rust and scale. This can best be done by rotating brass rods covered with carborundum in the holes. The final cleaning is done with wooden pins, and then a blast of dry air.

For filling the windows it is convenient to make a brass guide $\frac{3}{4}$ in. long which threads into the $\frac{5}{8}$ in. threads in the outer part of the insert. The brass guide has an inside diameter of $0\cdot255$ in. It is also necessary to have pistons of hard steel (Solar or Columbia Super die 58–60 R.C.) and of carboloy,

Table 1. Cell Dimensions (in.)

							Cell I	Cell II
Piston diameter	..	..	..	..	..	..	$0\cdot125$	$0\cdot500$
Piston taper	..	..	..	..	..	..	$0°$	$6°$
Diameter of flat	..	..	..	..	..	..	$0\cdot125$	$0\cdot093$
Jacket diameter	..	..	..	..	..	..	$3\frac{5}{16}$	$3\frac{1}{2}$
Insert diameter	..	..	..	..	..	..	1	$1\frac{7}{8}$
Window holes:								
(1) L	..	..	..	..	..	..	$0\cdot125$	$0\cdot125$
D	..	..	..	..	..	..	$0\cdot028$	$0\cdot037$
(2) L	..	..	..	..	..	..	$0\cdot125$	$0\cdot188$
D	..	..	..	..	..	..	$0\cdot046$	$0\cdot052$
(3) L	..	..	..	..	..	..	$0\cdot188$	$0\cdot188$
D	..	..	..	..	..	..	$0\cdot066$	$0\cdot082$
(4) L	..	..	..	..	..	..	—	$0\cdot188$
D	..	..	..	..	..	..	—	$0\cdot100$

Note: holes are number 1, 2, 3, 4 starting at the inside of the cell.
L=Length of hole.
D=Diameter of hole.

lapped to fit the $0\cdot250$ in. hole to $0\cdot0005$ in. The windows on the $\frac{1}{8}$ in. cell can be filled using the steel pistons only, and a pressure of 15 kilobars. For the $\frac{1}{2}$ in. cell it is necessary to use the carboloy pistons and 30 kilobars for the initial filling. The windows are then finished with the steel pistons.

A single crystal of NaCl is cut to fit roughly in the $0\cdot250$ in. diameter hole and about $\frac{1}{2}$–$\frac{5}{8}$ in. long. It is heated to about 500°C and thrust into the guide described above. The piston is inserted and pressure is quickly applied. It is desirable to work the salt in by cycling the pressure, e.g. 15 kilobars, release; 12 kilobars, release; 9 kilobars, release; 6 kilobars, release; 3 kilobars, release. This gives a clearer window. There is no advantage in holding the pressure for more than a fraction of a minute. The procedure is then repeated with the second window. A crystal about $\frac{1}{16}$ in. thick and just fitting the centre is heated and inserted in the centre. About 30 kilobars pressure is applied. (Flat pistons are used for both the $\frac{1}{8}$ in. and $\frac{1}{2}$ in. cells in this operation.) During this operation it is very desirable to screw solid steel plugs with polished ends tightly into the window holes as this gives much clearer windows. These plugs are also kept tightly screwed in place when the cells are not in use, as this maintains the condition of the windows. After one cycle of pressure one can usually see light through the windows, but it takes several further rounds before the maximum clarity is obtained. The centre section can be pressed out and replaced with a new salt pellet with or without a sample many times without damage to the windows. It is essential, how-ever, always to store the cell with a salt pellet pressed in the centre, as other-wise dirt and moisture deteriorate the windows. The steel retaining windows shown in our original paper are not necessary and are no longer in use.

Although the salt is relatively fluid, in these long thin holes the pressure drop is such that there is little or no distortion of the outside windows. With care and occasional repressing, the windows can be maintained for dozens of runs.

In addition to the common features of the two cells, there are a number of details which are more or less individual to one cell or the other; these are described below.

(ii) Cell I

The moving piston consists of a carboloy cylinder $0 \cdot 125$ in. in diameter and 1 in. long. It is given a 30° bevel on the edge and a hardened tapered ring of Solar or Labelle HT steel is seated on the bevel. This minimizes extrusion. The stationary piston consists of an anvil of hardened Solar steel which rests on a carboloy piston $\frac{1}{4}$ in. in diameter, ground to seat against the

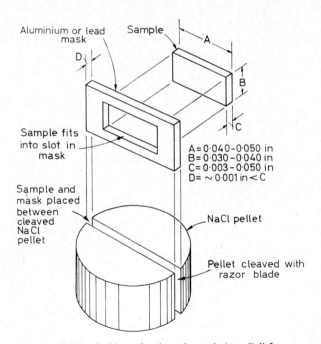

Figure 3. Method of introduction of sample into Cell I

taper of the insert. The anvil comes up to the bottom of the windows. The centre salt pellet is usually $0 \cdot 065 - 0 \cdot 070$ in. high. Two half-cylinders are cut to fit the hole and the sample is inserted in a thin layer between these. Unless the sample is quite soft and fusible it is generally desirable to mask it with aluminium foil as shown in *Figure 3*.

The basic calibration was made by inserting a layer of bismuth or tellurium in place of the sample and following the volume changes by piston displacement. It was possible to observe the transition in bismuth at 25 kilobars and tellurium at 41 kilobars with very little hysteresis. Secondly, the stretching frequency of the CN⁻ bond of the ion dissolved in NaCl was observed as a function of pressure to use for calibration of Cell II as discussed below. Many other shifts have been observed since the early calibration. Because of the very small bearing area the friction is very low (less than 5 per cent).

The pressure range of this cell is limited to about 54 kilobars by fracture of the moving piston in compression.

(iii) Cell II

The higher pressure range is obtained by making use of Bridgman's principle of 'massive support' plus the notion of a cell within a cell. Cell II

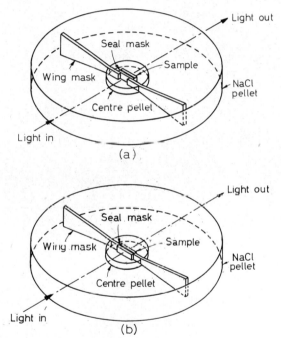

Figure 4. Two methods for introduction of sample into Cell II

consists of an apparatus much like Cell I but with $\frac{1}{2}$ in. diameter pistons. The piston faces are ground with a 6° angle leaving a flat 0·093 in. in diameter. The stationary piston threads into the brass guide and is inserted so that its flat comes at the centre of the windows. A single crystal of salt is weighed out to give a centre thickness of 0·010–0·012 in. and fused in place. The desired final centre thickness is obtained by scraping the outer edges of the pellet and re-fusing. The centre thickness is measured by the use of a specially built micrometer which measures the thickness of the pistons plus pellet in place in the bomb, and then of the pistons removed from the bomb. This is done at the beginning and end of each run, and the extrusion, if any, is assumed to be linear with applied pressure. As the calibration was made in the same manner and with the same assumptions, any errors should largely cancel out.

It is necessary to mask the sample to prevent light leak around the sides (and usually above and below). This is a relatively delicate operation. A typical masking is illustrated in *Figure 4*. It is desirable to insert the aluminium (or pipestone) masks while the centre thickness is still 0·008–0·009 in. and then to reduce the centre further, if necessary, with the masks in place. Considerable practice is necessary before hard samples, in particular, can be loaded without light leak. It is usually necessary to do the masking and loading under a magnifying glass.

As indicated above, relatively high pressures are obtainable in this cell because: (1) only the centre is stressed beyond the yield point, and (2) the salt in the centre and the central part of the piston is supported by the pressure in the salt along the taper.

The ultimate pressure range is limited by breakage of the piston and by its plastic and elastic distortions. These latter limitations are somewhat more severe than we had earlier thought.

The original calibration of Cell II was established from an extrapolation of the CN^- stretching frequency and from optical observation of the phase transitions in AgCl at 88 kilobars and in AgBr at 84·5 kilobars. Very few data were taken above 140 kilobars. Many shifts have since been measured in this range and give consistent results. In addition, it has been possible to make certain electrical resistance measurements since we have insulated one piston, as discussed in the section on the high pressure–high temperature optical cell. From these electrical resistance measurements and our optical calibration we find a transition in barium at 58–60 kilobars and one in bismuth at 88–92 kilobars. Bridgman[4] with *P–V* measurements found

Table 2. Pressure Calibration, ½-inch Cell.
Centre Pressure v. Applied Pressure for Various Centre Thicknesses.

Applied pressure	Centre thickness (thousandths of an inch)									
	3·5	4	5	6	7	8	9	10	11	12
5·6	30·4	28·4	24·3	20·3	17·7	15·2	13·2	12·2	11·7	10·6
11·2	55·9	51·7	45·7	39·6	35·5	31·4	27·4	24·3	23·3	21·3
16·8	81·2	75·0	67·0	59·8	52·7	46·7	41·6	37·5	35·0	32·4
22·4	101·3	96·4	86·2	78·1	71·0	61·9	55·8	50·7	46·7	43·6
28·0	119·8	115·7	101·5	96·5	86·3	77·1	69·0	62·0	57·8	54·8
33·6	136·0	133·0	124·7	115·0	102·5	91·3	82·2	74·1	68·0	65·0
39·2	148·0	146·0	139·0	131·0	119·2	105·5	95·0	85·2	78·1	74·1
44·8	157·0	155·0	149·5	141·0	131·0	118·3	106·5	96·4	88·3	83·2
50·4	166·0	163·0	157·2	148·1	139·5	129·0	118·7	106·5	97·5	91·3

All pressures in kilobars

transitions in barium at $58 \cdot 5$ kilobars and in bismuth at $88 \cdot 2$ kilobars. By electrical means[5] he found a transition in barium at 78 kilobars. Bundy[6] found a transition in bismuth at 120–125 kilobars, basing his scale on barium at 78 kilobars. The optical apparatus is not a good device for electrical resistance measurements because of flow of salt and sample, so our resistance results are in no sense standards. Nevertheless, it can be said that our optical calibration is in substantial agreement with Bridgman's volumetric measurements.

As mentioned above, our calibration in the higher pressure range was obtained by extrapolation of shifts obtained at lower pressures. In the range below 140 kilobars, where there is little plastic deformation and apparently not too much elastic deformation, this is satisfactory. A careful study of considerable data where the shifts were large gave convincing evidence that these extrapolations, and the correlating equations previously published[1,7,10], indicated too high a pressure in the region above 140 kilobars. A more accurate calibration has been prepared and is shown in *Table 2*. Because of the plastic and elastic effects, it cannot be fitted by any simple equation over the entire range. It agrees quite closely with the previous calibrations up to about 140 kilobars, and as very little data were published above this range, most of the published results are valid.

(iv) The Press

A wide variety of presses can, of course, be used with the optical cells. The one used in this work has the advantages of self-alignment with the pistons and relatively small outside diameter. The body and head are screwed together and consist of AISI 6150 or 4340 steel hardened to 44–46 Rockwell C. The threads tend to line up the body and head. In addition, a register $\frac{3}{8}$ in. long is ground in the body below the threads. This aligns with a similar register ground on the head above the threads. Three windows, $2 \times 2\frac{1}{2}$ in., are milled in the body to permit measurements of light transmitted, or scattered 90°. The body of our press is 6 in. O.D. and $4\frac{1}{2}$ in. I.D. A somewhat smaller press can be constructed for use with the $\frac{1}{8}$ in. cell only. Carboloy blocks 1 in. in diameter and 1 in. thick are inserted in the piston and the head of the press to prevent deformation. The piston seal used is an unsupported area seal, but O-rings could also be employed.

The press is portable and can be fitted into various spectrometers with minor modifications of the optics. It is used in our laboratory with a modified Beckmann DUR spectrometer for the range $0 \cdot 25$–$1 \cdot 0$ microns and a Perkin-Elmer single-beam, double-pass spectrometer for the infra-red. It is generally desirable to have a more highly focussed beam than is available in the standard spectrometer optics because of the small size of the holes.

(v) Experimental Results

The optical cell has been used to study a wide variety of phenomena, including the gap between the conduction and valence band in insulators, colour centres and impurity spectra in alkali halides, spectra of transition metal ions in complexes and chelates, spectra of rare earth salts, π-electron spectra of organic compounds, phosphor decay, and the mechanism and kinetics of phase transitions. Some 35 papers have been published, or are in press. It would be impractical to give any adequate review of the results. In *Figures 5–7* are shown a few curves which were obtained over a pressure

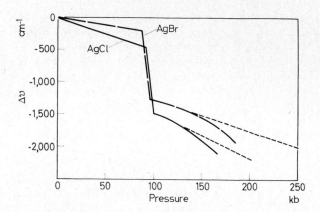

Figure 5. Absorption edge *v.* pressure, AgCl and AgBr

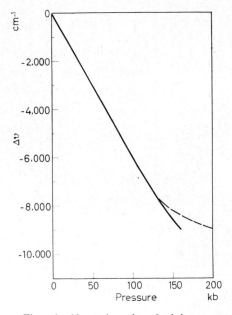

Figure 6. Absorption edge of sulphur *v.* pressure

range such that there is a significant difference between the most recent and earlier calibrations. These include the absorption edges of AgCl and AgBr[7], sulphur[8], and the shift of the Fe^{++} peak in garnet[9]. In each case the solid

32

curve is the result according to our present calibration; the dotted curve is the result as originally presented. These curves serve to correct the data in the literature and to illustrate the power of the technique.

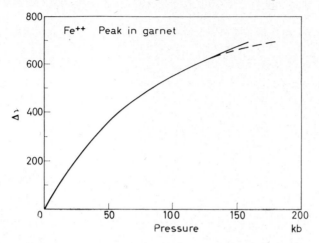

Figure 7. Δv v. pressure

II. High Temperature–High Pressure Optical Bomb

For a number of systems it is desirable to take spectra as a function of temperature at high pressure. Since external heating presents a multitude of difficult problems, a bomb involving an internal heater has been developed[10]. There are four basic problems to be solved in the design of such a bomb: (1) the insulation of a piston to provide an electrical lead, (2) the introduc-

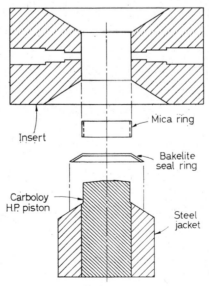

Figure 8. Insulation of high pressure piston

tion of heaters which do not interfere with the optics, (3) the calibration of temperature, and (4) the pressure calibration at high temperature.

To obtain an electrical lead, the bottom piston on the $\frac{1}{2}$ in. optical cell was ground undersize $0 \cdot 008$ in., and fitted with a mica sleeve and Bakelite collar (see *Figure 8*). The backing for the piston was insulated from the press by a Bakelite ring and a sheet of mica as illustrated in *Figure 9*. To prevent

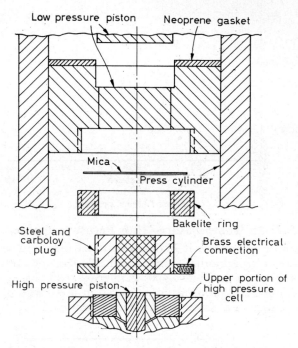

Figure 9. High pressure–high temperature cell

excessive extrusion of salt, pipestone (catlinite) was extruded in the space around the mica sleeve, using several applications of 30 kilobars pressure.

After a salt pellet of approximately the desired thickness was fused in place, the heaters were inserted as shown in *Figure 10*. Four No. 65 holes, located with respect to the centre as shown, were drilled in the salt. Powdered graphite was pressure-fused into the holes. The heaters can readily be located sufficiently accurately to give reproducible results. The sample and the pipestone masks used to prevent light leak were then inserted in slots cut for them. The cell and press were assembled, and connected to an a.c. source. The system consumed up to 400 amperes at 1–1·5 volts to obtain the higher temperatures.

The temperature calibration was made by observing the melting points of naphthalene, benzoic acid, hydroquinone, thallium nitrate, silver nitrate, anthracene, *p*-dichlorobenzoic acid, mercuric chloride, sodium nitrate, hexabromobenzene, and hexachlorobenzene. These covered a range from $80 \cdot 2 – 306 \cdot 8$ °C. The solid state transition in AgI at 145°C was also observed. Each material was in turn inserted in the slot and a slight pressure was imposed to make contact with the heaters. The recorded light transmission was followed as a function of increasing current. At the melting point there was a sharp cut-off of light and considerable oscillation in the transmission.

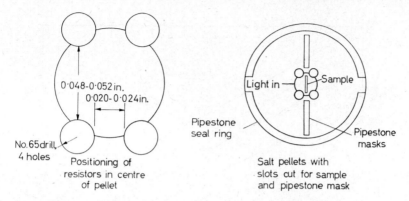

Figure 10. Centre loading for high pressure–high temperature cell

The temperature was found to be a linear function of the heating power of the form

$$T(°C) = W + 25$$

where W = watts of heating power.

The fit is within $\pm 5°$ at $307°C$ and is extrapolated for higher temperatures. Optical observations and measurements with a thermocouple inserted through a dummy piston indicated that a substantially steady state of temperature was reached in 30–45 seconds.

The pressure calibration of Section I was obtained at room temperature. Obviously there is some pressure redistribution in the salt at high tempera-

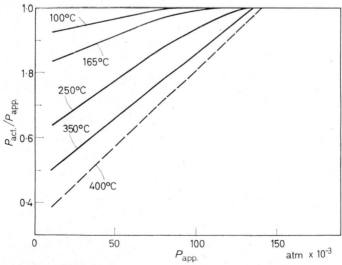

Figure 11. Pressure correction for high temperature

35

ture. There are not sufficient data available to permit a direct calibration at high temperature and pressure; hence the following method, which gives reproducible results, was developed.

Spectra were measured as a function of pressure at room temperature. The

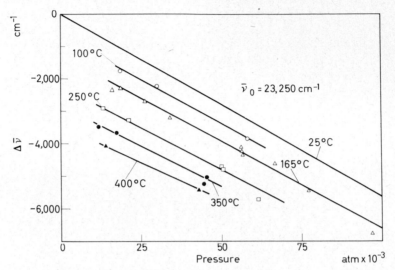

Figure 12. Sulphur: shift in absorption edge with temperature and pressure

system was then set at some elevated pressure and heated to a chosen temperature. A spectrum was taken at this temperature. The intensities at a number of given wavelengths were checked at the beginning and end of each spectrum to ensure that intensity was independent of time, and that there was no distortion of the spectrum. After the heating power was shut off, the

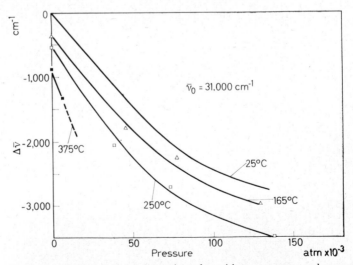

Figure 13. Olivine: shift in absorption edge with temperature and pressure

cell was quenched with a blast of compressed air for five minutes. Experiments with the dummy piston and thermocouple indicated that the centre temperature dropped below 50°C within 30 seconds. A second room-temperature spectrum was then obtained, which perhaps indicated a lower cell pressure than before heating. It was assumed that the pressure distribution obtained at high temperature had been quenched so that the second low-temperature spectrum established the pressure at high temperature. A higher heating power was next applied and the procedure was repeated. Normally a series of temperatures was run from one initial pressure, and then the bomb was dismantled and completely reloaded. By standardizing on the temperatures 165°, 250°, 325° and 400°C, the calibration shown in *Figure 11* was obtained. Above 30 kilobars it is reproducible to ±3 kilobars. The pressure from the room temperature calibration is the 'apparent pressure'. One would expect that the correction would be smaller at high pressure, for the melting point of NaCl increases rapidly with pressure, and the resistance to shear must also increase.

If one operates above 325°C and 100 kilobars, the pistons must be reground after each run, for there is considerable deformation of the Carboloy.

Examples of high pressure, high temperature data are shown in *Figures 12* and *13*, which exhibit the absorption edges of sulphur and of olivine. The latter is a mineral of considerable geological significance. Other data have been obtained at temperatures and pressures as high as 500°C and 150 kilobars.

III. High Pressure Electrical Resistance Cell
(*i*) *Apparatus*

To date, the most accurate measurements of the effect of pressure on electrical conductivity of metals, from the standpoint of an absolute pressure scale, are those of Bridgman[11,12] to 30,000 kg/cm², using pentane as a pressure-transmitting fluid. These data were used extensively for calibration purposes in this work.

Using a different technique, Bridgman[13] measured the resistance of 77 metals and alloys to an apparent 100,000 kg/cm². The apparatus employed consisted of two opposed cylinders of Carboloy, with truncated cone ends, press-fitted in hard steel outer jackets. The sample, encased in silver chloride and prevented from extruding by a 0·010 in. thick ring of pipestone, was compressed between the flat centre sections of the anvils. The anvils used by Bridgman were 1 in. in outside diameter, and were ground with 6° tapered ends with a ½ in. diameter central flat.

Pressures in the anvil apparatus were obtained from the applied force and the area of compressed material, this method having been assumed satisfactory by observation of the known transition in bismuth at 25,000 kg/cm² (this was discovered in Bridgman's 30,000 kg/cm² '*P–V*' apparatus)[14]. At higher pressures, however, a discrepancy between this 'anvil' scale and the '*P–V*' scale occurs, as is noticed by a comparison of the apparent transition pressures for thallium, cerium, and barium observed by the two methods.

The pressure limitation on the anvils was set by the high frequency of breakage which occurred when pressures in excess of the apparent 100,000 kg/cm² were generated.

A recent modification of the Bridgman design is that of Jura[15]. The Carboloy cylinders in this modification are subjected to a large radial compressive stress, which increases the compressive limit of the pistons. Pressures in the 400 kilobar range have been reported.

Other high pressure equipment, although not specifically designed for conductivity studies, has been successfully employed for this purpose. Bundy obtained the phase diagrams of bismuth[6] and rubidium[16] by measurement of resistance changes, using the General Electric 'belt' apparatus[17]. He was the first to observe the VI→VIII transition in bismuth, which has proved to be an important calibration point in the present work.

A schematic diagram of the resistance cell[18] used in the present work is shown in *Figure 14*. The Carboloy insert, grade 55A, was ground to a tight slip fit on the 0·875 in. diameter Carboloy pistons, and pressed into a Crucible

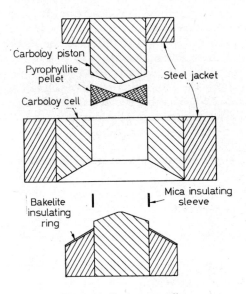

Figure 14. Resistance cell

Labelle HT steel outer jacket. The high pressure pistons were $1\frac{1}{4}$ in. long, 0·875 in. in diameter, pressed into AISI 4140 hard steel outer jackets. One end of each was ground in the Bridgman truncated cone shape, with an 18° taper and 0·090 in. diameter flat. Before use, one of the pistons was reduced in outside diameter by 0·004 in. in order to permit electrical insulation from the chamber wall (see section on insulation of high temperature optical cell). General Electric grade 999 Carboloy was used exclusively for the movable piston and most of the time for the stationary insulated piston (grade 883 was used occasionally, as detailed below).

A pellet of pyrophyllite, of the proper shape to fill the cavity and with a thickness at the centre of 0·012 in., was used as the supporting medium for the taper. Pyrophyllite was also used as a seal for the sample and silver chloride in the centre of the flat. (It was found quite important to control the centre thickness accurately; this was done to 0·0001 in.)

Force was applied by a short stroke, Bridgman unsupported area press with an 8 in. diameter piston. The piston was electrically insulated from the press with 0·004 in. thick mica.

Resistances were measured by observing the changes in potential across

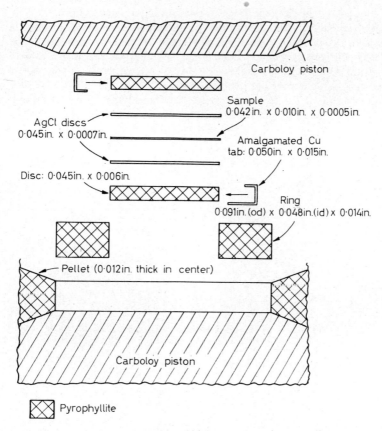

Figure 15. Centre assembly of high pressure resistance cell

the sample caused by a small, constant d.c. current passed through it. E.M.F. was measured with a Leeds and Northrup potentiometer capable of determining resistances to one part in one thousand.

After one piston had been insulated, the weighed pyrophyllite pellet was pressed together at two kilobars average pressure. The centre flat area was removed with a drill, and the centre pyrophyllite ring, coated with iron oxide, was placed in the hole. Into the ring were fitted, in order, a pyrophyllite disc, silver chloride plate, sample, silver chloride, and the upper pyrophyllite disc (see *Figure 15*). The total thickness of these components was about 0·0005 in. less than the thickness of the ring. Secondary contacts of 0·0005 in. thick amalgamated copper were used (as illustrated) with fragile or stiff samples (Bi, Rb, Ba, Fe, Pb, Ca). For ductile materials, a sandwich of the material in silver chloride was bent as a whole around the pyrophyllite discs, and contact with the pistons was made by the sample itself, through a small tab of amalgamated copper (Pb, Pt, Ca, Fe). The two methods gave identical results for the metals run in both ways. In the case of indium, the second method was used, except that silver chloride was placed only along the edges of the sample, to reduce chemical reaction. Rubidium was loaded by the first method, under an argon atmosphere.

After assembly, the pellet was pressed together at 2 kilobars average pressure. Resistance measurements were spaced in increments of 0·2–2 kilobars average pressure. Data were taken from the point at which the pellet and centre had crushed into a single conglomerate (about 40 kb centre pressure) to 50 kb average piston pressure.

The success of the apparatus was due largely to the discovery that the centre flat region of the Carboloy pistons could be successfully work-hardened without subsequent destruction. In this way both the elastic constants and elastic limit of the pistons were improved.

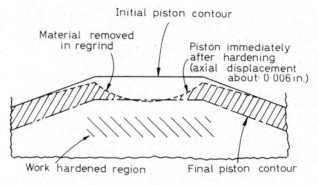

Figure 16. Deformation of piston during hardening

A new set of pistons was hardened by using a pellet of pyrophyllite 0·015 in. thick in the centre with the centre flat left untouched. Grade 883 pistons were compressed in sets to an average pressure of 25 kilobars; grade 999, to 14 kilobars. The resulting plastic deformation is shown in *Figure 16*. The material indicated by the cross-hatching was removed in a regrind leaving the newly formed flat in a strained condition.

In the majority of data runs, both pistons were totally destroyed. In a few exceptional cases, however, the stationary piston remained intact, was refaced as before, and re-used. These harder pistons enabled pressures of greater than 475 kilobars to be attained with ease. The only pistons which exhibited this behaviour were grade 883, and only these multiply-hardened pistons of this grade were used in data runs (the majority were grade 999 sets).

In the course of development of the cell, the importance of certain design variables was determined. The variations made, and the result of each, can be summarized as follows:

(a) Trial on 1·75 in. diameter all-Carboloy pistons: greater piston mass did not prevent failure of centre portion of piston.

(b) Trial on 1 : 1 mixture of iron oxide–epoxy resin in place of pyro-phyllite: internal friction was too small; large extrusion of centre material resulted.

(c) Centre thickness increase: extrusion of centre material was too great.

(d) Trial of 1·75 in. diameter pistons consisting of hard Crucible steel outer section and 0·875 in. diameter Carboloy centre (0·004 in. interference) steel did not prevent Carboloy from failing radially.

(e) Changes in Carboloy grade: grade 907, initially softer than 883 and 999, did not appear to work-harden as well as the latter grades. Grade 999 (and occasionally 883, as above) for both the movable and stationary pistons appeared to be the optimum combination.

(f) Change in angle of taper: angles smaller than 18° were found to cause an excess amount of force to be applied to the tapered section; angles of greater than 18° produced too much radial flow.

(ii) Pressure Calibrations

(a) Determination of bismuth and barium transition pressures—Because of the discrepancy existing above 25,000 kg/cm² between Bridgman's 'anvil' and 'P–V' scales with regard to transition pressures, the pressures of the barium transition and the highest bismuth transition were determined in the high pressure optical cell (see Section I). It is to be noted here that the calibration of the latter was based primarily on the 'P–V' scale (see section on calibration of optical cell), and thus direct comparison between it and the 'anvil' scale could be made.

The barium and high bismuth transitions were repeatedly observed at 58–60 kilobars and 88–92 kilobars, respectively. The final values used were 59 kb for the barium transition and 88 kb for the highest bismuth transition.

The 59 kb resistance transition in barium could then be identified with the volumetric transition at 60,000 kg/cm² (58·5 kb) and the 88 kb transition in bismuth with a volumetric transition at 90,000 kg/cm².

(b) Extrapolation of Bridgman's 30,000 kg/cm² resistivity data for lead, platinum and indium to higher pressures—It was found possible to correlate the resistance and density measurements of Bridgman to 30,000 kg/cm² in his P–V apparatus to obtain a slowly varying function of density, either as $\frac{R_0}{R} - 1$ versus $\frac{\rho}{\rho_0} - 1$, $1 - \frac{V}{V_0}$ versus $\frac{R_0}{R} - 1$, or $\ln \frac{R_0}{R}$ versus $\frac{\rho}{\rho_0} - 1$, which was ex-trapolated to the limit of Bridgman's density measurements. To extend the data to higher pressures, the P–V data of Rice, McQueen and Walsh[19], extrapolated to 25°C, were used.

The values of R/R_0 as a function of pressure so obtained are shown in Table 3 for lead, platinum, and indium. These metals were chosen because their resistance v. density curves changed less rapidly than did those of most metals, and because at least two different methods of extrapolation predicted con-sistent resistance changes at the higher pressures. Lead has a transition (dis-cussed in detail below) at 161 kilobars, which became an important fixed point in our calibration. It may be noted here that the resistance of lead just before the transition is 0·784 times its value at the upper bismuth transition.

(*c*) *Lead transition*—In the course of the present investigation, a transition was observed in lead which exhibited a 23·2 per cent increase in resistance. Bismuth and lead were run consecutively on the same sets of hardened pistons, and, with the upper bismuth transition as a reference point (90 kb), the above lead correlation was used to obtain centre pressure versus average piston pressure to the lead transition point. Five sets of runs gave values for the transition pressure of 161 kb±3 kb. The calibrations thus generated were straight lines from 50 to 161 kilobars, intersecting the axis at about 1–2 kilobars piston pressure (see *Figure 17*).

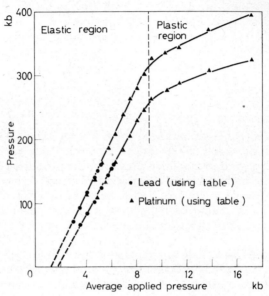

Figure 17. Typical calibration runs for grade 999 work-hardened Carboloy piston sets

(*d*) *Extension of calibration with platinum and indium*—The pressure calibration above 161 kilobars was determined for once-hardened and multiply-hardened piston sets through use of the extrapolated resistances for platinum and indium. This was done by overlapping the resistivity data of the two metals run with the same piston sets as used in the previous lead run. A plot of centre pressure versus average pressure was consistently linear to 9 kilobars average pressure (corresponding to 250–350 kilobars centre pressure, depending on the hardness of the particular piston set). *Figure 17* shows typical Pb–Pt runs for two piston sets used in extension of the calibration.

To 9 kb, no plastic deformation of the piston centres occurred; above this point the deformation was a direct function of the applied force. *Figure 18(a)* shows the 'dish' obtained upon exposure of a once-hardened piston to 400 kb, *Figure 18(b)* the strain pattern in the Carboloy underneath the centre flat of the piston in (*a*).

The resulting calibration obtained from platinum and indium above 9 kb for once-hardened 999 piston sets is shown in *Figure 19*, where the centre pressure at any given average pressure has been divided by the centre pressure found from the straight line extrapolation at 9 kb. A calibration was obtained in the same manner for multiply-hardened pistons.

Once the 9 kilobar linear relationship had been established, the following calibration procedure was adopted:

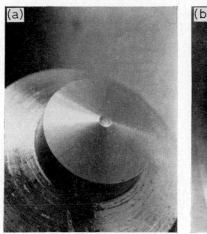

Figure 18. (*a*) Piston deformation. (*b*) Strain due to work-hardening

(1) The lead calibration to 161 kilobars was established for a particular piston set and the line was extrapolated to 9 kilobars average pressure.

(2) Pressures above 9 kilobars were obtained from the calibration of *Figure 19* for all 999 piston sets, and from a similar calibration for multiply-hardened 883 pistons.

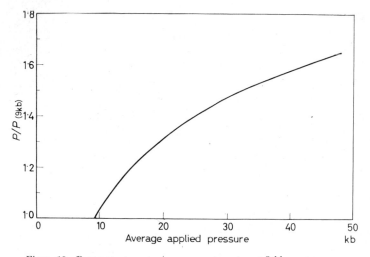

Figure 19. Pressure at centre/pressure at centre at 9 kb *v.* average pressure

(iii) Resistance of lead, iron, barium, calcium and rubidium at high pressure

(a) Lead—*Figure 20* illustrates the effect of pressure on the resistance of lead to **230** kb. The curve has been normalized at 90 kb, and, to 161 kb, represents the extrapolation given in *Table 3*. The transition observed was reversible,

Table 3. *Resistance (Relative to Zero Pressure Resistance) v. Pressure.*
Extrapolation of Bridgman's Data

P (kilobars)	$\frac{R}{R_0}$ (Platinum)	$\frac{R}{R_0}$ (Indium)	P(kilobars)	$\frac{R}{R_0}$ (Lead)
50	0·917	0·653	30	0·704
100	0·858	0·514	60	0·556
150	0·813	0·436	90	0·478
200	0·778	0·384	120	0·425
250	0·751	0·347	150	0·386
300	0·731	0·319	161	0·374
350	0·714	0·296	—	—
400	0·700	0·278	—	—
450	0·690	0·262	—	—
500	0·681	0·249	—	—

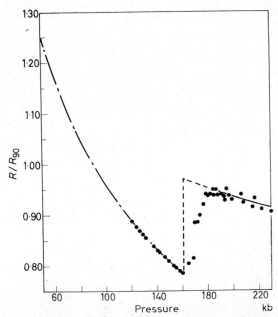

Figure 20. Resistance at *P*/resistance at 90 kb *v.* pressure
for lead

although the high pressure modification showed great stability upon release of pressure. The value of 23·2 per cent change across the transition was obtained as the average of 22 runs.

Since lead has the face-centred cubic structure at one atmosphere, it is proposed that the transition is electronic in nature.

(*b*) *Iron*—The resistance of iron to 425 kb is shown in *Figure 21*. A transition was observed at 133 kb; this value was obtained to ±1·5

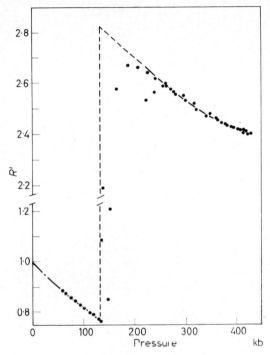

Figure 21. Relative resistance *v.* pressure for iron

per cent on four runs. The changes in resistance below the transition were fitted to an extrapolation of Bridgman's 30,000 kg/cm² liquid data similar to those for lead, platinum and indium. The resulting resistance change across the transition (using these corrections) was a factor of 3·66, although the uncorrected values were less than this. In *Figure 21* the extrapolation of Bridgman's data extends from one atmosphere to slightly beyond the first data point.

The transition pressure of 133 kb is in excellent agreement with a transition found at 131 kb in shock wave studies on iron[20]. This agreement provided an independent confirmation of the pressure scale obtained using the lead extrapolation. The value is in poor agreement with the data of Strong[21], although it is not certain that the same transition 'point' was measured in the two cases.

(*c*) *Barium, calcium and rubidium*—The pressure effect on the resistance of barium is shown in *Figure 22*. After the transition at 59 kilobars the resistance rises linearly to 144 kilobars, where a second transition occurs. The relative resistance shows a decrease with pressure after this point. Both transitions are completely reversible and the pressure of the higher transition was obtained as the average of four runs.

The data on barium were corrected by matching the data to the resistance

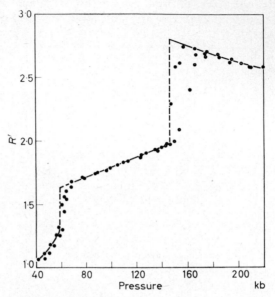

Figure 22. Relative resistance *v.* pressure for barium

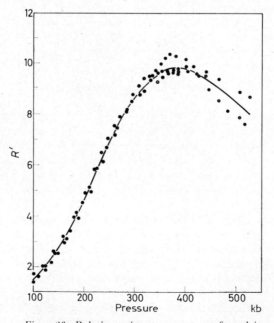

Figure 23. Relative resistance *v.* pressure for calcium

change obtained by Bridgman at the 59-kilobar transition (25 per cent). The resulting change from 40–59 kilobars appears to agree relatively well with the data of Bridgman, although, because of differences in the pressure scale used, direct comparison is impossible.

In *Figure 23* is plotted the resistance of calcium to 525 kilobars. A maximum of resistance occurs at 375 kilobars, this pressure being obtained to ± 15 kilobars on four runs. On release of pressure the resistance initially drops slowly, shows a small bump at a very low value of applied force, and decreases sharply below this point. Since the corrections applied by Bridgman were large, it was thought more useful to present the uncorrected

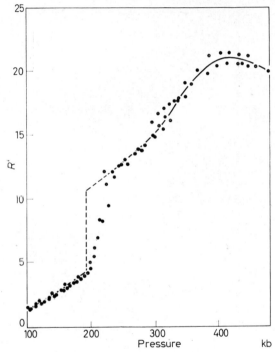

Figure 24. Relative resistance v. pressure for rubidium

data, as in *Figure 23*. Points below 100 kilobars on calcium (and rubidium) could not be obtained with accuracy, and are not shown. The resistance at 375 kilobars is $6 \cdot 78$ times the resistance at 100 kilobars.

The effect of pressure on the resistance of rubidium is shown in *Figure 24*. The data in this case are also left uncorrected. A transition was observed at 193 kilobars, as established in four runs. The resistance at the transition was $3 \cdot 31$ times that at 100 kilobars; the resistance increases above the transition to a maximum at 425 kb. Both maximum and transition are completely reversible, as shown in the case of the single run plotted in *Figure 25*. With decreasing applied force, the maximum (as in the case of calcium) shows a displacement toward lower pressures, a metastable behaviour similar to that observed by Bridgman in caesium.

Bundy[16] observed a transition in rubidium at about 75–80 kilobars on our scale accompanied by an increase of resistance of about 8–10 per cent. Because of the rapid rise of resistance of rubidium with pressure, and our difficulties with pressure in this range, it is impossible to say whether this occurred in our samples.

Of interest in both calcium and rubidium was the fact that, on incremental application of pressure immediately above the maxima, the resistance first rose slightly and then quickly fell to an equilibrium value. As the pressure was increased still further, this behaviour disappeared, or at least occurred too rapidly to be noticeable.

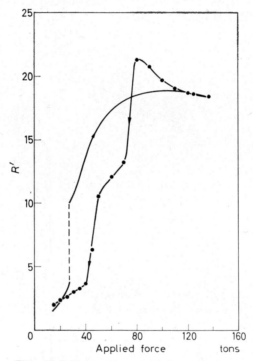

Figure 25. Relative resistance v. pressure (increasing and decreasing pressure) for rubidium

The results obtained at higher pressures for barium, calcium and rubidium help to explain the anomalous behaviour of the resistance of these materials at lower pressures, and aid in predicting the behaviour of similar metals. The calculations of Sternheimer[22] indicate the transition in caesium to be a discontinuous increase in the d character of the valence electron. On this basis Lawson[23] explains the large increase of resistance before the transition as increased scattering of the conduction electrons into vacant d states, whose density at the Fermi surface increases with pressure. Lawson interprets similar resistance behaviour in cerium and ytterbium as an increase (either discontinuous or gradual) in d character of the 4f electrons. The calculations of Manning and Krutter[24] for calcium show that the d band overlaps the first Brillouin zone at one atmosphere; the overlap increases linearly with decreasing interatomic distance.

On the basis of the present results, and those of Bridgman, for metals having 'vacant' d bands at one atmosphere with energies at or slightly above the highest occupied levels, a consistent picture of these materials can be formed. It is proposed that the transitions in rubidium and barium (at 144 kb) are electronic in nature, qualitatively similar to the transition in caesium. Indeed, the maxima in calcium and rubidium have some characteristics of transitions, albeit gradual ones. It appears likely that the anomalous behaviour of this class of metals is due to the fact that up to a certain pressure, the controlling effect on the conductivity is the increase with pressure in the number of vacant states of predominantly d character at the Fermi surface. At a high enough overlap this effect becomes secondary, and the resistance is determined mainly by the stiffening of the lattice with pressure. Between these two extremes, both factors contribute to the resistance behaviour. (There is, of course, always the possibility of discontinuous changes.) Whether the latter extreme, lattice stiffening, has been reached at the highest pressures in the metals studied is not certain. The maxima in calcium and rubidium resemble the one in strontium, and may represent the overlap of the first set of levels (of predominantly d character). In this case the resistance behaviour after the maximum has been passed may still prove anomalous.

Further work on these metals is anticipated to provide greater clarification.

(iv) Calibration Points

Table 4 contains the pressure 'set points' as established in this work (including also the 90 kb transition in bismuth noted by Bridgman and Bundy). The values listed, except in the cases of maxima, represent the pressures at the onset of the transitions, which appeared as extremely sharp points in all cases studied (generally $\frac{1}{4}$–$\frac{1}{2}$ of the transition could be accomplished by application of 5 kb greater pressure than that given in *Table 4*).

Table 4. Calibration Points

Element	Pressure (kb)	Character of Change
Bismuth	88	Sharp decrease in resistance (250–300%)
Iron	133	Sharp rise in resistance (366%)
Barium	144	Sharp rise in resistance (42%)
Lead	161	Sharp rise in resistance (23·2%)
Rubidium	193	Sharp rise in resistance (147%)
	425	Maximum in resistance
Calcium	375	Maximum in resistance

The two basic differences between Bridgman anvils and the cell just described are: (1) use of a smaller flat area, and (2) compressive support of the tapered section. Without either, or both, of these factors, it would undoubtedly be impossible to work-harden the pistons to the degree possible at present. (Tests indicate an increase in maximum pressure of at least 75 per cent for once-hardened pistons.)

Other advantages of the present design include: smaller over-all piston size (allowing greater Carboloy uniformity), minimal press requirements, and comparatively simple construction. A decrease in flat size, of course, increases the difficulties inherent in the loading of the cell.

The method of calibration is subject to considerable criticism and possible error due to gross extrapolation. On the other hand, it does permit future workers to translate our results in terms of their scale. There is also considerable consistency in the extrapolation and calibration curves obtained for the three metals, as previously detailed. It is the authors' opinion that while this 'continuous' calibration method may prove suitable for certain types of equipment, the most reproducible pressure calibration method still remains that of the use of a series of transition 'set points'. Since the pressures are undoubtedly not completely hydrostatic, the values of the fixed points are much more accurate than the fractional changes of resistance with pressure. It is hoped that the transition pressures obtained in this work will be examined critically by other investigators, as only in this way will the region of accurate high pressure calibration be extended.

References

[1] FITCH, R. A., SLYKHOUSE, T. E. and DRICKAMER, H. G., *J. Opt. Soc. Am.*, **47**, 1957 p. 1,015

[2] MAISCH, W. G. and DRICKAMER, H. G., *J. Phys. Chem. Solids*, **5**, 1958, p. 328

[3] JACOBS, I. S., *Phys. Rev.*, **93**, 1954, p. 993

[4] BRIDGMAN, P. W., *Proc. Amer. Arts Sci.*, **74**, 1942, p. 425

[5] BRIDGMAN, P. W., *Proc. Amer. Arts Sci.*, **81**, 1952, p. 165

[6] BUNDY, F. L., *Phys. Rev.*, **110**, 1958, p. 314

[7] SLYKHOUSE, T. E. and DRICKAMER, H. G., *J. Phys. Chem. Solids*, **7**, 1958, p. 207

[8] SLYKHOUSE, T. E. and DRICKAMER, H. G., *J. Phys. Chem. Solids*, **7** (L), 1958, p. 27

[9] BALCHAN, A. S. and DRICKAMER, H. G., *J. appl. Phys.*, **30**, 1959, p. 1,446

[10] BALCHAN, A. S. and DRICKAMER, H. G., *Rev. sci. Instrum.*, **31**, 1960, p. 511

[11] BRIDGMAN, P. W., *Proc. Amer. Acad. Arts Sci.*, **72**, 1938, p. 157

[12] BRIDGMAN, P. W., *Proc. Amer. Acad. Arts Sci.*, **79**, 1951, p. 125

[13] BRIDGMAN, P. W., *Proc. Amer. Acad. Arts Sci.*, **81**, 1952, p. 169; **83**, 1954, p. 1

[14] BRIDGMAN, P. W., *Proc. Amer. Acad. Arts Sci.*, **74**, 1940, p. 21

[15] JURA, G., HARRIS, R. E., VAISNYS, R. J. and STROMBERG, H., *Progress in Very High Pressure Research*, John Wiley and Sons, New York, 1961

[16] BUNDY, F. P., *Phys. Rev.*, **115**, 1959, p. 274

[17] HALL, H. T., *Rev. Sci. Instrum.*, **31**, 1960, p. 125

[18] BALCHAN, A. S. and DRICKAMER, H. G., *Rev. Sci. Instrum.*, March 1961

[19] RICE, M. H., McQUEEN, R. G. and WALSH, J. M., *Solid State Physics*, Academic Press, New York, 1958, vol. **6**, p. 1

[20] BANCROFT, D., PETERSON, E. L. and MINSHALL, S., *J. appl. Phys.*, **27**, 1956, p. 291

[21] STRONG, H. M., *Progress in Very High Pressure Research*, John Wiley and Sons, New York, 1961

[22] STERNHEIMER, R., *Phys. Rev.*, **78**, 1950, p. 235

[23] LAWSON, A. W., *Progr. Metal Phys.*, **6**, 1956, p. 1

[24] MANNING, M. F. and KRUTTER, H. M., *Phys. Rev.*, **51**, 1937, p. 761

3

OPTICAL STUDIES AT HIGH PRESSURES USING DIAMOND ANVILS

C. E. WEIR and A. VAN VALKENBURG

National Bureau of Standards, Washington, D.C.

E. LIPPINCOTT

Department of Chemistry, University of Maryland, College Park, Md

A PRESSURE cell capable of maintaining pressures up to 160,000 atmospheres has been constructed using a pair of type II diamonds for studies in the infra-red, visible and ultra-violet spectrum. Temperature variations from 175 to $-30°C$ have been obtained with the cell. Major effects observed in the infra-red spectrum of substances under pressure include shifts in absorption bands to both higher and lower frequencies, the occurrence of new bands as well as the elimination of existing bands, the splitting of bands, and changes in apparent band intensities. Examples of these effects, using the infra-red spectra of sodium nitrite, calcite, succinic acid, ice, and ferrocene, are given.

I. Introduction

The application of pressures up to 160,000 atmospheres to infra-red, visible, and ultra-violet spectroscopy now offers the investigator an effective tool to probe the behaviour of atomic forces. The most important factors affecting interatomic distances in solids are temperature, pressure, and geometrical configuration. Temperature, when used alone as a means of producing systematic variations in the interatomic distances of a given structure, cannot exceed the limits imposed by the thermal stability of the solid and the absolute zero of temperature. In general, a knowledge of the crystal potential energy function is insufficient to make use of the geometrical configuration as a means of varying intermolecular distances systematically. In comparison, the only limitation involved in the use of pressure is the failure of the pressure-producing vessel itself.

The work of Lawson and Ting-Yuan Tang[1], and later the work of Jamieson[2], demonstrated the use of a diamond pressure cell for producing x-ray powder diffraction patterns at pressures up to 30,000 atmospheres (see Chapter 4). A study of the absorption spectra of type II diamonds indicated the possibility of using a similar device to record infra-red, visible, and ultra-violet absorption spectra.

In the infra-red spectrum a typical type II diamond with a thickness of 2·4 mm has only one absorption band, which is near 5μ, as shown in *Figure 1*. It is transparent to 35μ, which is the long wavelength limit of most commercial infra-red prism spectrometers. A type I diamond shows an intense

51

absorption band near 8μ, as shown in *Figure 2*. Both type I and type II diamonds are transparent from 10μ to approximately 35μ. A number of diamonds, however, show gradations in absorption between types I and II. The reason for these differences in the infra-red spectrum is not known. Type II diamonds have been heated to 800°C in inert atmospheres and then

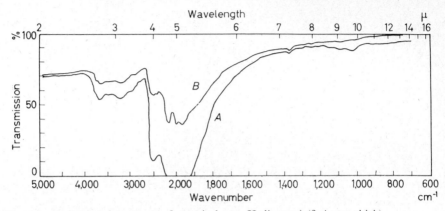

Figure 1. A. Infra-red spectrum of a typical type II diamond (2·4 mm thick)
B. Infra-red spectrum of a thin type II diamond (1 mm thick)

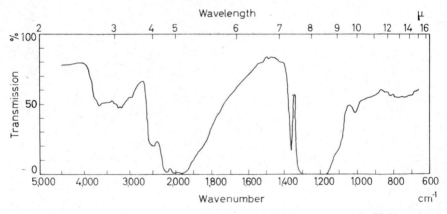

Figure 2. Infra-red spectrum of a typical type I diamond (2·4 mm thick)

rapidly cooled to room temperatures without any detectable change in the transmission spectrum[3]. Calculated pressures up to 160,000 atmospheres have been maintained on type II diamond anvils with this apparatus for periods of up to half an hour without any noticeable change in their transmission properties[4].

II. Apparatus

The first experimental pressure cell used was based on the design of

Jamieson[2], using the principle of squeezing material in a cylinder between two pistons. A type II gem diamond of emerald cut, weighing approximately $7\frac{1}{2}$ carats, was altered by polishing two flat parallel faces and drilling a 0.016 in. cylindrical hole parallel to these faces. Tempered steel pistons were fitted to the cylinder, and force was applied to the pistons by means of a calibrated spring activated by a hand screw mechanism. The samples to be examined were diluted with suitable material, such as KBr or NaCl, to obtain the correct concentration. In order to obtain the maximum transmitted energy, it was necessary to focus the beam to approximately 0.016×0.375 in. by using a lens system and adjustable slits.

The technique just described can be used to obtain data up to 30,000 atmospheres, but there are serious difficulties involved in the technique when applied to optical studies. For example, the cylindrical pressure chamber behaves as a complex lens system because materials under examination have indices of refraction different from those of the diluent, which in turn has indices different from that of the diamond. Careful orientation adjustments of the diamond cell, with respect to the focused beam, are necessary with each run. The mechanical difficulties of cleaning a 0.016 in. hole, and the repacking of new sample material for determining the correct concentration of diluent to sample as well as running the final patterns, require considerable patience. After a number of runs using this technique, the diamond split into two segments at an estimated pressure in excess of 10,000 atmospheres. Because of the difficulties inherent in this design, and the possibility of further diamond failures, a new design was constructed using the principle of Bridgman's anvil apparatus[5—7].

The apparatus is shown in *Figure 3*. Two gem-cut type II diamonds, each weighing 0.036 g, comprise the squeezer anvils. The culets of each diamond were ground off to form small flats parallel to the tables[6]. The specimen is placed between these small flats, which have an area of approximately 0.0002 sq. in. To minimize axial alignment problems, and to take advantage of the massive support principle, the two diamond surfaces are purposely ground to have different surface areas. Each diamond, A, is seated on its tabular face, which rests in a close-fitting recess in a stainless steel piston, B. Each piston is drilled longitudinally with a hole of 0.060–0.075 in. and is bored out with a tapering hole which extends to within $\frac{1}{16}$ in. of the diamond. This taper is designed to permit acceptance of the maximum flux from a cone of radiation which passes through both pistons, the diamonds, and the specimen contained between the diamond surfaces. The specimen itself is located at the focus of this beam.

The pistons are free to slide in a dural or bronze bearing, C, that screws into a large block of steel, carrying the pressure generating equipment. The threaded mount is used to enable ready interchange of bearings when desired. One piston rests against a thrust bearing, D, which also screws into the steel block. At the other end, a presser plate, E, bears against the other piston. The presser plate is connected to a lever that is pivoted in the block, and actuated by a calibrated spring, F, which bears against the upper end of the lever. The presser plate is bored out to permit entrance of the convergent cone into the piston. In operation, the position of the pistons may be varied by moving the thrust plate so that the presser plate is perpendicular to the axis through the diamonds. This positioning ensures the absence of components of force at right angles to the thrust axis. The spring is compressed by means of a manually operated screw, G, having 20 threads/in. In the present device, the lever arms are of equal length, but as there is negligible motion of the pistons, the lever arms may be varied to produce different pressure ranges using the same spring.

The whole unit is designed to be mounted in a commercial infra-red-beam condensing unit, and the cell is only 1 in. in length to fit into the highly restricted focal area of the lens system. The steel supporting block has been drilled to form a channel surrounding the diamond cell. By circulating

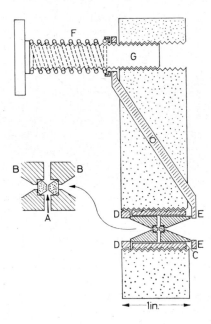

Figure 3. Schematic diagram of diamond 'squeezer' for infra-red transmission studies to 160,000 atm

liquids or gases through the channels, the temperature may be maintained at any convenient value for a given experiment. In practice, measurements have been performed to date in the temperature range $-30°C$ to $+175°C$. At lower temperatures cold N_2 gas was used, and at elevated temperatures heated air was used. Temperatures may be measured with a small thermocouple inserted through one piston and placed in contact with the diamonds. Adequate temperature control can be obtained by manual adjustment of the flow of gas through the channel system.

The force is determined by measuring the compression of the spring. Pressures are obtained by dividing the force by the area of the smaller of the two diamond faces, neglecting frictional forces. No greater precision is required at the present time. Experiments have shown that the thrust transmitted by the specimen may be measured by determining the resistance of a small coil of manganin wire placed under thrust plate D, if greater precision is desired.

The diamond-bearing surfaces are irregular octagons. The lengths of each

54

side and the external angles were measured using a micrometer eyepiece on a rotating stage microscope. The data were laid out on graph paper and the areas of the bearing surfaces determined by counting the squares. Two cells have been used with the smaller diamonds, having measured areas of 0·000156 sq. in. and 0·000182 sq. in.

III. The Nature of the Pressure

Some consideration of the nature of the pressure on the specimen is necessary, but only a qualitative discussion is possible at this time. In similar 'squeezers' using Carboloy, the anvils become concave on continued use and eventually confine the specimen in an enclosed capsule. Under these circumstances, one may be tempted to consider the specimen as subjected to reasonably hydro-static pressure. Even under these circumstances, however, there is consider-able uncertainty as to the hydrostatic character of the pressure[8,9]. In the diamond squeezer no plastic deformation of the surfaces has been observed, and there is considerably more uncertainty about the nature of the stress on the specimen. Marked lateral-extrusion tendencies, observed as changes in intensities, have been noted in some specimens. With diluents, the pressure on the specimen is more apt to be considered hydrostatic, but completely concordant data are obtained with or without diluents. Furthermore, all effects observed appear to be reasonably reversible and reproducible[4].

Therefore, although the uncertainties are fully recognized, the stress applied to the specimen will be considered to be a pressure, and no further discussion of its character will be made here.

IV. The Behaviour of the Diamonds

Optically, the diamond should be isotropic to visible light when placed between crossed polarizing nichols. Without a known exception, all the type II diamonds that were analyzed showed areas of birefringence. These areas were observed as wavy extinctions on rotations of the nichols, as cross hatched figures, as haloes, and as irregular light and dark areas. The presence of the birefringence areas indicates regions of stress and strain within the diamond. A noticeable shift of these areas was observed under the micro-scope when pressure was applied to the anvils. It was hoped that a pair of strain-free diamonds could be found, for then it might have been possible to determine the thickness of the specimen optically while under pressure, using birefringence techniques. Also, a rough determination of the compressibility of the specimen could be obtained using similar techniques.

After continued use of the diamond anvils at routine pressures of 50,000 atmospheres and room temperatures, fissure patterns were observed forming on the surfaces of the anvils. A quantitative analysis of the anvil alterations was not undertaken, as data involving crystal orientation, magnitude of the stresses and strains, and occasional misalignment of the anvils were not known. The fissure patterns on the larger diamond surface were significantly different from the corresponding smaller diamond anvil. *Figure 4* shows a typical fissure area of a larger diamond as photographed in white light. It will be noted that a series of approximately three concentric rings can be observed. These rings are opposite the face of the small diamond. Rarely do the fissures extend deep into the diamond and, in general, they appear to penetrate just below the surface, a distance of about $\frac{1}{64}$ in. With continued

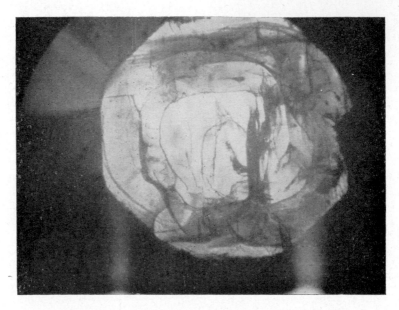

Figure 4. Fissure patterns on larger diamond anvil surface

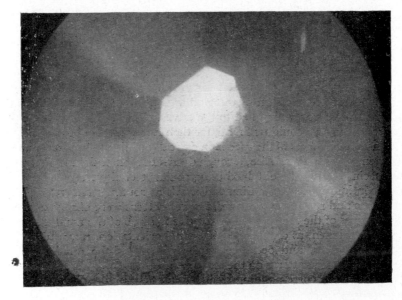

Figure 5. Chipping of smaller diamond anvil on pressure surface

use, the diamond surface becomes pitted as small diamond chips are dislodged. It is of interest to note that the shallow fissures do not appear to alter the mechanical or optical characteristics of the anvils. The appearance of pitted areas, however, renders the diamonds useless and they must be reground to a flat surface. In contrast, the smaller diamond anvils, *Figure 5*, do not show the concentric fissure rings. Chipping of the diamond adjacent to the pressure surface is the major factor in the alterations of the small diamond area. When chipping becomes too severe, the diamonds are reground.

V. Experimental Techniques

Commercial double-beam spectrometers equipped with beam-condensing units are used to cover the ranges 1μ to 35μ, and 250 mμ to $1,000$ mμ. The sample is held between the diamonds by the frictional forces resisting flow in a thin specimen. Fortunately, the thickness of the specimen retained after extrusion ceases is usually just adequate to obtain a reasonably characteristic infra-red spectrum. For organic compounds, this thickness is sometimes too small to permit observation of weak bands, while for some inorganic salts it appears somewhat too large for strong bands. The question of the hydrostatic nature of the pressure and the magnitude of the pressure gradients near the edges of the specimen makes it important that the pressure, calculated as force per unit area, should be checked by a calibration based on a phase change for a given substance at a known hydrostatic pressure and temperature. This was accomplished by using inorganic substances having transitions at known pressures, such as $NaNO_2$, KNO_3, etc.

Transitions were sometimes difficult to initiate, but once obtained they were usually readily reversible. By following transitions with different sets of diamonds it was possible to obtain information about the condition of the diamond surfaces. In some instances the transition was found to occur over a narrow pressure range (±300 atm) with only a single phase present at any time, while in other cases more than one band was present simultaneously over a rather wide pressure range, indicating the presence of a considerable pressure gradient. The latter situation usually occurred when the diamond surfaces had deteriorated markedly and a number of surface flaws were present, or with diamonds of very small surface area.

In order to obtain reproducible spectra and to lengthen the lifetime of the diamond anvils, it has been found to be extremely important to align the anvil surfaces prior to each run. To facilitate alignment, one diamond assembly is equipped with three small levelling screws. The two diamonds to be used are placed in position in a spare bearing and are observed in transmitted white light with a microscope focussed on the anvil contact surfaces. The levelling screws are adjusted until white light interference fringes appear. Further adjustments are made until the number of fringes is reduced to a minimum, and the resulting fringe system is centred on the surface of the smaller diamond.

In a typical experiment, the piston, with one of the diamonds, was inserted in the bearing and a small quantity of specimen was placed on the diamond surface with a spatula. The other diamond in its piston was inserted, and the thrust plate was screwed into place. The pressure was then raised to a few thousand atmospheres to produce a film between the diamond faces. The pressure cell was then placed in the focal point of the beam-condensing unit and its position adjusted in the beam to produce a maximum transmission at a wavelength where the specimen had no absorption bands. The pressure was then raised and lowered until no further evidence was found for extrusion of the sample between the diamond surfaces. The pressure was then raised to the maximum desired, and the spectrum run. Subsequent runs were made at successively lower pressures. When the lowest pressures had been reached, the whole set of runs was repeated by starting again at the higher pressures. In most cases the changes that occurred in the spectrum were reversible when run under these conditions. In a few experiments there was evidence of irreversible changes in the spectrum occurring at pressures in excess of 50,000 atm. This was indicated by the appearance of new bands that remained when the pressure was reduced to 1 atm. These irreversible changes may have been caused by a chemical reaction or the production of a dense phase, and have not been studied in detail.

In order to study strong absorption bands in detail, some materials were diluted with KBr or LiF. The dilutions were generally in 1 : 1 or 2 : 1 proportions. It was found that KBr extruded rapidly under pressure and was not satisfactory. LiF was a very satisfactory medium with little or no extrusion, but in dilute mixtures there exists the possibility of interaction with the dispersed substance. The complete range may not be studied with LiF because this material absorbs strongly above $14 \cdot 5\mu$.

VI. Discussion of Errors

Since the smaller diamond faces had an area of 1 to 2×10^{-4} sq. in., only a portion of the incident infra-red beam could be accepted by the cell. Thus it was necessary to restrict the reference beam so as to permit utilization of the full scale of the recorder. This was accomplished by placing a suitable screen or a sheet of perforated aluminium in the reference beam. The low available energy made it necessary to operate at high gain and to use a slow scanning speed. The scanning speeds used varied from $0 \cdot 08$ to $0 \cdot 5\mu$/min with a slit programme usually from three to four times that for the standard programme for the instrument. In studying a given specimen, all the instrumental settings were left unchanged. Because of the use of high gains, some of the recorded spectra showed considerable 'noise'.

Errors in reading the positions of absorption bands may occur because of the finite rate of scan and the limited amount of energy available. In cases where the exact position of a band was desired, the scanning speed was reduced, or the position was obtained from a manual setting. Since most of the work reported here is not concerned with the quantitative behaviour of the frequency shifts, no special effort was made to measure the positions with greater accuracy than that available from the normal scanning rate of the spectrum.

A number of sources of error may affect the intensities of the recorded bands. Among these are the errors associated with the finite slit width and scanning speeds. These errors are accentuated by the limited amount of energy passing through the small specimen. For a given run under a fixed set of instrument settings, there is the question of error associated with extrusion of the specimen. Also, the material may become increasingly more transparent to infra-red radiation at higher or lower pressures, depending on the condition of the specimen film. Initially, the powdered specimen is translucent to radiation with considerable scattering. This scattering is usually reduced as the pressure is applied, but sometimes increases at higher pressures, presumably because of a phase change. In general, bands tend to broaden at elevated pressures. The finite slit width used would act to increase the apparent intensity of the pressure-broadened bands. Since the intensity of most bands decreases at elevated pressures, this source of error produces an effect on intensity opposite to that observed.

The effect of the smaller amount of scattering at the higher pressure would be to furnish more energy to the detector, with the result that the apparent band intensity would appear slightly greater. In actual practice, most, but not all, bands show a decrease in intensity at higher pressures, and thus the effect of this source of error is opposite to the observed behaviour.

The effect of extrusion of specimen from between the diamond surfaces would produce a decrease in band intensity. However, a loss in intensity through extrusion should not be reversible for the types of material studied here. The extrusion is generally observed in all experiments as an irreversible, time-dependent decrease in intensity of all bands upon the initial application of pressure. In practice, quantitative intensity measurements were not considered feasible until the flow of specimen from between the diamond surfaces had ceased, as shown by the reproducibility of band intensities at different pressures. In addition, quantitative data were usually obtained by starting at the maximum pressure with subsequent measurements at successively lower pressures. Additional loss of material would be minimized by this technique. Furthermore, a few spectra have been obtained which show that in a given specimen, some bands increase in intensity, some decrease, and others show no change as the pressure increases. Such spectra show unmistakably that there is, at the very least, a marked relative intensity change between such bands. In addition, it is believed that the present data illustrate the behaviour of the absolute band intensities as a function of pressure. For obvious reasons, no great precision is to be expected in an individual quantitative measurement of absolute intensity, but data on the pressure dependence are believed to be qualitatively correct.

The apparent band intensities were calculated from plots of log I_0/I v. wave-number (or wavelength) followed by a graphical determination of the area. All results are given in ratios of the intensity at a given pressure to that at the lowest pressure recorded. In this manner, many problems associated with the computation of integrated intensities have been minimized or cancelled.

Intensity ratios calculated from the integrated expression for band intensities[10]

$$A = Kc^{-1}l^{-1}(\Delta\nu_{\frac{1}{2}})\ln(I_0/I)$$

gave results in essential agreement with those obtained graphically. In this equation $\Delta\nu_{\frac{1}{2}}$ is the band half-width, K is a proportionality constant, A is the band area, c is the concentration in moles per litre and l is the path length in cm. In these experiments, the product cl, which is a measure of the quantity of material in the beam, is considered to be constant.

VII. Experimental Results

In general, the infra-red spectrum of a substance shows a number of changes on application of pressure; these include shifts of absorption bands to both higher and lower frequencies from the positions of the bands at 1 atm, the occurrence of new bands, the splitting of bands from a change of site group and/or factor group selection rules, and changes in apparent band intensity. These effects may occur discontinuously for pressure-induced phase changes, and continuously because of the change of bond environment in a given phase on increasing or decreasing pressure. The shifts in absorption bands observed to date range up to a maximum of ± 10 cm^{-1} per 10,000 atm pressure, with greater shifts sometimes occurring for substances involving systems of hydrogen bonds. Appreciable changes in apparent intensity of many bands are observed at relatively low pressures, i.e. 10,000 atm, with larger changes occurring at higher pressures. The change of intensity is specific with respect to both the nature of the substance and the mode of vibration. We will illustrate these effects with results obtained from experiments on five substances: sodium nitrite, calcite, succinic acid, ice, and ferrocene [bis-dicyclopentadienyl iron (II)]. Comparable pressure studies were made on ferrocene in the ultra-violet and visible region of the spectrum as well in the infra-red region, and the results will serve to illustrate the application of the diamond cell in the range from $0 \cdot 30$ to 35μ respectively.

(i) Sodium Nitrite

The effect of a pressure-induced phase transition on the infra-red spectrum of an ionic solid may be illustrated by studies on sodium nitrite, in which a transition has been found to take place at a hydrostatic pressure of 14,500 atm[11]. This transition was studied by observing the behaviour of the 825 cm^{-1} $(12 \cdot 1\mu)$ absorption band corresponding to the nitrite ion bending mode of vibration. The frequency shifts discontinuously to near 855 cm^{-1} $(11 \cdot 7\mu)$ when this transition takes place. A similar shift may occur for the NO stretching frequency of the nitrite ion, but the intensity of this band was too great for accurate frequency determinations to be made. An example of this is illustrated in *Figure 6*. In these experiments, the pressure was raised to 14,000 atm, lowered a few thousand atm, raised again to 14,000 atm, and the process repeated several times. This transition served to check the pressure calibration in terms of the applied load and its relative sharpness furnished evidence that excessive pressure gradients did not exist in the specimen. The absence of excessive gradients provides evidence that the pressure is reasonably hydrostatic in nature. The transition was sometimes difficult to initiate but once obtained it was readily reversible. By following the transition with different sets of diamonds it was possible to obtain information on the condition of the diamond surfaces. When evidence of excessive gradients was observed the diamond surfaces were reground[6].

Other pressure-induced phase transitions have been found to have an effect on the infra-red spectrum of the specimen, although in some cases the transitions have been found to be rather sluggish. Some examples include KNO$_3$, AgNO$_3$, ferrocene, ice, CaCO$_3$, semicarbazide hydrochloride, and methylamine hydrochloride.

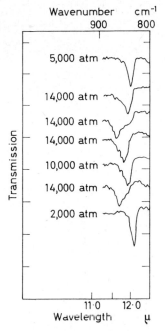

Figure 6. Behaviour of the 825 cm^{-1} nitrite ion bending frequency for the transition occurring in NaNO$_2$

(ii) *Calcite*

The vibrational spectrum of calcite is considered to be rather well understood, both in terms of frequency assignment and in the effects of crystal symmetry[12-16]. The free carbonate ion, CO$_3^{--}$, has D$_{3h}$ symmetry with four internal frequencies corresponding to a symmetric stretching, ν_1, an out-of-plane bending ν_2, a doubly degenerate stretching ν_3, and a doubly degenerate bending, ν_4. The selection rules for the calcite structure indicate that the ν_2, ν_3, and ν_4 fundamental frequencies should appear in the infra-red spectrum while ν_1 is predicted inactive. However, degenerate lattice frequencies of translational or rotational origins may interact with the degenerate frequencies to produce a splitting. This splitting is usually not observed in pellet or mull spectra of calcite taken at 1 atm. Spectra of calcite taken at various pressures are shown in *Figure 7(a)*, (*b*) and (*c*). One effect of pressure is observed to be a noticeable splitting of the degenerate fundamentals. The ν_3 fundamental at 1,463 cm^{-1} at 3,000 atm is split into two components which are separated by 103 cm^{-1} under a pressure of 31,000 atm. The splitting of the degenerate bending fundamental, ν_4, at 715 cm^{-1} is interesting in that three distinct components appear rather than two, as expected from a site group splitting*. These splittings are reversible and disappear when the pressure is lowered. The ν_2 mode at 883 cm^{-1} is not degenerate and shows no tendency toward splitting.

* Recent evidence indicates that the apparent splitting under pressure of the in-plane bending made for CO$_3^{--}$ ions is calcite is due to sum and difference tones of the fundamental made with rotational lattice modes of the CO$_3^{-}$ ion.

Evidence that the CO_3^{--} ion sites are deviating from D_3 symmetry is furnished by the appearance at 1,097 cm^{-1} of the forbidden symmetric stretching frequency, ν_1, at elevated pressures. This band shows a marked increase in intensity as the pressure rises, which is interpreted as a change of

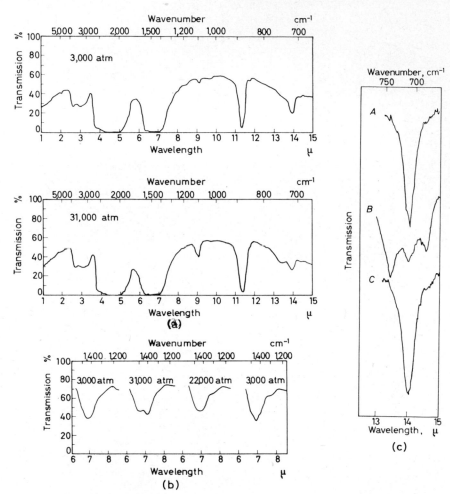

Figure 7. (a) Infra-red transmission spectra for calcite at various pressures: top, 3,000 atm; bottom, 31,000 atm
(b) Detailed study of 1,463 cm^{-1} band of calcite using LiF diluent
(c) Splitting of degenerate bending frequency with pressure in calcite: *A* and *C* 1 atm; *B*, 35,000 atm

selection rules from either a change of crystal symmetry as the result of a pressure-induced phase change or an increased perturbation of the internal frequencies by the more intense crystal field. We favour the former interpretation in that there is some evidence from the spectra that the splitting occurs discontinuously during a sluggish phase change. Pressure-induced transitions have been reported for calcite[17]. The former interpretation is also supported by the failure to observe this type of splitting under pressure in other carbonates having the calcite structure. If the splitting were due to an increased perturbation by the crystal field it should be a rather general effect in all carbonates.

It should be noted that with increasing pressure there is a definite shift of ν_1 to higher frequencies, as well as a shift of the centre of gravity of the two components of ν_3. The out-of-phase bending frequency ν_2 does not shift significantly.

(iii) Succinic Acid

The infra-red spectrum of succinic acid has been studied to pressures of 50,000 atm. The results of one series of spectra are given in *Figure 8*. These

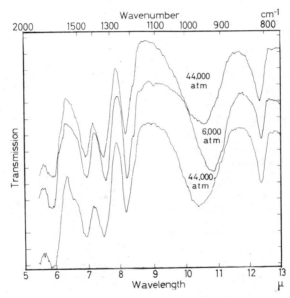

Figure 8. Infra-red spectrum of succinic acid at 6,000 and 44,000 atm

curves are spectra taken consecutively on a sample at pressures of 44,000, 6,000, and 44,000 atm respectively, after it was established that a fixed quantity of sample was remaining between the diamond faces. Most of the absorption bands show slight shifts to higher frequencies on application of pressure. The 930 cm^{-1} hydrogen-bonded out-of-plane O—H deformation frequency gives a relatively large shift of nearly 40 cm^{-1} to higher frequencies. The carbonyl band near 1,700 cm^{-1} appears to undergo a small but definite shift to lower frequencies. The behaviour for these two frequencies may be understood in terms of the effect of pressure on the hydrogen bond structure.

O · · · ·H—O

R—C   C—R

O—H· · · ·O

An increase of pressure on the sample would have considerably more effect on the relatively weak hydrogen bonds than on the normal covalent bonds for this system. The O · · · O hydrogen bond distance would shorten, with the result that with increasing pressure the hydrogen bonds would become stronger. This would result in an abnormally high out-of-plane O—H bending frequency and a lower carbonyl frequency. The O—H stretching frequency should shift to lower frequencies. This effect has been observed, but the O—H stretching frequency was very strong in this specimen and gave essentially 100 per cent absorption. In general, most large frequency shifts that have been observed for pressures under 50,000 atm occurred where hydrogen bonds were present in the structure. Similarly most shifts of frequencies to longer wavelengths that persist above pressures of 10,000 atm have been observed only when hydrogen bonds were present in the structure.

A study of the intensity behaviour of the bands in succinic acid on application of pressure was carried out by calculating the integrated area. The effect of the pressure was then expressed by taking the ratio of these areas. The only bands that were sufficiently free of band overlap to justify integration were the bands near 805, 930, and 1,205 cm^{-1}, respectively. For a change of pressure from 6,000 to 44,000 atm these bands show changes in area by factors of 1·26, 1·0, 0·82, respectively. Succinic acid is one of the few materials studied to date which shows both definite decreases and increases of integrated band area as a function of applied pressure. The general effects for most substances studied to date have been that most bands undergo a decrease of intensity. Sometimes they remain with essentially constant integrated intensity.

(iv) Ice

The structures of the dense forms of ice have been of considerable interest since the complexity of the system was revealed by Bridgman[18]. McFarlan[19] produced the various forms under pressure, cooled the system to a temperature sufficiently low that the pressure could be released without reversion to Ice-I, and obtained x-ray patterns in the metastable state at 1 atm. He found Ice-II and Ice-III to be orthorhombic and to contain distorted oxygen tetrahedra. Data for the higher pressure forms IV, V, and VI were obtained, but were not worked out because of their low symmetry.

Spectra obtained on ice under pressure[20] are shown in *Figure 9* as recorded successively for liquid water at room temperature and 1 atm; Ice-I at −7°C and 1 atm; ice at −26°C and 9,000 atm, obtained by cooling the previous specimen and then compressing; and ice at −27°C and 3,000 atm, obtained by decompressing from 9,000 atm. In view of the metastability of the forms of ice reported previously[18,19], and also observed here, the phases present at the elevated pressures are not certain. The run at 9,000 atm is in the Ice-VI field while the 3,000-atm run is in the Ice-II field, but so close to the II–III transition line that the temperature differential between specimen and thermocouple might place the run in the Ice-III field.

In Ice-I the band centred at 3,200 cm^{-1} corresponds to the hydrogen bonded O—H stretching mode and the 1,630 cm^{-1} band (on the shoulder of the diamond band) to the H—O—H bending mode. The broad band centred near 850 cm^{-1} corresponds to a libration mode of the H_2O molecule. When liquid water is frozen, the formation of the strong hydrogen bonds of Ice-I is accompanied by a shift of the stretching band to lower frequencies, a marked apparent decrease in intensity of the bending band, and an increase in intensity of the libration band[21]. In the spectrum at 9,000 atm the peak stretching frequency has shifted to 3,600 cm^{-1}, the bending band has a greatly increased intensity but has not shifted appreciably, and the libration band is either missing or has shifted to lower frequencies. These results are consistent with the interpretation that the hydrogen bonds responsible for the open structure of Ice-I have collapsed and, in the close-packed structure of the dense ice, hydrogen bonding produces a minor effect on the vibration

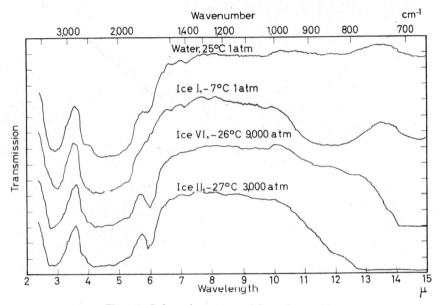

Figure 9. Infra-red spectrum of dense forms of ice

modes. Presumably, weak hydrogen bonds still exist in the dense ice but with the O—H · · · O angle deviating considerably from 180°.

The spectrum at 3,000 atm is in many respects intermediate between that of Ice-I and that at 9,000 atm.

(v) Ferrocene, $Fe(C_5H_5)_2$

Ferrocene is a suitable compound on which to make pressure studies in the ultra-violet and visible as well as the infra-red region of the spectrum. It has an absorption band near 430 mμ with an extinction coefficient of about the right magnitude for studies without dilution in the pressure cell. The vibrational spectrum is relatively simple and the assignment rather definite[22]. This compound contains unusual types of primary bonding in the presence of aromatic CC and CH bonds and covalent metal-ring bonds.

The details of the effect of pressure on the spectra of ferrocene will be reported elsewhere. However, a pressure-induced transition has been observed to occur near 10,000 atm as indicated by the discontinuous shift of the 434 mμ peak in the visible spectrum and the shift of the CC symmetric ring stretching frequency at 1,108 cm^{-1} to 1,135 cm^{-1}. The effect of pressure on the vibrational spectrum is a combination of a continuous change before and after the transition with a discontinuous change at the transition. In the infra-red spectrum given in *Figure 10*, the continuous changes are best illustrated by the intensity change of the absorption peaks associated with small frequency shifts. For example, the 476 (not shown) and 790 cm^{-1}

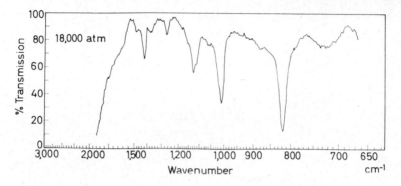

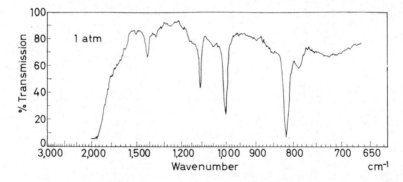

Figure 10. Infra-red spectrum of ferrocene taken at 18,000 atm and at 1 atm

bands have a greatly reduced intensity as the pressure is increased. At pressures considerably higher than that necessary for the transition, a new band appears at 1,260 cm^{-1}. The effect of pressure is most apparent on the vibrational frequencies which have been assigned to metal-ring and to CC modes of vibration.

The most prominent feature of the effect of pressure on the band at 434 mμ, which must be assigned to an electronic transition, is the large frequency shift to higher frequencies. The effect is illustrated in *Figures 11* and *12*. This band moves from approximately 23,100 cm^{-1} at 1 atm to 23,550 cm^{-1} at 10,000 atm and to 23,750 cm^{-1} at 40,000 atm, corresponding to an over-all 650 cm^{-1} shift in 40,000 atm. In addition, there appears to be a definite increase in band intensity. This large frequency shift of an electronic transition is to be compared with the rather small frequency shifts observed for vibrational transitions. Another interesting feature of this band is that

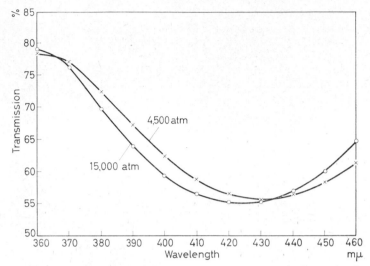

Figure 11. Spectrum of ferrocene at two pressures in diamond cell, 15,000 and 4,500 atm

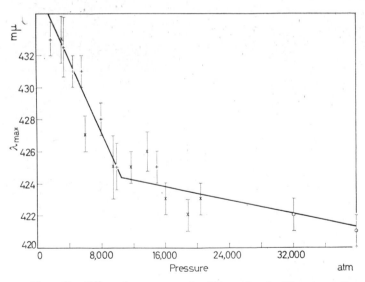

Figure 12. Effect of pressure on the 434 mμ band of ferrocene. Data taken from the same samples are marked +, ×, and O

there is no apparent frequency shift at the pressure-induced transition but only a change of slope of the frequency versus pressure relationship.

Both the visible and infra-red spectra were recorded on the same sample by

67

periodically transferring the pressure unit from the infra-red to the ultra-violet spectrometer respectively without a change of pressure.

VIII. Discussion of Experimental Results

In general, it has not been possible to interpret the changes in the infra-red spectra which occur on application of pressure in terms of the structures of the specific substances. The shift to higher frequencies which is observed at elevated pressures for many bands can qualitatively be interpreted as an increase of the importance of repulsive forces of neighbouring molecules as compared to attractive forces as the pressure increases. In cases where shifts to lower frequencies occur, it would appear that attractive forces of neighbouring molecules are initially exerting a greater influence on the atoms than the repulsive forces. Most of the shifts to lower frequencies observed to date have been for substances where hydrogen bonds are present in the structure. Such bonds are the result of relatively weak attractive forces between neighbours and it would seem that pressure tends to increase the strength of hydrogen bonds by increasing the attraction. Eventually, there must be some pressure at which the repulsive forces become larger than the attractive forces and shifts to higher frequencies should again take place.

If the cases where hydrogen bonds are present in the structure are excluded, it is clear that an applied pressure of the order of 40,000 atm has relatively little effect on the position of most vibrational absorption bands. This would indicate that such pressures do not produce significant changes in the bonds responsible for the spectra and that any phase changes that occur do not alter greatly the bond configuration of the molecule, although there may well be a change in space-group symmetry of the unit cell. For the organic materials studied here, the decreases in volume at pressures of the order of 40,000 atmospheres is approximately 20 per cent. Since the interatomic distances of atoms involved in the bonds do not change appreciably, there must be a large change in intermolecular distances. The present data indicate that the bonds are relatively insensitive to this change in intermolecular spacing. However, for pressures in excess of 50,000 atm, changes in structure may occur[4], and have been found in studies of p-nitrophenol conducted with this apparatus at a pressure of 160,000 atm.

The relatively large changes of integrated intensities which occur for pressures up to 50,000 atm suggest that relatively large changes in dipole moment derivatives are occurring for a number of modes of vibration.

The relatively large shift in the electronic absorption band at 434 mμ for ferrocene indicates that small changes of bond properties which occur on application of pressures may be associated with rather significant changes in the electronic spectrum of a substance. Drickamer[23] and co-workers have observed similar large shifts of electronic bands. From this point of view, it is not surprising that relatively large changes of intensity of infra-red peaks are observed.

References

[1]LAWSON, A. W. and TING-YUAN TANG, *Rev. Sci. Instrum.*, **21**, 1950, p. 815
[2]JAMIESON, J. C., *J. Geol.*, **65**, 1957, p. 334
[3]BUNTING, E. N. and VAN VALKENBURG, A., *Amer. Min.*, **43**, 1958, p. 102

REFERENCES

[4]Lippincott, E. R., Weir, C. E., Van Valkenburg, A. and Bunting, E. N., *Spectrochim. Acta*, **16,** 1960, p. 59

[5]Bridgman, P. W. and Simon, I., *J. appl. Phys.*, **24,** 1953, p. 405

[6]Weir, C. E., Lippincott, E. R. and Bunting, E. N., *J. Res. nat. Bur. Stand.*, **A63,** 1959, p. 55

[7]Jamieson, J. C., Lawson, A. W. and Nachtrieb, N. D., *Rev. Sci. Instrum.*, **30,** 1959, p. 1,016

[8]MacDonald, G. J. F., *Amer. Min.*, **41,** 1956, p. 744

[9]Clark, S. P., Jr., *Amer. Min.*, **42,** 1957, p. 564

[10]Ramsay, D. A., *J. Amer. Chem. Soc.*, **74,** 1952, p. 72

[11]Bridgman, P. W., *Proc. Amer. Acad. Arts Sci.*, **72,** 1937, p. 45

[12]Hexter, R. M., *Spectrochim. Acta*, **10,** 1958, p. 281

[13]Louisfert, J., *Compt. rend.*, **241,** 1955, p. 940

[14]Hornig, D. F., *J. chem. Phys.*, **16,** 1948, p. 1,063

[15]Halford, R. S., *J. chem. Phys.*, **14,** 1946, p. 8

[16]Cabannes, J., *Rev. sci.*, *Paris*, **80,** 1942, p. 407

[17]Bridgman, P. W., *Amer. J. Sci.*, **237,** 1939, p. 13

[18]Bridgman, P. W., *The Physics of High Pressure*, G. Bell and Sons, Ltd., London, 1952, pp. 242, 426

[19]McFarlan, R. L., *J. chem. Phys.*, **4,** 1936, pp. 60, 253

[20]Lippincott, E. R., Weir, C. E. and Van Valkenburg, A., *J. chem. Phys.*, **32,** 1960, p. 612

[21]Giguère, P. A. and Harvey, K. B., *Canad. J. Chem.*, **34,** 1956, p. 798

[22]Lippincott, E. R. and Nelson, R. D., *Spectrochim. Acta*, **10,** 1958, p. 307

[23]Parsons, R. W. and Drickamer, A. G., *J. chem. Phys.*, **29,** 1958, p. 930

4

DEBYE-SCHERRER X-RAY TECHNIQUES FOR VERY HIGH PRESSURE STUDIES

JOHN C. JAMIESON and A. W. LAWSON

University of Chicago, Chicago, Illinois

I. Introduction

THE motivation for high pressure structural studies stems from the existence of an increasing number of polymorphic transitions as the pressure range is extended. Until the crystal structures of these polymorphs are determined, the data on their physical properties are amenable to theoretical analysis only in very simple cases[1-4], and even then are subject to nagging doubts. Such doubts are not relieved by the knowledge that in those instances in which high pressure modifications have been successfully studied, only simple ionic crystals appear to conform to the theory. This agreement with theory is only qualitative; the observed transition pressures often deviate grossly from the predicted pressures. Apparently the soundest theoretical prediction[5] possible is that for the *reversible* transition between two phases, either stable or metastable, the phase with the greater density will be relatively stable at higher pressure with respect to the low pressure phase. If the transition is irreversible, no such statement can be made. Even in comparing two phases at zero pressure, the less dense of which is stable, it is not possible to assume that a transition to the denser phase will necessarily occur at high pressures because the less dense phase may have a larger compressibility.

It is sometimes assumed that a simple structure, thermodynamically stable at low pressures, but which undergoes a transformation at high pressures, will change to another simple but more closely packed polymorph. This assumption is unwarranted; the high pressure phase, although denser, may be very complicated in structure. It is even possible, in principle, that a 'close packed' structure (f.c.c. for example) may change to 'open' (b.c.c. for example) when changes in electronic band structure and hence atomic radius are involved. Finally, it is often assumed that the transformed phase of an initially homogeneous phase is itself homogeneous, whereas chemical decompositions[6] or reactions with the pressure media[7] are known to occur.

In addition to the structural aspects of x-ray crystallography, the techniques provide an additional source of information concerning compressibility and thermal expansion. They also provide a method of confirming the existence of a real phase transition in those cases where electrical and density measurements are ambiguous[8], either owing to a large hysteresis smearing a small discontinuity in physical properties or because of a direct conflict between two sets of data. Because the compressibility of two different materials can be measured simultaneously, the possibility exists of obtaining self-consistent data on systems studied under conditions in which the measurements of pressure are uncertain. Fortunately, diffraction studies can be carried out on very small samples. This fact permits the study of rare materials or anisotropic substances in which it is difficult to prepare suitable samples of the appropriate orientation. The method avoids spurious measurements[9] of compressibility associated with porosity of the sample, large pressure gradients, or uncertain corrections[10] for plastic deformation of the pressure vessel.

In view of all these possibilities, and of the uncertainties attached to experimental work in the very high pressure field, the need for experimental development of adequate crystallographic techniques is apparent. Despite this continued need, the progress in this field has been slow, and many of the procedures are reminiscent of an art rather than a science. The basic reason for this slow development is the fundamental prerequisite of a satisfactory high pressure container to which the x-ray techniques must play a subordinate role.

Two principles dominate the experimental approach to the problem. Firstly, in contrast to the usual procedures of very high pressure techniques in which the investigator is inclined to think in terms of relatively bulky and heavy equipment, diffraction studies demand that the experimentalist think in terms of the smallest possible apparatus in order to avoid intensity and absorption problems and large geometrical correction factors and to permit ease of adaptation to standard x-ray equipment. Secondly, in all work to date, static high pressures must be confined by a suitable pressure vessel. For x-ray diffraction work, the number of available materials is relatively limited, being confined at present to substances whose mean effective nuclear charge $\bar{Z}$ is less than about 6. In other words, this requirement on $\bar{Z}$ means that the pressure vessel must be constructed of compounds formed by combinations of elements in the first row of the periodic table, e.g. Be, C, LiH, BN, LiF, B_4C, BeO, etc. It is not unusual that such materials do not satisfy the mechanical requirements imposed on pressure vessels by the large stresses which they must support. For this reason, we have not included any organic materials in the list of recommended possibilities, although it is conceivable that these may become practicable as general understanding of high pressure design improves.

If one bears in mind these two overriding principles—namely, the necessity for miniature apparatus and low $\bar{Z}$—the course of the historical development of the high pressure diffraction art is not difficult to understand. In this connection, it is interesting to note that very high pressure techniques, such as solid pressure media and supported pistons, were used in high pressure diffraction studies relatively early, because in general they simplify rather than complicate the procedures.

II. Quenching Experiments

Buerger[11] has classified structural transformations into two broad categories: displacive and reconstructive. Loosely defined, displacive transformations can be described in terms of a gross macroscopic shear on which small relative readjustments of atomic separations may be superimposed. Reconstructive transformations, on the other hand, involve rather gross atomic

71

rearrangements whose kinetics are rate-limited by the factors controlling diffusion in the solid state. Typically found among the latter are transformations in covalent crystals in which bonds must be broken and reformed to effect the structural change. Because reconstructive processes in general proceed much more slowly than displacive transformations, they are easier to repress by rapid cooling or increases in pressure which decelerate diffusion. Conversely, once they have been induced, it is relatively easy to preserve metastable modifications by proper thermal and pressure cycling.

Advantage of this fact has been taken in a number of instances to produce new phases or metastable high pressure modifications in such a form that they could be studied crystallographically outside a pressure vessel. Some examples are given in *Table 1*. The usual procedure is to pressurize the material at high temperatures, or in some labile phase such as the melt or a solution, so that the material is in the equilibrium field of the high pressure modification. The temperature is then dropped rapidly to a lower temperature at which the pressure is released isothermally.

The first, but still among the most interesting, of the high pressure phases to be studied by x-ray techniques was black phosphorus[12]. This semiconducting phase is prepared by heating ordinary white phosphorus, which is a good insulator, to about 200°C at 10 kb. After an incubation period lasting from minutes to hours, depending on the exact temperatures and pressure, the transformation runs almost explosively. The temperature is then lowered, the system depressurized, and the sample upon removal is stable in air without protection for many years. Material originally prepared in this manner by Bridgman has been extensively studied by the usual Debye-Scherrer techniques by Hultgren and Warren[13], who have resolved its orthorhombic structure. Krebs[14] has discovered how to prepare black phosphorus at one atmosphere with Hg as a catalyst.

Similar quenching studies have been conducted on a number of the high pressure phases of water by McFarland[15]. Another example is the metastable phase of SiO_2, coesite, named after Coes[16-18] who first made it in the laboratory. It has recently been found associated with large meteorite craters.

Most conveniently, the pressure quenching is carried out at room temperature, so that, if the new phase is indefinitely metastable, the sample may be removed from the high pressure apparatus and studied in a usual type of diffraction equipment. Otherwise, the high pressure apparatus must be dismantled at some lower temperature, the sample removed under refrigerated conditions, and studied in a low temperature camera.

The Bridgman[19] anvil shearing apparatus or the Griggs-Kennedy[20] simple squeezer lend themselves most easily to this type of before-and-after study. These relatively simple and inexpensive systems may be operated to pressures in excess of 60 kb from 80°K to 900°K, and even to 1,300°K at reduced operating pressures. Because of the large pressure gradients involved in these techniques, the samples are usually highly distorted with small grains, suitable only for Debye-Scherrer studies. Occasionally, however, where the kinetics are particularly favourable, sufficiently large crystals may be grown to permit Laue pictures to be obtained.

The requirements for quenching experiments seem to exclude a large number of interesting transformations from study by these techniques. Jacobs[21] carried out extensive experiments with an anvil shearing apparatus in an effort to preserve the high pressure modifications of various

Table 1. *Various High Pressure Transformations Studied by X-Ray Diffraction Techniques*

(a) *Structural changes observed by x-ray diffraction*

Substance	Transition type	References
H_2O II	High-pressure form, cubic	16, 48, 52
H_2O III	High-pressure form, tetragonal	16, 48, 52
P	Cubic→ orthorhombic	12, 13, 15
SiO_2	Quartz→ coesite	17, 18
KNO_3 III	Aragonite→ rhombohedral	40
KNO_3 IV	Aragonite→ orthorhombic	35
CS_2	Liquid→ polymer (?)	6
AgI	ZnS→ NaCl	23, 26
RbI	N₋Cl→ CsCl	23, 41
RbBr	N₋Cl→ CsCl	49
RbCl	N₋Cl→ CsCl	41
KI	N₋Cl→ CsCl	5, 87
WO_3	Not resolved	46
HgSe	Decomposed	46
$CaCO_3$ II	Calcite, anion disorder	5
Ce	f.c.c.→ f.c.c.	28, 29, 30
$CsClO_4$	Not resolved	23
Hg	Volume change	42
Bi	Not resolved	37, 44
BiSn	Intermetallic phase formed at 15–20 kb; structure not resolved	49, 51
MnAs	Same as thermal transformation at 40°C, 1 atm	49

(b) *Reported phase changes so far unobservable by x-rays*

Substance	Transition type	References
Cd	Resistance change	5, 7
AgCl	Shear transition at 13 kb	19, 49
MoS_2	Resistance transition at 20 kb	49, 50

(c) *Substances examined by x-rays in which no transformations were observed*

Substance	Maximum pressure	Remarks
Graphite	30 kb	Contraction of 6·2 per cent in c_0, 0·4 per cent in c_0
V_2O_3	20 kb	No transition noted
SbSn	20 kb	No transition noted

metals such as Hg, Ba, Bi, Cs, Tl, etc. The anvil shearing apparatus was surrounded by a metal can with styrofoam insulation on its cylindrical surface. The top and bottom of the anvil were thermally insulated from the press. After the pressure had been applied, and the specimen sheared to assure transformation, the can was filled with liquid N_2. The press was then disassembled with the anvil maintained at 80°K, the sample removed and mounted on an x-ray diffractometer, and a diffraction pattern taken, while the sample was being bathed in a continuous stream of liquid N_2. Despite these elaborate attempts, no success was encountered. Apparently all these metallic phases transform by a diffusionless process which cannot be prevented from taking place by lowering the temperature to that of liquid N_2.

Despite these abortive experiments on displacive transformations, further systematic exploitation of the quenching technique on the many hitherto unstudied reconstructive transformations is clearly indicated. So far such efforts have been primarily confined to systems of particular interest to the geochemist, such as the carbonates and silicates.

III. High Pressure Techniques

The earliest diffraction experiments on samples confined quasi-permanently by hydrostatic pressure were carried out by Frevel[22], who used a

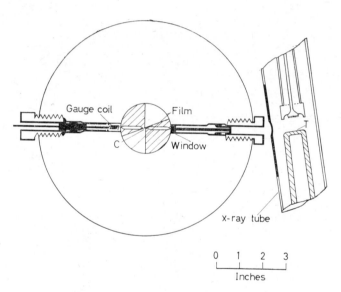

Figure 1. Schematic arrangement showing He-filled pressure vessel with Be window and film internally mounted (After Jacobs[9])

silica capillary as a pressure vessel. Owing to the low tensile strength of silica, his experiments were perforce limited to pressures below 1 kb.

The first successful efforts above this pressure range were those of Jacobs[9], whose apparatus is shown schematically in *Figure 1*. The x-rays were admitted to the hardened steel bomb by a thin beryllium window. Both target and recording film were contained within this bomb, whose internal diameter was about 5 cm. The pressurizing fluid was helium gas. Owing to the size of the container and the tendency of He to penetrate his available steel at high pressures, Jacobs worked only up to 5 kb. An additional experimental difficulty was imposed by the tendency of the helium to strip the emulsion

74

from the film unless pressurization and de-pressurization of the system was carried out sufficiently slowly to permit diffusive equilibrium to take place between the helium dissolved in the film and its environment. Furthermore, elaborate precautions had to be employed to remove trace impurities from the helium gas to prevent excessive absorption of the x-rays.

Despite these difficulties, Jacobs[9, 23] was able to study the phase transitions in AgI, RbI, and $CsClO_4$. He showed that the transition in AgI at about 3 kb is from a zinc blende structure to a rock salt modification. Furthermore, the discrepancy between his values[24] for the compressibility of aluminium and previous values led Bridgman to review his earlier dilatometric experiments, resulting in a revision of these data to lower values.

More modern techniques of packing He under pressure and better pressure vessels now make the Jacobs technique feasible up to perhaps 20 kilobars. The development of such apparatus would still be quite valuable as its precision both of pressure measurement and lattice parameter measurement in this truly hydrostatic pressure range fills a gap not covered by the higher pressure apparatus described below. The gas-film problem apparently has not been solved to date.

A single crystal diffractometer using a gas pressure medium has been developed by Vereschagin *et al.*[25]. This camera, which covers approximately the same pressure range as that of Jacobs, was used to study the compressibility of NaCl. No work on transformation has been reported. This fact is hardly surprising in view of the general experience that single crystals normally shatter at phase transitions and the virtues of a single crystal camera could not be exploited in the study of phases stable only at higher pressures.

IV. Miniature Pressure Vessels

The difficulties of using photographic film inside a pressure vessel and generating high pressures with gases such as helium have led to several alternative experimental approaches. One of these is based on the use of a miniature bomb of low Z in which the pressure may be generated either hydrostatically by a fluid, or quasi-hydrostatically by a plastic solid of low shear strength.

It is interesting to trace the evolution of these miniature bombs, which reflect some of the difficulties inherent in very high pressure techniques. The first experiments[26] were conducted with a polycrystalline Be bomb made from machinable beryllium as cast by the Brush Beryllium Corporation. This material is extremely large-grained, about 10 to 20 grains/cm². Attempts to use fine-grained, sintered beryllium were unsuccessful and may account for the lack of success of a much earlier effort[27]. Roughly speaking, the vessel is a right circular cylinder, approximately a centimetre in height with an outer diameter of approximately $\frac{1}{4}$ in. The sample is contained in some semi-fluid medium, such as Duco cement, in a small circular axial hole about 0·031 in. in diameter. The pressure is applied to the sample either by hardened drill rod or carboloy pistons. The x-ray beam, usually MoK_a radiation, traverses the beryllium cylinder containing the sample normal to its axis and is diffracted to a simple semi-cylindrical film holder mounted concentrically with the bomb.

Several severe limitations are associated with this design. Firstly, the beryllium bomb and the sample are both polycrystalline, and one therefore obtains two Debye-Scherrer patterns, one characteristic of the beryllium and the second characteristic of the sample. These patterns must be disentangled before any analysis of the diffraction pattern of the sample can be carried out. Secondly, it is difficult to estimate the pressure with any certainty. The usual procedure is to calculate the pressure by dividing the total load on the pistons by the nominal base of the cylindrical hole retaining the sample. As in many experiments involving quasi-hydrostatic very high pressure techniques, this estimated pressure is likely to exceed the actual effective hydrostatic pressure by as much as 30 per cent. This is particularly true when the pressure in the Be bomb has exceeded 20–30 kb so that appreciable flow occurs and the vessel becomes progressively distorted with use. A further

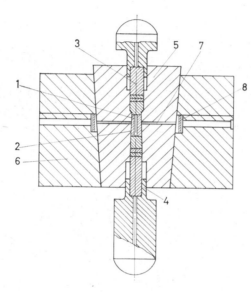

Figure 2. Schematic arrangement of conical Be pressure vessel externally supported to withstand pressures up to 30 kb. (After Vereschagin and Brandt[31])

complication of this approach is the finite size of the sample. This involves not only an appreciable correction for sample size but also makes it virtually impossible to obtain diffraction patterns of materials of high Z without further modifications of the technique.

Despite these difficulties, a large number of experiments were run and at least one successful structure analysis[28] was carried out on cerium, which transforms from face-centred cubic to face-centred cubic with a large volume decrease. This analysis has subsequently been confirmed by low temperature experiments[29] carried out at atmospheric pressure, and further dilatometric analysis of the transformation under pressures indicates that the transformation terminates at about 225°C in a critical point[30].

The mechanism for generating pressure in the polycrystalline Be vessel was a simple spring-loading device antedating the type shown in Figure 8. The relative arrangement of the spring-loading mechanism, bomb and film holder have been described in detail elsewhere[26]. No particular precautions were used in aligning the mechanical system because the progressive distortion of the cylinder did not seem to warrant them. The lack of careful alignment undoubtedly contributed materially to the excessive friction already mentioned. Despite this high friction, significant alterations in the diffraction patterns of calcite and bismuth were obtained, indicating that pressures up to perhaps 30 kb were produced. The failure to unravel these patterns was due in part to the complexity of the pattern and in part to the heavy background generated by the polycrystalline vessel. If some care is not exercised in careful aligment of the x-ray beam relative to the sample, the pattern may be further complicated by the appearance of diffraction lines from the pistons.

Several of these difficulties were partially overcome in subsequent modifications of the basic design. Vereschagin[31] and his collaborators have built an arrangement schematically shown in *Figure 2*. In this design, the Be pressure vessel is supported by a conical collar in which appropriate narrow slits are cut to admit the x-rays. The photographic film recording the diffraction pattern is wrapped around this supporting collar. The collar is subjected to a differential counterthrust in the usual way in order to relieve the peripheral tensile stresses produced in the Be cone by the internal pressure.

An effort[28] to improve the quality of the diffraction patterns obtained by this technique was made by the substitution of single crystal Be bombs for the polycrystalline containers. The pressure vessel was cut with its axis parallel to the axis of hexagonal symmetry of a large Be crystal in order to keep the direction of easy slip in a plane on which the resolved shear stress is low. Despite these precautions, the single crystal vessels flowed very rapidly at pressures above 10 kb and for this reason proved unsatisfactory. The quality of the diffraction pictures obtained at low pressures, however, were markedly improved and suggested an intensive search for other suitable single crystal containers. This search was further encouraged by the difficulty and cost of machining beryllium under conditions safe for laboratory personnel. As a result, the diamond pressure containers described in the next section were developed.

V. Miniature Diamond Bombs

The improved quality of the diffraction patterns obtained with the single crystal Be bomb, compared to those obtained with polycrystalline bombs, results from the fact that instead of obtaining Debye-Scherrer diffraction rings from the container as in the latter case, one obtains only sparsely separated, intense Laue spots which are easily identifiable. It seemed reasonable therefore to suppose that a single crystal diamond could be substituted for the single crystal Be, with the same gain in quality of pattern, considerable gain in inherent strength and life, but at some cost in increased absorption since Z for carbon is 6 whereas that for Be is only 4.

Dies with tapered inlet and outlet throats had long been used for drawing wire. Before 1940, these dies had been largely imported from Holland but, during World War II, this source became unavailable. Consequently, considerable research[32,33] was undertaken in this country into the problem of drilling holes in diamonds. This work, which has been summarized elsewhere, led to considerable and progressive improvement in this technology.

At the time of the first interest in single crystal diamond cells, it did not appear economically feasible to drill a straight hole only $0 \cdot 015$ in. in diameter through an industrial diamond. As a result, the split diamond bomb was developed[33]. This design is shown in *Figure 3*. In essence, two diamonds are used, each having parallel optically flat surfaces ground on them. On one of the flat surfaces of each diamond a hemi-cylindrical groove is lapped so that when the two halves are clamped together a cylindrical cavity $0 \cdot 015$ in. in diameter is formed. Flats are then ground perpendicular to the axis of this hole. The clamp, also shown in *Figure 3*, is made of hardened tool steel. One side of the clamp has a small entrance pinhole to admit the x-rays while the other has a slit cut in it to permit the diffracted beam to emerge from the opposite side. The recorded angular range of 2θ is limited to $45°$ by the clamp. A second clamp was built to permit observation of 2θ values ranging from $70°$ on one side to $20°$ on the other. No advantage accrued, however,

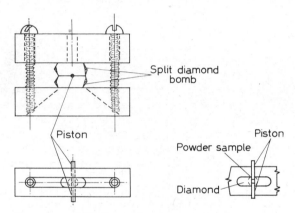

Figure 3.   Split-diamond pressure cell and steel clamp   (After Lawson and Tang[34])

since no 2θ values greater than $45°$ were recorded for any of the materials studied with this device.

This split-diamond bomb, fabricated by Arthur Crafts and Company of Chicago, Illinois, was used in conjunction with the spring-loading device and film holder previously used with the Be bombs. The only reported study[33] resulting from work with this device is that of the relatively low 4 kb transition in KNO_3 using filtered Mo radiation. Actually, some forty exposures on various substances at pressures ranging up to 25 kb were made before fracture of one diamond occurred. This fracture took place as pressure was being increased on a graphite sample near 18 kb. Small 'wing' flaws, described in more detail in a later section of this chapter, had already developed early in the use of the bomb. It is not known whether the ultimate failure was related to these flaws, which are normal to the axis of the pistons, or to a slight misalignment of the clamp.

One annoying feature of the split diamond scheme is the tendency of the sample to extrude between the diamonds. This extrusion is more likely to occur when a lubricant such as zinc stearate[36] is used to reduce friction, or a diluent such as carbon black is used to minimize absorption. When such extrusion occurs, the pressure is either lost completely, or is at best uncertain. Even if pressure is partially retained, the x-ray geometry is not satisfactory.

The complications of extrusion phenomena and clamp alignment associated with the split diamond technique were overcome by two different approaches which we shall discuss in chronological order.

Subsequent to the construction of the split-diamond bomb, advances in the technology of drilling diamonds made it possible to procure a single crystal diamond[5] with a small cylindrical hole of uniform bore. A 0·015 in. hole, 0·172 in. long, was drilled in a three-carat diamond by the Indiana Wire Die Company, Fort Wayne, Indiana. Except for flats ground perpendicular to this hole, the original crystal faces were untouched. A photograph of this cell is shown in *Figure 4*. Later, it was found convenient to have four other flats ground and polished on its vertical surface so that the interior of the

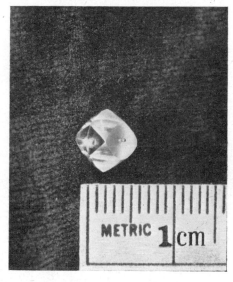

Figure 4. Single crystal diamond cell (After Jamieson[5])

diamond could be inspected. This diamond, with associated steel pistons, was used with the same press and film holder assembly as the previously described bombs. An extensive series of pictures was taken in conjunction with a study of the phase diagram of $CaCO_3$. Typical diffraction patterns obtained with this arrangement are shown in *Figure 5*, where they are compared with pictures taken with various other cells.

A careful history of this diamond has been kept and in this case, at least, it is possible to give an account of the progressive development of strain and flaws. On delivery, the diamond was found to be optically isotropic by microscopic examination. The Laue diffraction spots obtained before any application of stress were uniformly intense except for those portions coming from a thin layer surrounding the central cylindrical hole. The same set of Laue spots was obtained as the pressure was increased in small stages to 25 kb and also during a similar release of pressure. In this manner, the development of the strain induced by the internal pressure could be studied as a function of distance from the axis. After one cycle of pressure, the region of strain returned to that initially found on the thin layer around the hole. After several further excursions to 25 kb, the diamond developed a permanent set, revealed by a mottled appearance of the Laue spots. This

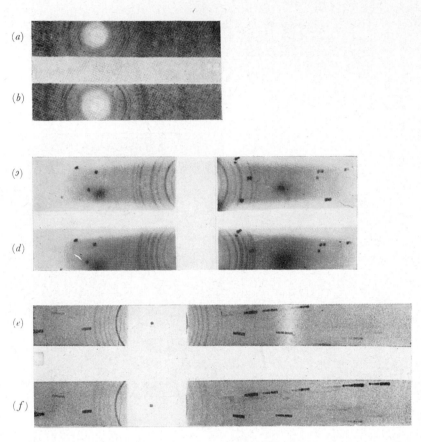

(a)

(b)

(c)

(d)

(e)

(f)

Figure 5. A comparison of diffraction patterns obtained by various techniques showing the progressive improvement. (a) and (b) were taken with the poly-crystalline Be cell and illustrate the low and high pressure modifications of Ce, respectively (after Lawson and Riley[26]). (c) and (d) were obtained with the split diamond cell and illustrate the low and high pressure modifications of KNO_3IV, respectively (after Jamieson[35]). (e) and (f) show the low and high pressure modifications of $CaCO_3$, respectively, obtained with the single crystal cell (after Jamieson[5])

remnant distortion after the release of pressure was also observable optically because of the associated stress birefringence detectable in polarized light. A similar effect had previously been recorded with the two halves of the split diamond bomb.

After the second exposure to pressure a flaw appeared near the central hole where the stress is a maximum. This flaw resembled a tiny wing, and was strikingly similar to those already mentioned in connection with the split diamond.   Two more pressure cycles developed the pattern exhibited in *Figure 6*.   The angle between the two pairs of intersecting flaws is appropriate for two intersecting (111) cleavage planes.   This identification seems reasonable since the diamond was initially oriented by the manufacturer with a cubic axis parallel to the axis of the hole and x-ray investigation in the laboratory confirmed this orientation.   In the third dimension, the flaw

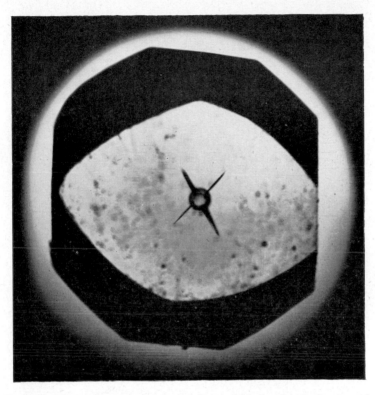

Figure 6.   Picture illustrating the wing flaws which developed after several excursions to high pressures with single-crystal diamond cell (After Jamieson[5])

planes appear somewhat curved and, at least to the eye aided by a microscope, seem to be formed by steps.   Although the flaws extend roughly one quarter of the way from the hole to the outer surface of the diamond, they did not seem to affect its durability.   At least thirty further excursions to 25 kb did not seem to induce any growth in the existing flaws nor did any further detectable flaws appear.   Apparently, the flaws act as stress relievers for the diamond.   These flaws must have exceedingly small openings near the wall of the chamber as there is no evidence that any sample material ever intruded into the flawed region.   If such intrusion had occurred, it is highly likely that the diamond would have failed immediately by propagation of the flaw.

Although this last design eliminated some of the problems associated with the split diamond technique, it did not resolve the difficulty associated with the size of the hole ($0\cdot015$ in.). In particular, even with the sample substantially diluted with carbon black or zinc stearate, samples with high Z, such as bismuth, are difficult to study owing to excessive absorption of the x-rays by the sample. Dilution ultimately fails to improve the situation owing to the inescapable background absorption and scattering by the diamond. For the same reason, one cannot compensate for self-absorption by use of longer exposure times. The basic reason for this problem may be seen from an approximate calculation similar to that of Buerger[47] for estimating the optimum size of single crystals used in diffraction studies. For the intensity I of a diffracted beam corresponding to a sample of thickness t and absorption coefficient μ, contained within a material of thickness t_d and absorption coefficient μ_d, we have

$$I = k I_0 t^2 e^{-\mu t} e^{-\mu_d t_d} \tag{1}$$

where $k I_0 t^2$ is the intensity of the diffracted beam in the absence of sample and diamond absorption, and k is a factor which allows for the geometry of the sample. For a cylindrical diamond with $t_d = 3$ mm, $e^{-\mu_d t_d} = 0\cdot5$ for MoK$_a$ radiation if we neglect the variation of μ_d and t_d with strain. Buerger shows that a maximum in diffraction intensity occurs for $t = 2/\mu$. For this thickness

$$I_{max} = \frac{4 I_0 k}{e^2 \mu^2} e^{-\mu_d t_d} = \frac{I_0 k}{4 \mu^2} \tag{2}$$

Typical values of $I_{max}(k I_0)^{-1}$ are 10^{-3} for NaCl, 10^{-5} for RbCl, and 10^{-7} for HgSe. With the geometry employed in the previous experiments, good patterns were obtained for RbCl by varying the effective t by dilution of the sample with zinc stearate, but none could be obtained for HgSe.

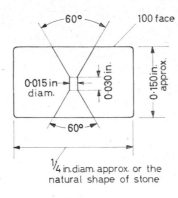

Figure 7. Schematic diagram showing design of G.E. diamond cell (after Kasper et al.[37]). A good quality diamond crystal about $\frac{1}{4}$ inch in diameter is used

An ingenious modification of the single crystal diamond design has been developed by Kasper[37] and his collaborators to overcome the difficulty with self-absorption. The principal feature of Kasper's approach is the use of a thin foil sample imbedded in a zinc stearate pressure medium. The details of Kasper's bomb are shown in Figure 7. It will be noted that the diamond pressure cell used by Kasper does not have a uniform base except near the centre. The cells were cut and drilled by the Wayne Die Company, Hillside, New Jersey, from strain-free rhombic dodecahedra. Two opposite corners were ground off to produce two parallel (100) faces. A circular hole with a 0·015 in. diameter was drilled normal to these faces along the 'hard' (100) direction. The 60° tapered throats at the top and bottom of the cell are similar to those in a wire die. Although this design simplifies the construction of the bomb, the piston design must be altered to accommodate these

SKETCH OF HIGH PRESSURE APPARATUS

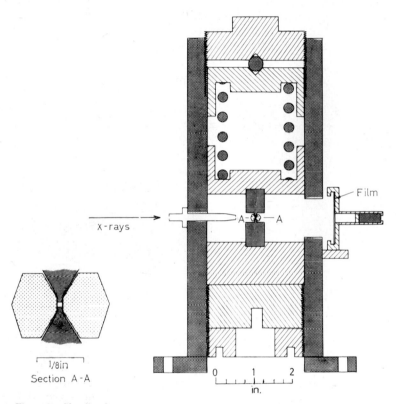

Figure 8. Sketch of a cross section of the complete pressure apparatus using the diamond cell of *Figure 7*. The conical pistons are driven together by a helical spring which is compressed by a screw

throats. The pistons, either hardened steel or Carboloy, are ground to have a matching 60° taper near their ends with a projecting cylindrical termination from 0·010 in. to 0·020 in. in length to fit the 0·015 in. diameter hole. It was found that this last fit must be exceedingly good in order to achieve the highest pressures and avoid excessive hysteresis. Once again, the use of zinc stearate as lubricant was found helpful.

Because the General Electric group have engineered the simple spring

83

loading mechanism first introduced by Riley and Lawson[26], it seems desirable to describe it in some detail. The mechanism is shown to scale schematically in *Figure 8*. The diamond cell, shown in *Figure 7*, is at A. The lower piston is mounted in a relatively massive steel block which is locked in position. The upper moving block carries the other piston and is motivated by a calibrated steel spring which is loaded through a ball bearing by a screw drive. A full rotation of the screw corresponds to a 50 lb. force which is translated into a 20 kb pressure on the working area of the piston. The actual pressure on the sample, corrected for friction, must be ascertained independently. Jamieson[5] reports a lattice parameter for KI of $4 \cdot 13 \pm 0 \cdot 02$ Å at a pressure of 20 kb, where he finds a partial transformation. Kasper *et al.*[37] report a lattice parameter of $4 \cdot 12 \pm 0 \cdot 02$ Å at a pressure somewhat greater than 22 kb. The agreement, although not excellent, is within experimental error and gives some indication of the reproducibility attainable in different laboratories.

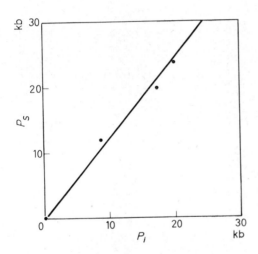

Figure 9. Pressure P_s as estimated from load on pistons *v.* internal pressure P_s estimated from Bridgman's compressibility measurements and observed lattice parameter (After Jamieson[5])

To give some idea of the magnitude of the friction encountered, it seems wise to give a résumé of the experience with KI. This material was chosen for calibration because of its large compressibility, because its NaCl structure facilitates the determination of its lattice parameter, and because of its transition to a CsCl structure near the top of our working pressure range. Bridgman's 1940 data on volume decrements[38] are used to calculate the internal pressure from the observed lattice parameter. In this way, one can plot the nominal pressure estimated from the spring deflection against internal pressure and obtain a measure of the friction in the system. Such a plot is shown in *Figure 9*. The results are given only for increasing pressure, for reasons discussed below, and are terminated at 27 kb nominal pressure by the appearance of the high-pressure form of KI. It is thought safe to extrapolate the curve to 30,000 bars, the present upper limit of work. It is interesting to compare these measurements with a rough derivation of Bridgman's[38] on the effect of friction between a solid and the walls of the pressure vessel in which it is contained. Bridgman assumes that the pressure is constant perpendicular to the walls and, in the absence of transitions, he obtains

$$P = P_0 \, e^{-2\mu l/r} \tag{3}$$

for a piston advancing onto a sample in a blind hole; P is the quasi-hydro-static pressure, l the distance from the piston face, r the chamber radius, μ the coefficient of friction, and P_0 the stress at the piston face. If we further assume that the pressure is symmetrical about the mid-point of the sample in the present case where two pistons are used, the same formula applies. However, l is now permitted to take values only up to $L/2$, where L is the sample length, μ is unknown for mixtures of KI and zinc stearate against diamond, but Bridgman[39] states that 0·1 is a common value in the realm of plastic flow, so we shall adopt that value. For KI at $P_0=30$ kb, $L=0\cdot015$ in., and $r=0\cdot0075$ in., equation (3) gives a pressure at the centre of the sample of 24,600 bars as compared with 24,400 bars from the calibration curve in *Figure 9*. The agreement is due partly to a cancellation of errors, since P_0 is actually reduced by a slight extrusion of material between the piston and the diamond, while the x-ray line spacings correspond to an average pressure somewhat higher than that at the centre.

If a transition occurs, it will occur first nearest the pistons. Equation (3) still holds approximately. As the piston force is increased, the central pressure increases only slowly until the transition is complete throughout the cell. When the piston is decreased after an initial excursion to the maximum, the central pressure may remain constant and actually surpass the decreasing piston pressure until the effect of friction can be overcome by the developing pressure gradient.

Highly absorbing specimens such as Bi were prepared by Kasper as very fine discrete particles dispersed in glyptal cement, and in the form of flat strips from 0·001 to 0·005 in. thick. The fine powder was spread on a microscope slide moistened with glyptal. After it had dried, the material was stripped away and mounted in zinc stearate in the centre of the diamond cell. The best compromise between intensity and spottiness in the pattern was achieved with particles about 30μ in diameter. The pattern of Bi achieved with this arrangement was superior to any achieved by any technique so far developed. Because the range of stability of Bi II is only about 2 kb wide, there is considerable uncertainty as to whether all the lines measured by Kasper pertain to one, two or three phases. For this reason, Kasper has been reluctant to publish any interpretation of his data.

In obtaining the diffraction pattern, a radiograph of the pressure cell is taken before exposure to ensure that the alignment is satisfactory and that the pistons will not produce any confusing extra lines in the picture. To check on the displacement of the pistons and to ascertain that the pressure is not lost in the course of a run, two micrometer dial gauges are mounted on the side of the spring-loading apparatus to give a continuous indication of the piston separation. This practice, coupled with optical examination by a low-power microscope, is an important contributing factor to Kasper's success in obtaining relatively good data. In all, 17 lines from Bi were recorded, although some were of dubious validity.

Kasper has also examined the 50–50 Bi–Sn system, in which Bridgman[51] reported the formation from the elements of a new compound BiSn at pressures of 15–20 kb. This is interesting because the elements are only slightly soluble in each other at 1 atm. Kasper found that at about 15 kb there occurred a sharp change in electrical resistance and in the diffraction pattern. The lines of Bi and Sn disappeared and were replaced by a new set. The exact structure of this high pressure phase has not yet been worked out. Upon release of pressure there occurred a sharp change in resistance and a reversion to the patterns of Bi and Sn.

VI. The Anvil-Type Spectrometer Apparatus

Our group has developed an alternative technique[44] to avoid the absorption problem. The design chosen was compounded from two sources: the simple squeezer of Griggs et al.[20] and the clamping scheme of Chester and Jones[43]. Both ideas have been heavily modified for the present work. The x-rays are diffracted by a flat specimen exposed to quasi-hydrostatic pressure generated by opposed diamond pistons (see *Figure 11*).

The unit was designed to be mounted on a General Electric XRD-5 x-ray diffractometer using filtered Mo radiation, although with suitable modification the unit could be used on any other x-ray diffractometer. It simply replaces the normal sample holder and the instrument is used in the usual fashion, a major advantage conferred by the clamping scheme.

Figure 10 shows a cross section of the new device. The upper cylindrical portion D is demountable from the base A to which it is securely attached by means of dowel pins (not shown) in the dovetail slide B, which is positioned horizontally in the x-ray beam by the micrometer screw C.

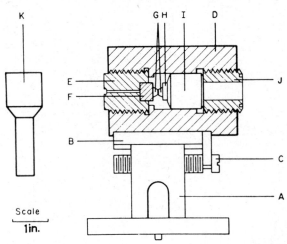

Figure 10. Anvil apparatus for obtaining diffractometer traces (After Jamieson, Lawson and Nachtrieb[44])

The cylinder D is a holder for the working parts of the apparatus and is machined from SAE steel 1020. The threaded plug E contains the Carboloy insert F which supports the opposing diamond pistons G. Both F and G have been modified in later work as described below. The movable piston I contains the Carboloy block H and is manufactured from 4140 steel, heat treated and drawn to 40 Rockwell C. This block in turn is held by the threaded plug J. Both J and E are 4140 steel hardened and drawn to 40 Rockwell C. In use, E is advanced to its shoulder, then a small amount of sample trapped between the diamond faces. In an auxiliary press, the Solar piston K is used to advance I until the desired pressure is reached. I is clamped by the threaded plug, after which the stress applied by K is released. During this operation, only the portion of the apparatus contained by D is

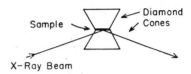

Figure 11. Configuration of diamonds in anvil apparatus and x-ray beam (After Jamieson, Lawson and Nachtrieb[44])

involved. After clamping, this portion is mounted on its base on the x-ray diffractometer. Pressure is estimated by measuring the area of the sample after exposure and knowing the applied stress.

During initial testing, one of the tapered pistons shown in *Figure 11*, which contained a 'knot', broke at about 12 kilobars. It, and the Carboloy insert F, were both replaced by an optically polished single crystal sapphire flat which was successfully used in several studies ranging up to a nominal 35 kilobars before failure necessitated its replacement. At the same time, the other conical diamond was replaced with a diamond having natural faces on which was ground an optical flat, normal to the diamond cubic axis, of somewhat larger area (approx. $\frac{1}{4}$ sq. in.) than the working face of the origina cone. This replacement was made for fear of further breakage. Our present experience indicates that this change was probably unnecessary, and that the original design would have proved satisfactory if the diamond had been 'knot' free.

The preparation of the sample depends on its mechanical properties. If the material is refractory powder, it is prepressed into a thin disc less than $0\cdot002$ in. thick. The area is kept less than quarter the area of the diamond face so that some support for the stressed area of the diamond is gained. If the material is a soft metal such as the bismuth used in many of our test runs, it is pressed into a flat sheet, trimmed, repressed, etc. The resultant discs (again less than quarter the area of the diamond face) are then mounted in the diamond press, brought to pressure and clamped in position. During this procedure, further flow occurs and, depending on the shear strength of the material and the pressure, the sample further decreases in thickness until the viscosity of the material and friction against the platens prevents further appreciable flow within the time required to obtain a diffraction pattern. In the case of bismuth, this quasi-equilibrium thickness after exposure to 30 kilobars is only about $0\cdot0004$ in. Because of the enormous deformations produced in the sample by this history, it is reasonable to expect that a certain amount of preferred orientation will be produced in the sample. Furthermore, it is clear that a large pressure gradient will exist in the sample, although most of the gradient is presumably confined to a region corresponding to 3 per cent of the radius near the periphery[19]. For both of these reasons, the intensities of the powder diffraction lines may be strongly affected, and caution must be exercised in their interpretation.

The most extensive studies using the anvil technique were carried out on bismuth. During the course of these experiments, several difficulties were encountered which led to modifications of the original design.

The most exasperating difficulty has been the fracture of the diamond pistons, seven having been destroyed in about thirty exposures to pressure. Three, two of which contained either knots or visible flaws, failed on the initial application of pressure at a relatively low stress level. One failed owing

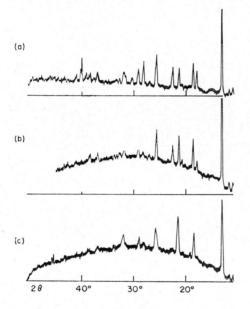

Figure 12. Diffractometer traces obtained with anvil apparatus on Bi (After Jamieson, Lawson and Nachtrieb[44])

to the accidental application of an excessive torque by the clamping screw The remainder failed for uncertain reasons after successfully withstanding considerably high pressures. In all cases but one, the failure resulted in complete shattering with only moderate regard for cleavage. The failures may be due to shifting alignment or the tensile stresses developed by sample flow and extrusion. Some of the diamonds were etched in hot HNO_3 in an effort to avoid this early failure. While this treatment removed scratches only visible with an interference microscope, etch pits as deep as 1μ developed. In any case, this etch did not prevent fracture at the low stress in use.

Because of the high incidence of piston failure, one of the diamond cones was replaced by an optically flat sapphire, which in turn, for reasons described below, was ultimately supplanted by a Carboloy block with a platinum film. This film was thick enough for the complicated diffraction pattern of the Carboloy to be replaced by the much simpler pattern of Pt.

Despite these difficulties, easily discernible diffraction spectra were obtained for Bi, of which typical examples are shown in *Figure 12.* When estimating the pressure by dividing the total load on the diamond by the sample area, it was initially thought that the bottom trace shown in *Figure 12* corresponded to Bi II. The top two traces are Bi I, without and with an overlying diamond respectively. A fourth trace not shown, similar but with even greater line loss and remaining line intensification, was tentatively identified as Bi III. However, a comparison of our results with those of Kasper *et al.*[37] revealed that the two sets of *d* values obtained by these different techniques were radically different.

An investigation of the reasons for this discrepancy revealed that in all likelihood several contributory factors were operative. Firstly, at higher pressures, the deformation of the pistons results in the formation of a double convex, lens-shaped sample so that ultimately the two platens touch along their periphery. When this occurs, the nominal pressure calculated by our procedure grossly overestimates the actual pressure. Secondly, despite precautions taken to preclude it, the flow of the sample during loading appears to produce marked orientation effects which result in a severely distorted and misleading Debye pattern. Thirdly, it is clear that if a phase transformation does occur, a coexistence of the two phases owing to the radial pressure gradients existing in the sample will lead to a superposition of diffraction patterns.

Some of these difficulties may be avoided by further modifications in design not yet fully exploited. The lens effect is accentuated by the use of asymmetrical pistons. It may be avoided to a large degree by the use of a containing ring made of a material with a higher shear strength than the sample. The use of such a ring requires the presence of some internal calibration agent such as KI if the pressure is to be known because it distorts the pressure distribution in a manner not easily calculable.

The flow orientation effects can be reduced by variations in the technique of sample preparation. The inclusion of some hard amorphous second phase such as lithium borate glass will reduce the flow and distribute it in such a way that a random orientation can be simulated. Care must be exercised that the stress concentrations present in such a matrix do not lead to fracture of the diamond at a very low nominal pressure or to such a poor distribution of stress that the pressure is never effectively transmitted to the sample.

The simultaneous coexistence of two or more phases in the stressed region is not necessarily a difficulty but, in principle at least, can be advantageous in indexing diffraction lines of transformed phases closely related in structure to the lower pressure modification.

The foregoing corrective measures have not been employed on Bi samples, but have been tested in model experiments on the 3 kb transition in AgI. If, for instance, AgI is mounted in Duco cement, only three of the first ten lines are easily discernible in the high pressure modification and their intensities are seriously warped by orientation effects. On the other hand, the same material mounted in a thermal setting epoxy resin such as araldite gives rise to nine of the first ten lines with approximately the theoretical intensity distribution. These experiments were carried out with the samples retained by thin (0·005 in.) mild steel rings.

With this experience at hand, we are now faced with the problem of interpreting the reversible disappearance of a large number of lines in the diffraction patterns of Bi as illustrated in *Figure 12*. We believe that the second of the three patterns is characteristic of the amorphous phase of Bi produced by evaporating the metal onto cold substances. The radial distribution function of this phase is very similar to that in the liquid, which has a co-ordination number close to that occurring in a body-centred cube. It is entirely possible that such a phase was produced by melting of the thin Bi wafer by the heat generated during rapid compression and subsequent rapid cooling by conduction to the pistons. The region of the third diffraction pattern remains a mystery but may be a mixture of lines from several phases of highly preferred orientation or merely a distorted picture of Bi I. The problem is complicated by the fact that Bi I is known to recrystallize very rapidly at room temperature. Experimentally, the intensity of the observed peaks is a function of time. Because the spectrometer cannot distinguish between Laue spots from large grains and Debye-Scherrer rings, it is impossible to make any further statement at the present time.

An analysis of Kasper's data for Bi II suggests that this phase is some distortion of a body-centred cube. Such an interpretation is consistent with the known radial distribution function for the liquid and the horizontal equilibrium line separating Bi II and the melt in the T–P plane. The full resolution of the structure has not yet been carried out and may be possible only with the introduction of inductive chemical arguments of a plausible but not conclusive nature.

VII. Prospects

At present, Kasper's version of the single crystal diamond cell appears to be the most successful design. The ultimate possibilities of the anvil-type apparatus should not, however, be disregarded. The substitution of gem-quality diamonds for the obviously flawed industrial diamonds will undoubtedly reduce the high incidence of fracture. The clamp design of *Figure 11* is adequate for working pressures of 200 kb. Howes and Tolansky[45] have reported cubic planes of diamonds withstanding stresses up to 140 kb before the formation of cracks. Weir, Lippincott, and Van Valkenburg, working with gem-quality diamonds, have consistently operated a press of similar design (see Chapter 3) at 50 kb with occasional excursions to 160 kb in their infra-red studies.

We feel that the use of such high-quality diamonds would not only materially extend the working range of the anvil apparatus, but would hasten the development of more satisfactory techniques of sample preparation by reducing the time lost through piston failure and the inevitable delay due to the continuing scarcity of replacements.

The authors are currently working with a compound anvil design which would avoid the use of diamonds completely. Essentially, the technique consists of mounting a fine wire at the centre of a thin wafer of some relatively stiff amorphous material. This wafer is pressurized in clamps at some moderate pressure, say 10 kb, before the wire is further independently stressed by advancing opposing miniature Carboloy pistons concentric to the wire. The details of this apparatus are not given here because the design is not yet sufficiently developed. We mention it only to emphasize the fact that many of the very high pressure techniques described elsewhere in this book have not yet been fully mobilized for the attack on the structure problem. We anticipate the advent of many more ingenious developments as more diverse thinking is brought to bear in very high pressure physics by the many new workers entering this rapidly developing field.

In conclusion, we would like to emphasize the need for collaboration with experienced crystallographers. Many of the experiments described here have been carried out by people primarily interested in other aspects of high pressure phenomena who have been forced into the structure problem by necessity. More rapid progress with the successful resolution of high pressure structures will ensue only after more expert attention has been attracted to this essentially virgin but promising field of investigation. If our account of preliminary efforts helps to call attention to the need for further effort along these lines, it will have served its cause.

References

[1]BARDEEN, J., *J. chem. Phys.*, **6,** 1938, p. 367

[2]STERNHEIMER, R., *Phys. Rev.*, **78,** 1950, p. 235

[3]BORN, M. and HUANG, K., *Dynamical Theory of Crystal Lattices*, Oxford, 1954

[4]LÖWDIN, PER-OLOV, *Adv. phys. Sci., Moscow*, **5,** 1956, p. 3

[5]JAMIESON, J. C., *J. Geol.*, **65,** 1957, p. 334

[6]BRIDGMAN, P. W., *Rev. mod. Phys.*, **18,** 1946, p. 1

[7]BRIDGMAN, P. W., *The Physics of High Pressures*, 2nd ed., Bell, 1949

[8]LAWSON, A. W., *Progr. Metal Phys.*, **6,** 1955, p. 1

[9]JACOBS, R. W., *Phys. Rev.*, **54,** 1938, p. 325

[10]BIRCH, F. W., *Handbook of Physical Constants, Bull. Geol. Soc. Amer.*, 1942, p. 36

[11]BUERGER, M. J., in *Phase Transitions in Solids*, SMOLUCHOWSKI *et al.*, John Wiley and Sons, New York, 1951

[12]BRIDGMAN, P. W., *Proc. Amer. Acad. Arts Sci.*, **62,** 1927, p. 207; **70,** 1935, p. 71

[13]HULTGREN, R. and WARREN, B. E., *Phys. Rev.*, **47,** 1935, p. 808

[14]KREBS, H., WEITZ, H. and WORMS, K. H., *Z. anorg. Chem.*, **280,** 1955, p. 119

[15]McFARLAN, R. L., *J. chem. Phys.*, **4,** 1936, p. 60; **4,** 1936, p. 253

[16]COES, L., Jr., *Science*, **118,** 1953, p. 132

[17]MacDONALD, G. F., *Amer. J. Sci.*, **254,** 1950, p. 713

[18]BOYD, E. R. and ENGLAND, J. L., *J. geophys. Res.*, **65,** 1960, p. 749

[19]BRIDGMAN, P. W., *Proc. Amer. Acad. Arts Sci.*, **71,** 1937, p. 387

[20]GRIGGS, D. T., FYFE, W. S. and KENNEDY, G. C., *Bull. geol. Soc. Amer.*, **66,** 1955, p. 1,569

[21]JACOBS, I. S., *4th Annual Report to ONR on High Pressure Physics*, University of Chicago, 1950

[22]FREVEL, L. K., *Rev. Sci. Instrum.*, **6,** 1935, p. 214

[23]JACOBS, R. B., *Phys. Rev.*, **54,** 1938, p. 468

[24]JACOBS, R. B., *Phys. Rev.*, **56,** 1939, p. 211

[25]VERESCHAGIN, L. F., KABALKINA, S. S. and EVDOKIMOVA, V. V., *Pribory i Tekh. Eksperimenta*, **3,** 1953, p. 90

[26]LAWSON, A. W. and RILEY, A. N., *Rev. Sci. Instrum.*, **20,** 1949, p. 763

[27]COHN, W., *Proc. Amer. Phys. Soc.*, **63,** June 1922

[28]LAWSON, A. W. and TANG, T. Y., *Phys. Rev.*, **76,** 1949, p. 301

[29]SCHUH, A. F. and STURDIVANT, J. H., *J. chem. Phys.*, **18,** 1950, p. 145

[30]BEECROFT, R. I. and SWENSON, C. A., *J. phys. Chem. Solids* (in press, 1960)

[31] VERESCHAGIN, L. F. and BRANDT, J. V., *Dokl. Akad. Nauk SSSR*, **108,** No. 3, 1956. See also Soviet Physics *Doklady*, **1,** 1956, pp. 312–13

[32] PETERS, C. G., NEFFLEN, K. F. and HARRIS, F. K. *NBS Research Paper* 1657, U.S. Govt. Printing Office, Washington, D.C., 1945

[33] GRODZINSKI, P., *Diamond Technology*, Waterlow and Sons, Ltd., London, 1957

[34] LAWSON, A. W. and TANG, T. Y., *Rev. Sci. Instrum.*, **21,** 1950, p. 815

[35] JAMIESON, J. C., *Z. Krist.*, **107,** 1956, p. 5

[36] GUENGANT, L. and VODAR, B., *C.R. Acad. Sci.*, Paris, **239,** 1954, p. 431

[37] KASPER, J. S., HILLIARD, J. E., CAHN, J. W. and PHILLIPS, V. A., *W.A.D.C. Tech. Rept.* 59–747, General Electric Co., Schenectady, N.Y., 1960

[38] BRIDGMAN, P. W., *Proc. Amer. Acad. Arts Sci.*, **74,** 1940, p. 21

[39] BRIDGMAN, P. W., *Proc. Amer. Acad. Arts Sci.*, **72,** 1937, p. 45

[40] BARTH, T. F. W., *Z. phys. Chem.*, **B43,** 1939, p. 448

[41] VERESCHAGIN, L. F. and KABALKINA, S. S., *Dokl. Akad. Nauk SSSR*, **113,** 1957, p. 797

[42] SWENSON, C. A., *Phys. Rev.*, **111,** 1958, p. 82

[43] CHESTER, P. T. and JONES, G. O., *Phil. Mag.*, **44,** 1953, p. 1,281

[44] JAMIESON, S. C., LAWSON, A. W. and NACHTRIEB, N. D., *Rev. Sci. Instrum.*, **30,** 1959, p. 1,016

[45] HOWES, V. R. and TOLANSKY, S., *Proc. Roy. Soc.*, London, **A220,** 1955, p. 294

[46] Unpublished research, University of Chicago

[47] BUERGER, M. J., *X-Ray Crystallography*, John Wiley & Sons, Inc., New York, 1942

[48] KAMB, W. B. and DATTA, S. K., *Acta Cryst. Camb.*, **13,** 1960, p. 1,029

[49] KASPER, J. S., Private communication

[50] BRIDGMAN, P. W., *Proc. Amer. Acad. Arts Sci.*, **81,** 1952, p. 165

[51] BRIDGMAN, P. W., *Proc. Amer. Acad. Arts Sci.*, **82,** 1953, p. 71

[52] KAMB, W. B. and DATTA, S. K., *Nature*, **187,** 1960, p. 140

5

HIGH TEMPERATURE METHODS AT HIGH PRESSURE

H. M. STRONG

General Electric Research Laboratory

I. Introduction

THE purpose of this chapter is to describe some of the progress which has been made on handling the problems of heating substances while they are exposed to high pressure.

At pressures less than 10 kilobars and temperatures under 600°C the entire apparatus may be placed in an oven for external heating. As temperatures and pressures are both increased the rapidly decreasing strength of the materials of the pressure chamber requires that the heating be limited to the specimen only, keeping the pressure chamber cool. Because of these conditions one has to deal with a number of new problems, such as insulating the heated zone from the pressure vessel, avoiding chemical reactions between heater, specimen, and the sample holder, transmitting pressure, measuring temperature, and determining the effect of pressure on thermocouples. This chapter describes some of the progress that has been made in these problems.

The simplest ways of heating are to pass an electric current through the specimen or through a tube or resistance wire helix which contains the sample. In some early forms of high pressure apparatus it was difficult to arrange for the passage of a large electric heating current and a thermite reaction was used instead. The thermite reaction is capable of producing temperatures up to 3,000°K for a very short time interval. Bridgman[1] used thermite extensively in his experiments of 1947 on the direct conversion of graphite to diamond. His specimen was surrounded by a thermite mixture, and was set off by an igniter which was adjusted to fire at 10 to 15 kilobars. Liander and Lundblad[2] also used the thermite reaction in their diamond experiments. The charge was ignited by passing a current through a small silicon carbide heating rod. With the development of high pressure apparatus in which the piston (or pistons, in the case of multiple piston equipment) and the pressure chamber are thermally and electrically insulated from one another, it is no longer necessary to use the rather inconvenient thermite reaction for heating. Using electric current heating, the sample can be heated in a controlled manner over a prolonged period of time.

Some of the methods of current heating are illustrated in *Figure 1*, where the principal design requirements are shown. The heating element itself should have a higher resistance than the current path leading up to it and it is very important to provide thermal insulation at the terminal connections so that the pistons will not be damaged by overheating due to their nearness to the source of heat. The current ring, with its insert of thermal insulating material, and the current disc serve the purpose of insulating while providing an electrical conduction path to the specimen. *Figure 1(a)* illustrates how a specimen for growing diamonds was heated by passing an electric current directly through a rod of nickel surrounded by a sleeve of carbon. In this particular example the diamonds grew at the interface betweeen the nickel and graphite.

Heating by means of a platinum helix surrounding the specimen is illustrated in *Figure 1(b)*. A coil heater requires more machining work to install but has the advantage that its resistance increases with temperature,

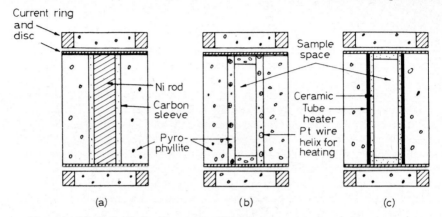

Current ring and disc

Ni rod

Carbon sleeve

Pyro-phyllite

Sample space

Ceramic

Tube heater

Pt wire helix for heating

(a) (b) (c)

Figure 1. Methods for heating under high pressure. (a) Current passes through sample, in this case a nickel rod in a graphite sleeve : diamonds grew at interface between them ; (b) sample is heated by a platinum wire helix ; (c) a tube heater with ceramic liner for containing the sample

giving a measure of the temperature of the heater. By keeping the heating-coil resistance constant, a fairly steady temperature within the specimen can be maintained.

The tube heater of *Figure 1(c)* probably has the greatest utility. It is quite easy to install and it provides a steady source of heat because it is not subject to the variations in resistance peculiar to the directly heated sample, where phase transformations or chemical reactions within the specimen can modify the resistance of the heater. Probably the most useful material for the tube is carbon. Other materials may be used, such as nichrome, stainless steel, tantalum or platinum. The tube must be designed to have high resistance compared to the rest of the heating current circuit.

The currents required for heating under high pressure are often very high because of low heater resistance and high thermal conduction from the specimen to the pressure chamber. The heating current circuit should be capable of delivering 500 to 1,500 amperes at one to three volts.

II. The Insulating Sample Holder

Before the discovery of the high pressure and temperature properties of pipestone (catlinite) and pyrophyllite, the problem of thermal insulation for high pressure work was a puzzling one. Of the various substances considered, all had either the fault that their melting points were too low or that they were too hard and stiff for transmitting pressure from pistons to sample. While pipestone and pyrophyllite appeared to have the low melting point fault, they were nevertheless tested by Bundy at the General Electric Company Research Laboratory as high temperature insulation for high pressure work. Fortunately, neither of them melted at the temperatures expected when under pressure because new solid phases were formed instead which possessed very much higher melting points than the original materials. Today, it is known that several relatively soft materials can serve the purposes of thermal insulation and pressure transmission at very high pressures and temperatures.

One of the best all-purpose materials, because of its availability in uniform large machinable blocks, is pyrophyllite, $Al_2O_3 \cdot 4SiO_2 \cdot H_2O$, of the type quarried in the Transvaal[3] near Johannesburg. This deposit furnishes a very fine grain, soft, machinable material which is almost ideal for high pressure sample holders and gasket material. The African deposit is associated with lava intrusions and is supposed to be a metamorphic clay derived from volcanic ash. Its chemical composition is as follows:

Table 1. *Approximate Composition of African Pyrophyllite (by weight per cent)*

Silica	..	..	..	..	54–56
Alumina	..	..	..	..	32–33
Titanium oxide	..	..	..	..	2·0–2·6
Ferric oxide	..	..	..	..	0·6–2·4
Lime	..	..	..	..	0·3–0·7
Magnesia	..	..	..	..	0·36–0·78
Volatile	..	..	..	..	6·5–6·8
Sulphur	..	..	..	..	0·06–0·17

The bulk specific gravity of pyrophyllite is 2·64 and its true specific gravity is 2·8. Its melting point is about 1,400°C. Its thermal conductivity

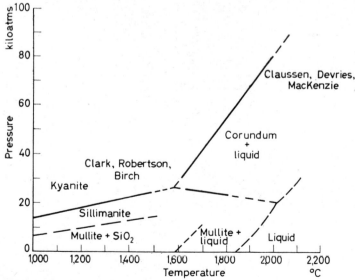

Figure 2. The region of stability of kyanite, the dense form of $Al_2O_3 \cdot SiO_2$

has been reported variously from $0 \cdot 002$ to $0 \cdot 011$ cal$°$C^{-1}, sec^{-1}, cm^{-1}. At room temperature it has a volume electrical resistance of about 85×10^6 Ω cm.

In high temperature experiments run at pressures less than about 25 kilobars, it was noticed that the pyrophyllite tended to melt to a sort of glassy material. At higher pressures under conditions of high temperature, the original light grey stone was transformed to a fine white crystalline sub-

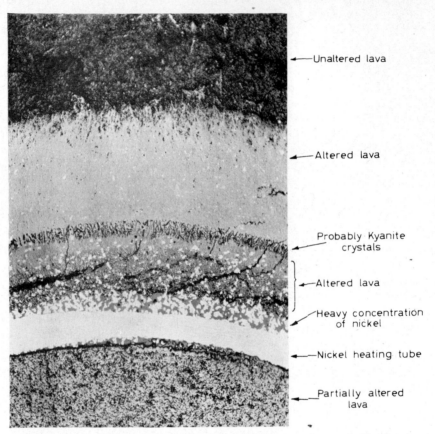

Figure 3. A photograph at 100 $\times$ of the changes which occur in pyrophyllite (lava) under pressure. X-ray diffraction patterns taken on the altered lava show the presence of kyanite and coesite

stance. The transformed material had a density close to $3 \cdot 3$ gm/cm^3 and was found by Wentorf, Jr., of the General Electric Company Research Laboratory, to contain kyanite and coesite. Kyanite has the composition Al$_2$O$_3 \cdot$SiO$_2$. Coesite has the composition SiO$_2$ and is a high pressure modification of quartz[4]. This modification of pyrophyllite gives the impression of not melting at temperatures under about 2,700°C at pressures in the neighbourhood of 50 kilobars. Close inspection of the tiny crystals of transformed stone show that they are sometimes slightly rounded as though they had melted to a viscous glassy substance. Fortunately, sample holders made of pyrophyllite preserve their shape and hold the sample firmly in place up to temperatures in excess of 2,500°C.

Claussen, DeVries and MacKenzie[5], of the General Electric Research Laboratory, have studied the region of stability of kyanite at pressures above 25,000 atm. The stability at lower pressures was studied by Clark, Robertson and Birch[6] at Harvard University. The results of these studies are shown in *Figure 2*. A photomicrograph of pyrophyllite transformed under pressure is shown in *Figure 3*. As it was very difficult to obtain equilibrium conditions in this type of system, the equilibrium lines (*Figure 2*) were located by approaching them from both directions. The equilibrium lines were drawn in the location where a new phase first started to appear and are claimed to be approximate only.

III. The Problem of Pressure Stability at High Temperatures

The phase changes which occur in pyrophyllite under high temperature and pressure tend to complicate the problem of measuring and maintaining steady pressures unless the piston or pistons are free to move in so as to compensate for the volume losses which are associated with the transformation to kyanite and coesite. If, due to frictional resistance in the gasketing around the pistons, the pistons are not free to move and compensate for the volume shrinkage, then there will be a loss of pressure within the specimen.

It is very difficult to measure pressure under conditions of high temperature because there is no known sensing element which is not affected to some

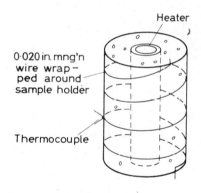

Figure 4. Method of installing a pressure-sensing manganin wire element and making the external connections

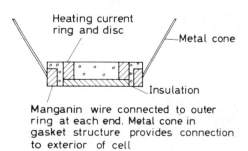

Manganin wire connected to outer ring at each end. Metal cone in gasket structure provides connection to exterior of cell

extent by the high temperatures which prevail near the reaction zone. Nevertheless, some attempts were made to follow the pressure changes by the use of manganin wire, whose electrical resistance is responsive to pressure changes, but whose resistance is nearly constant from room temperature to about 200°C. To keep the manganin wire as cool as possible, it was wrapped spirally around the outside of the sample holder for a belt[7] apparatus as illustrated in *Figure 4*. The wire was provided with a thermocouple in order to keep track of its temperature.

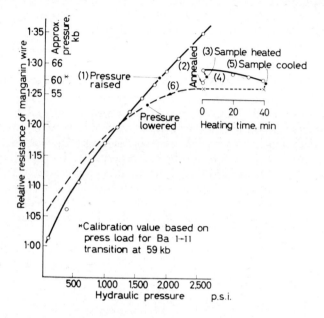

Figure 5. Variations of resistance of manganin wire with (1) press load, (2) annealing, (3) sample temperature raised, (4) while heating sample, (5) when sample was cooled, and (6) lowering the pressure. The reference point 60 kb was based on Ba I → II transition. The pressure scale 55 to 66 kb was computed using the manganin wire pressure coefficient of $2·5 \times 10^{-6}$ ohm/ohm bar

With increase of press force upon the sample, the resistance of the wire increased due to increase of pressure and due to work-hardening and distortion in the wire. When the final pressure was reached the wire was partially annealed by passing a heating current through it for several minutes while measuring its temperature with the attached thermocouple. Annealing temperatures of 400 to 600°C were tried. This treatment lowered the resistance of the wire. However, it was not possible to stabilize completely the wire resistance, because upon continued heating the resistance of the wire tended to decrease very gradually.

After annealing the wire, the sample was heated. Upon the first application of temperature to the specimen, while the wire was still cool, its resistance rose sharply. The magnitude of the initial sharp increase in resistance of the manganin wire indicated a pressure increase of a few thousand kilobars, due to thermal expansion of the sample. During prolonged heating the resistance of the manganin wire tended to decrease. This decrease was regarded as the slow ageing decrease mentioned above and a decrease resulting from an actual loss of pressure within the sample holder due to additional transformation of pyrophyllite and transformations in the reaction zone. The resistance behaviour of the manganin wire is illustrated in *Figure 5*. The resistance changes occurring during the sample-heating period were indicative only and were not interpreted quantitatively because of the aforementioned difficulties in stability of resistance of the manganin wire under high temperature. The sharp changes occurring when the sample was first heated and later cooled were probably due to pressure increase and decrease. The decrease in resistance upon lowering the applied force must also have been a real pressure effect. The indicated pressure changes due to heating or cooling in this example were 3 to 5 kb.

IV. Special Sample Holder Materials

Sample holder materials are chosen for ease of pressure transmission and physical and chemical stability under the experimental conditions used. Selections may be made from a wide range of materials, or material combinations, so that the desired properties can often be closely approximated. The high pressure behaviour of a few materials other than the pyrophyllite already mentioned will be described briefly below.

Granular sodium chloride may be pressure moulded to nearly its theoretical density and machined to particular shapes for use as a sample holder. It transmits pressure to the specimen rather easily and has been used for containing samples heated to 1,500°C at pressures above 50 kb. Unlike pyrophyllite under these conditions, sodium chloride does not undergo a transformation to a more dense phase with resultant loss of pressure. Instead it may melt close to the heated specimen thereby providing some pressure increase due to volume expansion. The molten salt then forms a hydrostatic pressure medium. But sodium chloride cannot be depended on to form its own gasket, as pyrophyllite does, since it flows so much more easily. Sodium chloride should be enclosed in an outer shell of pyrophyllite.

Silver chloride and silver sulphate are very soft solids and remain so under high pressures. Unable to support much shear stress, they transmit pressure as nearly hydrostatically as possible in a solid medium. Silver chloride, and probably silver sulphate, too, decompose under pressure at a few hundred degrees and become electrically conducting. Silver chloride has a phase transformation at 88 kb with a volume loss of 1·6 per cent. Like sodium chloride, these two substances must also be surrounded by a pyrophyllite gasket enclosure.

The hexagonal form of boron nitride is available in moulded machinable shapes out of which sample holders can be made for use at temperatures over 3,000°C at pressures above about 25 kb. A small amount of ammonia may be evolved from boron nitride and it should not be used in contact with metals under conditions which may catalyze the formation of cubic BN[25]. These metals are the alkali and alkaline earth metals. Boron nitride is quite stiff

99

under pressure at room temperature, resembling pyrophyllite in this respect. At high temperature it may flow more easily, but there are no data concerning its high temperature flow characteristics. An alternative is to restrict the use of BN to a thin sleeve adjacent to the reaction zone.

Sintered magnesia and alumina are quite rigid and probably unsuitable for use as sample holder materials. However, they are obtainable in pure forms which are attractive for their chemical stability at very high temperatures. It is convenient to use them as thin sleeves next to the reaction zone. The sleeves can be machined from moulded stock sintered at moderate temperatures.

V. Pressure-Transmitting Properties of Sample Holders

In an ideal straight piston and cylinder pressure apparatus the pressure on the sample is simply the piston force divided by its area. But in a real apparatus an appreciable part of the force is used to overcome friction between the piston and cylinder wall and the frictional resistance to flow and compression within the sample holder itself. In apparatuses using tapered pistons a compressible gasket is required, either one that forms by extrusion of sample holder during the compression, or one that is placed there initially. For these devices, the press load is divided between gasket and sample and the build-up of pressure within the reaction zone depends upon how this load is distributed between the two. If the region of the reaction zone is highly compressible, then the shoulders of the pistons will take the larger portion of the load on the gasket structure. The opposite will be true for a relatively incompressible sample structure.

The sample holder which surrounds the specimen may transmit the applied force to the sample or it may not, depending upon its physical properties. A hard, rigid, incompressible sample holder will bear the burden of the press load while the sample which it contains may feel relatively little pressure. A sample holder that is too compressible will not be sufficiently pressurized before the gasket structure absorbs the bulk of the press load. It is due to this interplay of effects among gasket, sample holder and the specimen itself that each type of high pressure sample structure requires its own pressure calibration, using the pressure reference transformation points in bismuth, thallium, caesium and barium. These transformations are easily detected by the sharp electrical resistance changes associated with the transformations in thin wires placed axially in the cell. Some of the varying pressure transmitting effects of different sample holder materials are illustrated below for room temperature conditions. It is unfortunate that a high temperature calibration scale has not yet been established.

In a sample holder having a considerable amount of shear strength, such as pyrophyllite, the transition begins at the ends of the wire and proceeds along the wire towards the middle. When the pressure-sensitive wire is surrounded by soft materials, such as sodium chloride or silver chloride, practically the entire wire undergoes the pressure transition at the same instant. In the customary calibration of the belt apparatus the transition wire is surrounded by a small silver chloride sleeve placed inside the pyrophyllite sample holder. This arrangement gives quite a sharp bismuth transition as illustrated in *Figure 6*, Curve 1. When the wire is surrounded solely by pyrophyllite, the transition starts at the same press load, but is extended over about 10 tons of press force before the entire wire is transformed to the high pressure modification (Curve 2).

A moulded boron nitride sample holder required a higher press load to start the transition and the transition was also dragged out over a range of

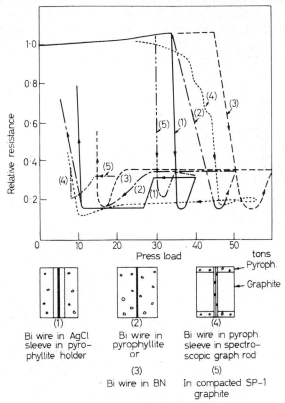

Figure 6. Contrasting behaviour of 25 kb Bi transition in a few different types of sample holders. Silver chloride, sodium chloride, and National Carbon Co. SP-1 graphite give sharp transitions at low total force. Pyrophyllite, moulded boron nitride, and spectroscopic-grade rod carbon require larger press loads and the transition was spread over a large range of forces as it progressed along the wire from ends to centre. Sample (1) and curve (1) illustrate the customary type of calibration

about 10 tons before it was completed (Curve 3). This was very surprising because boron nitride has the graphite structure and the same slippery feel to the touch but under pressure it apparently developed very high shear strength.

Both high and low shear strengths were observed for sample holders composed of graphite. The type of sample tested is illustrated in *Figure 6*, samples 4 and 5. The holder was all graphite except for thin pyrophyllite

discs at each end and a thin sleeve of pyrophyllite around the bismuth wire
for insulation. When the sample holder was composed of spectroscopic rod
graphite of density $1 \cdot 7$ gm/cm³ (made by National Carbon Company) the
bismuth transition ran in steps by a kind of stick-slip process between about
39 and 46 tons press load (Curve 4). But using another grade, identified by
the symbol SP-1 (also made by the National Carbon Company) quite a
different result was obtained. This graphite was a very pure powder easily
compressed into coherent pellets having a density of $2 \cdot 1$ gm/cm³. In a
sample holder of this graphite, the bismuth transition ran very sharply at a

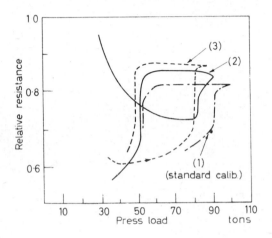

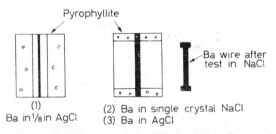

Figure 7. Barium transitions at approximately 60 kb in
pyrophyllite, silver chloride and sodium chloride. The
barium wire had actually decreased in diameter where it
passed through the NaCl part of the sample holder, and
increased in diameter at the pyrophyllite ends

press load of only 29 tons (Curve 5). Of the two graphites, the latter showed
the larger and more perfect crystal development in x-ray diffraction tests.
These structural differences clearly had much to do with the shear strength
of the graphite under pressure.

Examples of other materials exhibiting quite low shear strengths were
sodium chloride and silver chloride. Sample holders composed of either of
these substances and having thin pyrophyllite end discs (like sample 4,

Figure 6) to prevent blow-out, gave sharp bismuth transitions at press loads of only 29 to 30 tons.

Tests on the barium transition at approximately 60 kilobars are illustrated in *Figure 7*. Curve 1 shows the press load required to obtain this transition in the usual manner using a pyrophyllite sample holder with a silver chloride sleeve surrounding the barium wire. Curve 2 shows the press force required for obtaining the barium transition in a sodium chloride single crystal sample holder. The press load required to reach this pressure was almost 10 tons less than required for the pyrophyllite sample holder. Curve 3 shows the same experiment conducted in a silver chloride sample holder where even less press force was required to reach 60 kb. In all these examples the transition ran quite sharply. In other cases where the barium wire was not surrounded by a soft material such as sodium chloride or silver chloride, the barium transition was extended over a considerable range of press force, and usually ran at a substantially higher press load.

These examples of pressure behaviour of various sample holders apply to room temperature only. In some of the materials used, high temperature would undoubtedly soften the sample holder material so that the extended transitions observed at room temperature might be found to run considerably more sharply if they could be observed. However, this argument probably does not apply to some forms of carbon, whose strengths may increase with increasing temperature.

VI. Thermal Conductivity of the Sample Holder

In high temperature, high pressure work the thermal conductivity in the sample holder is one of its important properties, because the sample holder has to protect the chamber walls from the intense heat in the centre. In order to do this the thermal resistance of the sample holder must be very high compared with the thermal resistance of the walls of the pressure chamber. The thermal conductivity of pyrophyllite, catlinite, talc, sodium chloride, etc., and its variation with pressure are therefore of considerable interest in the design of high pressure apparatus and experiments. Bridgman[9] made observations on the thermal conductivity of a number of materials including pipestone (catlinite) under pressure. His data for pipestone running between 0 and 12 kilobars are shown in *Table 2* below. The experience at the General Electric Research Laboratory indicated that pipestone, pyrophyllite, and

Table 2. Bridgman's Values for the Thermal Conductivity of Pipestone at 30°C*

Pressure kg/cm²				Thermal conductivity cal/cm sec °C
0	..	..	..	0·00438
2,000	..	..	..	0·00506
4,000	..	..	..	0·00544
6,000	..	..	..	0·00563
8,000	..	..	..	0·00574
10,000	..	..	..	0·00587
12,000	..	..	..	0·00596

* Orientation of heat flow with respect to bedding plane not specified.

103

talc differed little from one another with respect to thermal conductivity, but that the thermal conductivity of sodium chloride was a little higher than either of these three. These qualitative results on thermal conductivities and their variation with pressure were based on the amount of heating power required to reach certain temperatures in the different materials.

Tests made on the thermal conductivity of pipestone and pyrophyllite at room pressure are listed in *Table 3* below.

Table 3. Thermal Conductivity of Pipestone and African Pyrophyllite at Zero Pressure in Temperature Range of 60–70°C*

Specimen	Thermal conductivity cal/cm sec °C
Pipestone	0·0118
African pyroph llite 'Wonderstone' fine grain	0·0105
African pyrophyllite coarse grain	0·0095

* Conductivity values taken in direction of bedding plane. The tests were performed at the General Electric Research Laboratory.

These values are about twice as high as those obtained by Bridgman on pipestone. The ones on pyrophyllite are in agreement with those of Carte[10] in South Africa, who has studied pyrophyllite and finds a difference of 2 to 1 in directions parallel and normal to the bedding plane. His values parallel to the bedding plane are 0·0119, 0·0100, and 0·0085 at 0°C, 100°C and 200°C respectively. These are in close agreement with the values shown in *Table 3*.

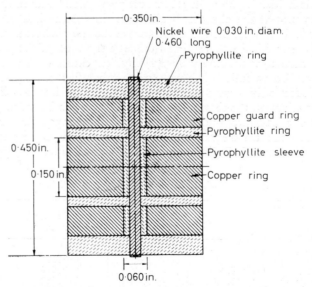

Figure 8. High pressure thermal conductivity cell. The thermal conductivity of pyrophyllite was obtained by comparing the temperature gradients across the pyrophyllite sleeves and copper rings for a known amount of cylindrical heat flow

The thermal conductivity of pyrophyllite was tested under pressure by Bundy in a sample structure of the design illustrated in *Figure 8*. The thermal conductivity was obtained by observing the temperature drop across the pyrophyllite sleeve for a known heat flux from the nickel wire. The results are shown in *Table 4* and indicate that the thermal conductivity at these pressure levels was quite constant. This was in agreement with the earlier

Table 4. Thermal Conductivity of Pyrophyllite at High Pressure and Temperature*

Pressure kb	Temp. of N. rod °C	Thermal conductivity of sto:e cal/cm sec °C
34	1,530	0·0112
52	1,580	0·0114
65	1,610	0·0105

* Conductivity values taken in direction of bedding plane.

rough observation that the power required to heat the sample to a given temperature was proportional to the temperature and independent of the pressure. In Bundy's tests, the temperature was high enough to transform pyrophyllite to kyanite and coesite.

VII. Electrical Conductivity of Pyrophyllite

The electrical conductivity of pyrophyllite was observed as a function of temperature at room pressure by Hall and as a function of temperature at 70 kb by Bundy, both of the General Electric Company Research Laboratory.

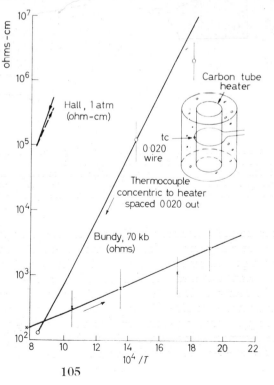

Figure 9. Electrical resistance of African pyrophyllite as a function of temperature. Hall's tests were made on a block of pyrophyllite at atmospheric pressure. Bundy's tests were done at about 70 kb and were based on resistance between the thermocoup'e wire and carbon tube heater arranged as shown in the sketch. The return curve follows a much different course probably because phase changes have occurred in the pyrophyllite

These results are illustrated in *Figure 9*. The data showed the normal behaviour for materials of this type in that the electrical conductivity increased rapidly with temperature. It never increased enough, however, to cause a noticeable reduction in the apparent resistance of the heater, but at high temperatures its resistance may be low enough to interfere seriously with sensitive electrical measurements, such as thermo-electric potentials.

VIII. Methods of Measuring Temperature

(i) Thermocouples

The most direct way to measure temperature inside the high pressure apparatus is to use a thermocouple. A resistance thermometer may also be used, but the mechanical hazards involved in its use in solid high pressure media make it unattractive. Thermocouples have their disadvantages too,

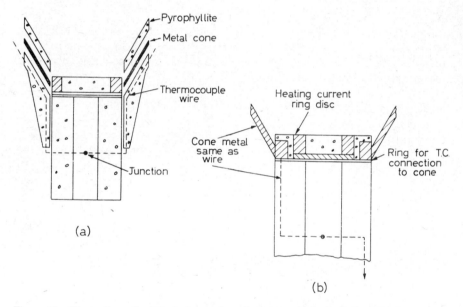

Figure 10. Illustration of methods for getting thermocouple leads through high pressure gasket structure. (a) Wires led through holes or slots in outer pyrophyllite gasket. (b) Wires are connected to metal cones at opposite ends of sample holder through double end ring assembly. Cones must be made from same pair of metals as the wires. The gasket structures are illustrated for one end only. The opposite ends have identical structures

because their thermal e.m.f.'s are influenced by pressure to some extent, and the stretching and working that the wires receive when the cell is loaded are apt to generate very weak couples in other locations. The first difficulty is the important one and will be discussed in more detail below.

In many of the present-day high pressure apparatuses a pyrophyllite gasket is used to give side support to the piston faces and to seal in the sample. This pyrophyllite gasket furnishes a fairly good path through which to lead the thermocouple wires. An illustration of how this has been done is shown in *Figure 10(a)* for the belt apparatus. The wires can be led through small

106

holes drilled in the conical part of the first gasket or laid in slots filed into the gasket from the outside. The wire is put in the slot and then covered over by a cement made of pyrophyllite stone powder and waterglass.

One way to avoid threading wires through the gasket structure is illustrated in *Figure 10(b)*, which shows the belt sample with a double end ring. One ring is used for the heating current and the other is used for a connection to the thermocouple wire. The outer ring is in contact with the metal cone in the gasket structure, which is used as a connection for the thermocouple to the outside. The metal cones are composed of the same thermo-electric metals that are used in the thermocouple itself. Otherwise additional

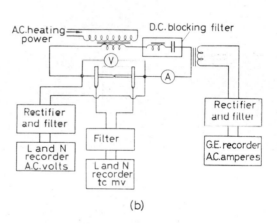

Ni disk and wire lead

Ni
Ni 20 Co
MgO

Ni 20 Co disk and wire lead

(a)

Figure 11. This illustrates an electrical circuit arrangement by which a thermocouple acts as a heating element as well as a means of temperature measurement. The element could be used in the form of a helical coil to heat a volume within it

A.C. heating power   D.C. blocking filter

(V)   (A)

Rectifier and filter

Rectifier and filter

Filter

L and N recorder A.C. volts

G.E. recorder A.C. amperes

L and N recorder tc mv

(b)

junctions would develop which might cause considerable error in the temperature reading.

In multiple piston apparatuses there is a temptation to use a pair of the pistons for connections to the thermocouple inside the pressure cell. Doing so makes other junctions which interfere with the calibration of the thermocouple inside the cell.

When the apparatus does not possess a gasket structure, thermocouple wires must enter through a hole in the chamber. The apparatus of Boyd and England[11], constructed at the Geophysical Laboratory and shown in Chapter 8, illustrates how this can be done quite successfully.

On occasion thermocouples have been used as both heating element and temperature probe. This scheme was used in determining the melting points of some metals. A schematic diagram showing such an arrangement is illustrated in *Figure 11*. The end discs were made of the same metals as the thermo-electric elements, whose leads were threaded through the gasket structure in the usual manner, while the heating current came through the pistons, also in the normal manner. The alternating current circuit contained a condenser with a choke in series to reduce the apparent resistance of the condenser. The purpose of the condenser was to prevent the thermo-couple from being shorted by the secondary winding of the heating power transformer. The thermo-electric circuit was provided with suitable filters to block the a.c. voltage pulses. This made it quite easy to read the thermo-electric output while at the same time the wire was being heated by an alternating current. If the thermocouple pair were made into a helical coil so as to enclose a specimen, then the heating element could measure its own temperature while heating a sample.

(ii) Effect of Pressure on Thermocouple Calibration

When a metal is exposed to very high pressures, its physical properties may be substantially modified. In a certain sense it becomes a different metal. Because of this, one might expect that a thermocouple exposed to high pressure would read the temperature differently from a thermocouple out in the room. The correct way to observe the effect of pressure on the thermo-electric effect is illustrated in *Figure 12*, which shows the experiment of Bridgman[12] in schematic diagram. In Bridgman's experiment both branches

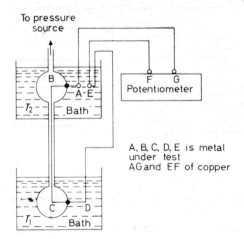

Figure 12. A schematic representation of Bridgman's pressure thermocouple experiment. The thermo-electric junctions were located at the pressure seal where the wire passed from high to low pressure

of the thermocouple pair were composed of the same metal, but the part exposed to pressure was in effect a different metal. Opposite ends of the pressure cell were held at different temperatures and the hot and cold junctions were located at the points where the wire passed from high pressure to low pressure. Bridgman found there was a pressure effect on the thermo-electric potential of individual metals. The strength of the effect varied widely between metals and for many of them it was non-linear in both temperature and pressure. His studies were carried to pressures of 12,000 kg/cm^2

at 100°C as a maximum. When combining a pair of metals to form a thermo-couple to be used under pressure, the algebraic sum of their individual pressure e.m.f.'s must be used to correct the temperature calibration.

The range for pressure e.m.f. studies was extended by Bundy[13] to 72 kb at 100°C using the belt apparatus illustrated in *Figure 13*. In the latter

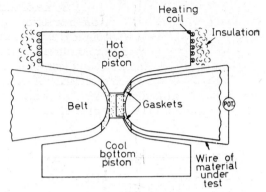

Figure 13. Bundy's arrangement for testing pressure thermocouples to a temperature of 100°C at 70 kb

experiment, as in Bridgman's, one end of the pressure cell was heated and the other was cooled. The wire of the material under test was run continuously from a connection on the potentiometer through the pressure region and back to the other side of the potentiometer. The hot and cold junctions were located in the pressure cell gaskets where the wire passed from low pressure to high pressure and thence from high pressure back to low pressure.

Bundy's measurements on pressure thermocouples agreed with Bridgman's

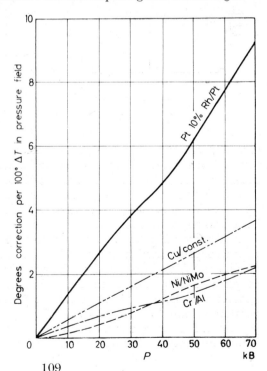

Figure 14. The number of degrees to be added to thermocouple readings at 100°C as a function of pressure up to 70 kb

results rather closely over the range covered by Bridgman. The algebraic sum of the pressure e.m.f.'s for different thermocouple metal pairs provide the actual correction to be applied to thermocouples at different pressures and temperatures. *Figure 14* shows the corrections to be added to the thermo-couple readings of four different kinds of thermocouples for pressures up to 72 kb at a temperature of 100°C. Some of these corrections appeared to be substantial. For example, if the correction curve for a platinum platinum 10 per cent rhodium thermocouple is extrapolated to 100 kilobars at 1,000°C, it would show that it read temperatures about 130°C too low. However, it is not certain that the thermocouple corrections can be extrapolated this far. The additional result which throws doubt upon the possibility of a long extra-polation is illustrated in *Figure 15*. This shows a comparison between a platinum–platinum 10 per cent rhodium thermocouple and a chromel–

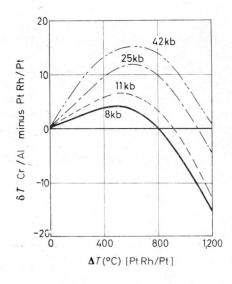

Figure 15. Chromel–alumel thermo-couple deviations from platinum–platinum 10 per cent rhodium tempera-tures for temperatures up to 1,200°C at pressures up to 42 kb

alumel thermocouple to 1,200°C at pressures ranging from 8 to 42 kb. At first their independent temperature readings deviate from one another in a manner predicted by the correction curve of *Figure 14*, but at a temperature of about 500°C the deviation reached a maximum and then increased in the opposite direction. It is, of course, impossible to say which thermocouple (or both) was responsible for this behaviour.

Another way of testing thermocouples under pressure is to compare several thermocouples simultaneously under the same pressure and temperature conditions. This has been done for possibly six different types of thermo-couple, including those illustrated in *Figure 14*. The result was that at 70 kilobars and about 1,000°C the various thermocouples read the same tem-perature within a range of 20°C. If the thermocouples used had both positive and negative errors, then the correct temperature would have been within this range. However, there was the very real possibility that all of the thermocouples tested deviated in the same direction, in which case the temperature error would have been larger than 20°C.

(iii) Absolute Temperature Measurement at High Pressure

An ingenious method of temperature measurement was proposed by Garrison and Lawson[14] which makes use of the thermal noise phenomenon in resistors. This phenomenon is apparently quite independent of the absolute pressure. Hence, in principle, it should be possible to make the correct temperature measurement under any pressure whatsoever simply by observing the thermal noise of a resistor. The phenomenon is entirely independent of the chemical composition and past history of the material being used in the resistor. In practice there are a number of physical limitations and experimental difficulties which might reduce its accuracy under conditions of very high pressures and temperatures to something less than what Garrison and Lawson obtained at room pressure.

The basis of operation of a noise thermometer is shown by the Nyquist formula for the mean square voltage fluctuations arising from thermal agitation in a network in which there is no net current flow, namely

$$\bar{V}^2 = 4kRe(Z)\,T\varDelta f$$

If one knows the Boltzmann constant k and $Re(Z)$, the real part of the complex impedance of the network, and the magnitude of the mean square fluctuations over a range of frequencies $\varDelta f$, the absolute temperature T of the resistor will be determined. In Garrison and Lawson's experiment, they measured an unknown temperature T_2 by comparing the noise voltage of an independent circuit at temperature T_2 with the noise voltage of another circuit at known temperature T_1, using the same amplifier on both noise signals by switching back and forth. Their measurements up to 1,200°K agreed to within 0·1 per cent with the readings obtained from a carefully calibrated platinum–platinum 10 per cent rhodium thermocouple.

Garrison and Lawson at the University of Chicago tested for the effect of pressure on the thermal noise element by exposing it to a pressure of 10 kilobars in a pressure bomb in equilibrium with room temperature. Temperatures measured by the resistance element inside the bomb were found to be correct. At pressures not exceeding 10 kilobars, it should be possible to heat the bomb to a few hundred degrees centigrade and further check the theoretical prediction that a thermal noise resistance element is independent of pressure. If so, a thermal noise thermometer should provide an excellent means for calibrating a thermocouple to very high pressures and temperatures.

A simple but non-absolute method for estimating thermocouple pressure

Table 5. Resistances and Temp. Coeff. for Platinum at Pressures (kg/cm²) of:

	0	4,000	8,000	12,000
0°C	1·00000	0·99224	0·98476	0·97756
100°C	1·38680	1·37638	1·36618	1·35622
Temperature coefficient ..	0·003868*	0·003871	0·003873	0·003874

* Value given by American Institute of Physics Handbook (McGraw-Hill Book Co., New York, 1957) is 0·00392.

errors would be to compare a resistance element with a thermocouple. Bridgman[15] has already observed that the variation of the temperature coefficient of resistance of most metals with pressure was quite small. For example, the resistances for platinum at temperatures of $0°$ and $100°C$ at pressures up to 12,000 kg/cm^2 were as shown in *Table 5*.

The table indicates that the temperature coefficient of resistance increases with pressure at a small and decreasing rate. A linear extrapolation of the change between 0 and 12,000 kg/cm^2 to 100,000 kg/cm^2 (100 kb approximately) indicates a possible increase in the coefficient of about 1·3 per cent. If it can be assumed that the error in the coefficient is no larger than this at 1,000°C, then it should be possible to measure the temperature correctly to within about 15° at 1,000°C, the tendency being to read a temperature lower than the true temperature. Actually, since the direction and approximate magnitude of the change are known, allowances could be made.

Since thermocouple errors are not always linear with pressure and temperature, it would seem that a comparison between thermocouple and a platinum resistance element would be worthwhile as an aid in narrowing the range of uncertainty that exists in present high pressure temperature measurements.

(iv) *Approximate Methods of Temperature Measurement and Control*

In carrying out a series of high pressure experiments, it is convenient to measure and control the temperature in terms of heating power input. Once the temperature scale has been established by comparing a thermocouple reading or certain known melting points to power input, then the temperature in the high pressure cell can usually be reproduced to within ± 1 or 2 per cent, using the power input alone as the means of measurement. In order for this method to be successful, the elements of the heating circuit must be made to within close dimensional and resistance tolerances.

IX. Attainment of Temperatures of about 3,000°C

There are few insulating materials which will withstand temperatures in excess of 3,000°C without melting*. To maintain temperatures near this level for an extended period of time is very difficult indeed, since the surrounding ceramic insulating material tends to become electrically conducting even if it does not actually melt. This increased conduction on the part of the ceramic changes the apparent resistance of the heating element and therefor the power dissipation in the heating circuit. Thus is it almost impossible to maintain a steady temperature above this extreme high level by present techniques. One method of surmounting these difficulties in certain cases is to heat the specimen by discharge of a very strong pulse of heating current through the specimen from a large condenser. When using this technique, the temperature of the specimen at peak is estimated from the strength of the input pulse which is usually observed on an oscilloscope, while allowing for the time duration of the pulse and the thermal diffusivity of the surrounding insulating material. Using the techniques just described,

---

* Boron nitride is good for steady temperatures to perhaps 3,500°C[26].

Bundy has reached temperatures of about 4,000°C at pressures in the neighbourhood of 80 kilobars.

X. Melting of Metals

In making observations on the effect of pressures on the location of phase transformations and melting points, the problems are to be able to detect the occurrence of the transformation and to measure the pressure and temperature when the transformation occurs. This detection is easy if it is accompanied by a change in thermal conductivity, latent heat or electrical properties of the sample.

The measurement of temperature and pressure is not so easy. The errors in temperature measurement have already been discussed. Up until the time of writing this at least, no means of accurately measuring very high pressures when the temperature is also high has yet been discovered. So far the pressure calibration of high pressure apparatus has depended upon the volume or the electrical resistance transitions observed by Bridgman[16] in the metals bismuth, thallium, caesium and barium. The volume and resistance transitions were observed separately by Bridgman, and when first discovered appeared to occur at somewhat different pressures. It is now believed that both volume and resistance transitions occur simultaneously and their values as given by Bridgman, Balchan and Drickamer[17] at the University of Illinois, Kennedy and LaMori[18] at the University of California and Boyd and England [11] are as follows: bismuth 25 kb, thallium 36·7 kb, caesium 41 kb, barium 59 kb and bismuth 88 kb. These are the principal room-temperature reference points for determining the pressures produced within the pressure cell in terms of the press load applied to the pistons. Except for bismuth, the locations of these transitions at elevated

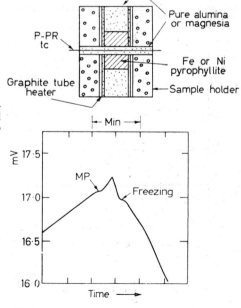

Figure 16. The detection and measurement of the melting point of a metal under pressure from a latent heat step in a rising time–temperature curve

113

temperatures is unknown. Consequently, the best that can be done at present is to establish the desired pressure in the pressure cell at room temperature and then heat the sample.

The combined effects of heating the specimen and the phase changes occurring in the sample holder with its associated volume shrinkage are

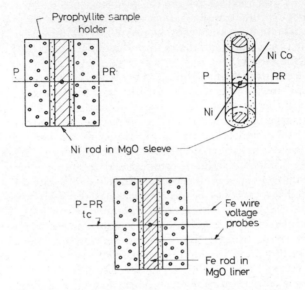

Figure 17. Method of observing the melting points of iron and nickel in resistance-heated rods, using the resistance change at melting and thermocouples to detect and measure the melting point

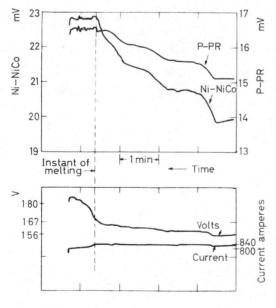

Figure 18. Thermocouple records and resistance increase at the melting point of nickel. The thermo-electric e.m.f. of the Ni–NiCo junction increased steadily up to the instant of melting, but the P–PR junction probably started to alloy and lose calibration near the melting point

likely to cause some deviation in pressure from its calibrated value. Except in cases where it is possible to eliminate the friction on the sides of the pistons and thus make it possible to compute pressure from force over area, it is necessary to live with this uncertainty. One way to try to get some idea of the effect of thermal expansion uncertainty of the heated zone on pressure is to vary the sample size and the volume of the heated zone in order to note its effect on the location of the phase transformation being studied. This was done to determine the melting point of nickel.

The melting points of iron and nickel were determined by techniques illustrated in *Figures 16* and *17*. In the first instance, the sample was contained in pure magnesia or alumina capsules inside a carbon tube heater. A platinum–platinum 10 per cent rhodium thermocouple passed directly through the sample and registered the occurrence of melting by a latent heat step in a slowly increasing temperature–time curve. In the second example, the sample was heated directly by passage of a current through the specimen and melting was detected by the occurrence of a sharp increase in electrical resistance and the simultaneous attainment of an upper limit in the e.m.f. of the thermocouples inserted in the specimen. The detection of a thermocouple maximum e.m.f. was made quite simple in the case of nickel by using a nickel–nickel cobalt alloy thermocouple. The nickel melted before the alloy and signalled the melting of the nickel rod very clearly. *Figure 18* illustrates the behaviour of thermocouples and current and voltage in the neighbourhood of the melting point. In the case of nickel

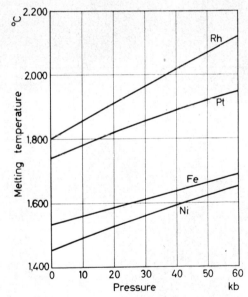

Figure 19. The fusion curves of Ni, Fe, Pt and Rh on the revised pressure scale

the effect of thermal expansion on the pressure was studied by observing the melting point for samples in which the volume of the heated zone was varied by 40 to 1. In this instance the pressure difference due to the difference in the volume of the heated zone was within the errors of measuring the melting point temperature and could have been as much as 5 kb.

115

The fusion curves of nickel, iron, platinum and rhodium are illustrated in *Figure 19*. They are replotted from their original published forms, in which the pressure calibration was based on the electrical resistance transitions of the four calibration metals. The revised scale is based on the volume transitions of these metals. The curves for platinum and rhodium start at melting points well below the melting point of the pure metal. This was due to the fact that although pure metals were placed in the pressure cell, they became slightly contaminated during the course of the experiment and this lowered their melting points substantially. In the case of nickel and iron it was easier to keep the chemically pure metal relatively clean.

The fusion curves of tin and indium up to about 75 kb on the new pressure scale were obtained by Dudley and Hall[20]. They used the multi-piston tetrahedral apparatus of Hall[21] with a pyrophyllite sample holder. The occurrence of melting was detected by a sharp increase in electrical resistance and the temperature was measured with a platinum–platinum 10 per cent rhodium thermocouple. The fusion curves for the same two metals were also determined by Kennedy[22], and their two sets of curves agreed to within about 10°C. *Tables 6* and *7* give some of the results of their measurements.

Table 6. Melting Points of Indium at Pressures up to 75 kilobar

Pressure kb	Melting temperature °C	
	Dudley and Hall[20]	Kennedy[22]
0	156	156
10	202	200
20	242	242
30	275	280
40	325	320
50	360	
75	410	

Table 7. Melting Points of Tin at Pressures up to 75 kilobars

Pressure kb	Melting temperature °C	
	Dudley and Hall[20]	Kennedy[22]
0	232	232
10	268	258
20	294	285
30 (triple point) ..	317	305
40	368	360
50	414	
75	494	

The fusion curves of several other metals melting at temperatures less than 800°C were determined by Butuzov, Gonikberg *et al.*[23] for pressures up to 34,000 kg/cm².

References

[1] BRIDGMAN, P. W., *J. chem. Phys.*, **15**, 1947, p. 92

[2] LIANDER, H. and LUNDBLAD, E., *Ark. Kemi*, **16**, 1960, p. 139

[3] NEL, L. T., JACOBS, H., ALLAN, J. T. and BOZZOLI, G. R., 'Wonderstone', *Union of S. Africa, Dept. of Mines Bull. No. 8*, 1937 (Publ. of Geol. Survey Div.)

[4] COES, L., Jr., *Science*, **118**, 1953, p. 131, and BOYD, F. R. and ENGLAND, J. L., *J. Geophys. Res.*, **65**, 1960, p. 749

[5] CLAUSSEN, W. F., DEVRIES, R. C. and MACKENZIE, J. D., *WADD Tech. Rept. 60-634*, Wright Air Force Development Division, Air Research and Dev. Command, USAF Wright-Patterson Air Force Base, Ohio

[6] CLARK, S. P., Jr., ROBERTSON, E. C. and BIRCH, F., *Amer. J. Sci.*, **225**, 1957, p. 628

[7] HALL, H. T., *Rev. sci. Instrum.*, **31**, 1960, p. 125. Also chapter by BUNDY, F. P.

[8] BRIDGMAN, P. W., *Proc. Amer. Acad. Arts Sci.*, **71**, 1937, p. 387; *Phys. Rev.*, **48**, 1935, p. 825; and *J. Geol.*, **44**, 1936, p. 653; and LARSON, E. S., *Amer. J. Sci.*, **36**, 1938, p. 81

[9] BRIDGMAN, P. W., *Amer. J. Sci.*, **7**, 1924, p. 81

[10] CARTE, A. E., *Brit. J. appl. Phys.*, **6**, 1955, p. 326

[11] BOYD, F. R. and ENGLAND, J. L., *J. geophys. Res.*, **65**, 1960, p. 741

[12] BRIDGMAN, P. W., *Proc. Amer. Acad. Arts Sci.*, **53**, 1918, p. 269

[13] BUNDY, F. P., *Progress in Very High Pressure Research*, Collected papers of Sagamore Conference, Lake George, N.Y., 1960. John Wiley and Sons, New York. (To be published in *J. Appl. Phys.*)

[14] GARRISON, J. B. and LAWSON, A. W., *Rev. Sci. Instrum.*, **20**, 1949, p. 785

[15] BRIDGMAN, P. W., *The Physics of High Pressure*, Chapter IX, G. Bell and Sons, Ltd., London

[16] BRIDGMAN, P. W., *Proc. Amer. Acad. Arts Sci.*, **76**, 1948, p. 55; **81**, 1952, p. 165; **74**, 1942, p. 425

[17] BALCHAN, A. S. and DRICKAMER, H. G., Private communication. (To be published)

[18] KENNEDY, G. C. and LaMORI, P. N., *Progress in Very High Pressure Research*, 1960, (See ref. 13)

[19] STRONG, H. M., *J. geophys. Res.*, **64**, 1959, p. 653; STRONG, H. M. and BUNDY, F. P., *Phys. Rev.*, **115**, 1959, p. 278

[20] DUDLEY, J. D. and HALL, H. T., *Phys. Rev.*, **118**, 1960, p. 1,211

[21] HALL, H. T., *Rev. sci. Instrum.*, **29**, 1958, p. 267

[22] KENNEDY, G. C., Private communication

[23] BUTUZOV, V. P., GONIKBERG, M. G. and SMIRNON, S. P., *Dokl. Akad. Nauk SSSR*, **89**, 1953, p. 651 (Transl. Nat. Sci. Found., USA NSF-tr-76 Sept. 1953); BUTUZOV, V. P. and PONYATOVSKII, E. G., *Kristallografiya* **1**, 1956, p. 572; **1**, 1956, p. 736; BUTUZOV, V. P., *Kristallografiya* **2**, 1957, p. 536; BUTUZOV, V. P., PONYATOVSKII, E.G. and SHAKHOVSKOI, G. P., *Dokl. Akad. Nauk. SSSR*, **109**, 1956, p. 519

[24] FITCH, R. A., SLYKHOUSE, T. E. and DRICKAMER, H. G., *J. opt. Soc. Amer.*, **47**, 1957 p. 1,015

[25] WENTORF, R. H., Jr., *J. chem. Phys.*, **34**, 1961, p. 809

[26] WENTORF, R. H., Jr., *J. phys. Chem.*, **63**, 1959, p. 1,934

6

A MULTIPLE PISTON, HIGH PRESSURE, HIGH TEMPERATURE APPARATUS

BALTZAR VON PLATEN

Götgatan 16, Stockholm

I. 'Demiurge and the Diamonds'—a Hypothesis

LET me begin by telling a story.

It was a fine autumn day, and I had just entered the University of Lund in the south of Sweden. As I passed the School of Botany, I saw that one wall was covered with Virginia creeper. Its leaves were a beautiful red. Every autumn brought the change from green to red, and passers-by would pause at the display of colour in sudden admiration. I was one of these passers-by, and had no idea that my pleasure in this seasonal beauty would later play an important role in my life, that it would reveal the clue to the problem of achieving very high pressures in large volumes of the order of a thousand cubic centimetres or more. I had no suspicion that later this sight would show me the way to construct a machine which makes diamonds, the machine now owned by ASEA*.

A couple of years later I was studying at the Royal Institute of Technology in Stockholm. Although botany was not one of our studies, Tarras Sällfors†, a friend of mine, was very interested in the subject. One day I happened to describe the autumn in Lund, and the colours, and I asked him why the leaves of the creeper turned red in the autumn as they died.

'Your question reminds me of a hypothesis—or call it a speculation— which a philosopher described to me not long ago,' answered Tarras, and continued:

'He was not a biologist himself, and certainly didn't want his thoughts on the subject to be described by so scientific a word as "hypothesis". He just called it an interesting speculation, and I think you will find it interesting too. But there is something else I must say first. . . .'

'Perhaps you know,' Tarras continued, 'that the natural force which solved the problems of life on this earth was symbolically represented in antiquity by the spirit called Demiurge or Demiurgos. God himself gave Demiurge the task of solving these problems, and to help him He gave him divine understanding. He made Demiurge into the world's greatest inventor. The five senses, sight, hearing, touch, taste and smell, are his inventions, and so is the human brain—perhaps the most wonderful of all. Demiurge has made thousands upon millions of inventions, all necessary to support life.'

---

* ASEA: Allmänna Svenska Elektriska Aktiebolaget (Swedish General Electric Company Ltd).

† Former General Director of Swedish Industrial Organization Committee, *obit* 1960.

118

'And I imagine he invented something useful for the leaves of that Virginia creeper too,' I said.

'Of course. Now I will tell you what the philosopher told me.

'You asked why these leaves turned red in the autumn when they die. Well, our philosopher supposed that they do this not because they are dying, but because they don't want to die. Each autumn, when they feel that they have not much longer to live, a physico-chemical process takes place in them which gives them those beautiful colours. We know that certain molecules in the leaves disintegrate, and that this must happen sooner or later—that is, either before the leaves die, or after. The fact that it happens before they die was taken by my philosopher friend to be a typical example of adaptability in the world of living organisms. He assumed that there must be some good reason for this to happen, and came to regard the process as a weapon which Demiurge had given the leaves and taught them how to use in the unequal struggle against Death's advance. This seems to be a paradox, because with this weapon the leaves actually help their enemy Death to carry out part of his work of destruction—namely, the disintegration of molecules. During the last part of their lives, the leaves co-operate with the enemy by doing a job that he would otherwise have had to do soon after their death. He would have to do it anyway, because it is part of his task of bringing about the dissolution of the leaf's organism.

'But this co-operation with Death, the philosopher speculated, was nothing more nor less than a way of tricking him. The leaves had to meet Death half way; but Death did not understand that in teaching them this, Demiurge was giving them an extra couple of weeks of life, and giving us the beautiful blaze of autumn.'

Not being a biologist, I allowed this speculation of Tarras' philosopher to become an accepted scientific fact in my mind, as though it were one of the real inventions of Demiurge.

The years passed. I was fully occupied with other work and thought very little about the problem of making diamonds. Then, between Christmas of 1930 and the New Year, I happened to be visiting a friend, John Tandberg, now a professor and well-known physicist in Sweden. On a table there was a publication which I glanced at quite by chance. It showed the function between pressure and temperature during the crystallization of carbon into diamond. Discussing the subject with him, he was doubtful whether steel could stand up to such enormous pressures.

Some hours later when I was thinking over what he had said, I happened to remember what Tarras had told me about the leaves. In my mind's eye I saw a mass of red leaves with Demiurge in the background. All at once a thought struck me and an association of ideas sprang to life. It was utterly unexpected, for up to then I had done no work at all on the diamond problem, though I had often been tempted to get to grips with it. Suddenly I saw how Demiurge's principle for prolonging the life of the leaves could be applied to a machine for making diamonds. One had merely to convert botanical facts into mechanical ones, and the parallel between the corresponding details seemed to me to be quite complete. It was as though Demiurge himself had told me a great secret, in words like this:

'You must show as much care for your diamond machine as I showed for my leaves when I taught them how to meet Death by doing some of his work for him. You know your machine must fall to pieces when it is destroyed—when it is killed—by the enormous pressure. And the form of these pieces will be wrong, since the dead steel has not been invested with the wit and knowledge that I gave to the leaves. Your machine will be destroyed in the same way as my leaves died before they learned what to do from me. You must let your machine go to meet Death by dividing it up into pieces, but you must give these pieces the shape that the machine itself would have wished, had it been a living organism like the leaves. Then it will stand much higher pressures, and live longer. And then you will be able to make diamonds.'

The association of ideas had now led to a hypothesis.

As we know, a hypothesis is an assumption we make to help us understand certain facts more easily or more thoroughly. We may not, however, make just any assumption at all. We must show logically that it is likely to be correct. The likelihood that a hypothesis is correct is derived not directly from scientific facts, but from a philosopher's speculations. This made it necessary to describe my own hypothesis together with the circumstances of its origin, otherwise it might have seemed abrupt and obscure.

We also know that a more general way to understand facts, for example, thoughts or phenomena, is to combine them logically into a system or several systems. These may themselves be combined into supersystems. A hypothesis always implies the building of a system, or an attempt to do so. This process of combination or synthesis is constantly being carried on, intuitively and subconsciously, by most human beings. It is a form of understanding. When it is performed consciously and the system is brought towards the point of completion, it becomes science, and with it the view of a complex of problems becomes clearer and the perspective widens. And so the process helps us to find the right path, or the direction of that path, towards the result we wish to achieve. This may be diamonds, or millions of other concrete or abstract things.

There is little doubt that the phenomenon upon which our present hypothesis rests has been known for many years in other branches of technology. If this is so, there can be no doubt at all that when it was first observed it was at once fitted into one or several systems. None of these, however, happened to be any that could lead us to our goal—that is, the making of diamonds. My hypothesis fitted the phenomenon into an entirely different system, which proved to be one of those that led to the right direction, since it led to the construction of ASEA's diamond machine and the production of diamonds with this machine in February, 1953.

In other words, my hypothesis forced me to think along a certain line which proved to be one of the correct ones. I say 'one of the correct ones' because we know that quite apart from the present hypothesis, other lines have led to the same goal—man-made diamonds.

II. General Design Considerations

Before we try to realize the hypothesis in the construction of a diamond machine, we should first glance at the mathematical implications. We will find it convenient to consider first a thick-walled cylindrical tube.

Figure 1 is a diagrammatic drawing of a tube whose inner diameter is $2a$ and whose outer diameter is $2c$. The thickness of the wall, $c-a$, is taken to be fairly great, since the tube is to withstand a positive pressure p of about 6,000 kg/cm² in its interior. Following the hypothesis, the tube must be divided into pieces so that its strength will be greater, or put another way, so that the maximum strain occurring shall be a minimum for a given constant pressure p. The only way—or in any case, the most direct way—of dividing the tube, is shown in the drawing. Thus the inner part of the tube is divided into a fairly large number of pieces 31, which inside and outside are bounded by the cylindrical surfaces 32 and 33, and on the sides by the plane surfaces 34, the continuations of these planes intersecting in the tube's central axis. The thin column (not specially marked in the drawing)

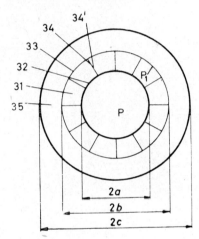

Figure 1. Cross section of a thick-walled tube, showing method of sub-division of wall

between two proximate surfaces 34, is called 34'. We suppose that inside the tube which had been divided up in this way, and in contact with it, is a skin or thin shell of, say, soft iron. This skin is not shown in the figure, and its presence has no effect on our calculations of the tube's durability. It performs more or less the same functions as the inner tube of a car tyre, merely preventing the medium which is under pressure from forcing its way into the columns 34'. These are assumed to communicate with the surrounding atmosphere.

We now ask ourselves to what radius, b, the columns 34' shall extend, so that the greatest strain in the steel shall be a minimum for a constant value of pressure p. If b exceeds a, $(b>a)$, and is, of course, not imaginary, then it can be proved mathematically that the hypothesis will be useful, at least in this case.

Since the number of pieces 31 is assumed to be fairly large, the tangential strain in each one may be disregarded. The pressure p_1 between each such piece 31 and the unsplit, integral cylinder or tube 35 will then be

$$p_1 = p \cdot \frac{a}{b}$$

121

We look now at *Figure 2*, which shows the integral tube 35. The pressure inside it is p_1, as stated above. The forces on an infinitesimal element of it, of the shape shown, are σ_r, $\sigma_r + d\sigma_r$, and σ_t. The radii of the element are r and $r + dr$. The element is contained by a sector making the infinitesimal angle $d\phi$.

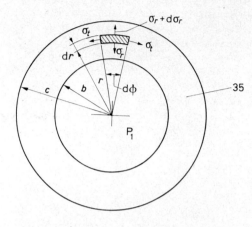

Figure 2. Cross section of a thick-walled tube, showing forces on an infinitesimal element

Since the element is in equilibrium we obtain, by a pair of simple operations which do not need to be repeated here, the expression

$$\frac{d}{dr}(\sigma_r r) = \sigma_t \tag{1}$$

Introducing the radial displacement u of the element, we obtain by a further pair of operations the differential equation

$$r^2 \cdot \frac{d^2 u}{dr^2} + r \cdot \frac{du}{dr} - u = 0 \tag{2}$$

From the solution of this equation we obtain integration constants, which depend on

$$\sigma_r = -p_1 \quad \text{when } r = b$$
$$\sigma_r = 0 \quad \text{when } r = c$$

It will then be found that

$$\sigma_r = p \cdot \frac{ab}{c^2 - b^2} \cdot (1 - \frac{c^2}{r^2})$$

$$\sigma_t = p \cdot \frac{ab}{c^2 - b^2} \cdot (1 + \frac{c^2}{r^2}) \tag{3}$$

$$\therefore \quad \sigma_j = \sigma_t - \sigma_r = 2p \cdot \frac{ab}{c^2 - b^2} \cdot \frac{c^2}{r^2} \tag{4}$$

As we know, σ_j is greatest, i.e. $\sigma_j(b)$, on the inside of the integral tube; that is, when $r = b$. This can also be seen from equation (4).

$$\therefore \quad \sigma_j(b) = 2p \cdot \frac{ac^2}{b(c^2 - b^2)} \tag{5}$$

By derivation from equation (5), and with the derivative equal to zero, we obtain the most advantageous depth of the column, b_{opt}; that is to say, the value of b that we require.

$$\therefore \frac{d\sigma_j(b)}{db} = -2pac^2 \cdot \frac{c^2-3b^2}{b^2(c^2-b^2)^2} = 0 \tag{6}$$

$$\therefore \quad c^2 - 3b^2 = 0$$

$$\therefore \quad b_{opt} = \frac{1}{\sqrt{3}} \cdot c \tag{7}$$

The advantage to which the hypothesis pointed is thus valid for a cylindrical tube, but only if certain conditions are fulfilled; that is, only if

$$a < \frac{c}{\sqrt{3}}$$

By dividing the tube into pieces 31, tangential tensions are prevented in the region between radii a and b. Thus the tube is stronger. Or one could say that it is stronger because tangential tensions have been eliminated from a region where radial tensions are far more dangerous, allowing the steel in this region to concentrate entirely on withstanding the latter. The tangential tensions are absorbed instead by parts of the tube farther away from the centre, which, before the inner part was divided, contributed very little to containing the pressure in the tube. A logical result of this operation is that the pieces have a very small, but sufficient, freedom of movement in the direction of the eliminated force, i.e. tangential.

The formulae governing the durability of a thick-walled cylinder and those governing the durability of a thick-walled sphere are very similar. Thus we see without further calculation that the hypothesis holds good for this sort of vessel also, and thus will be valid for another part of the diamond machine which we shall call the high-pressure component.

III. Description of High Pressure Apparatus

Having shown mathematically that the hypothesis is likely to be useful, we may now describe ASEA's diamond machine. It consists of three main parts: the high-pressure component, a cylindrical tube, and a mounting. The two latter together, the tube and the mounting, form the low-pressure component. As we know, the high-pressure component must be built for a pressure of several tens of thousands of atmospheres, or say 100,000 kg/cm², whilst the greatest pressure in the low-pressure component has up to now been only 6,000 kg/cm².

Figure 3 shows the high-pressure component diagrammatically, whilst *Figure 4* is an actual representation of a shell 50 which is almost perfectly spherical and whose diameter is about 52 cm. It is set into the cylindrical tube just mentioned, which has a diameter of 53 cm. This tube is closed at the top by a piston or plug 45 and at the bottom by another, 47. The pressure inside the tube and surrounding the shell is the above 6,000 kg/cm² at its maximum. This pressure also acts on the plugs 45, 47, so the maximum force upon them will be 13,200 metric tons. This force, or forces, is absorbed by the mounting, whose two pieces 10 directly oppose them (as shown in *Figure 3*). *Figure 5* (p. 128) shows the mounting. It consists mainly of the pieces 10, the rectangular pieces 11, and the binding-mantle 12. Its construction will be described in more detail later.

When the machine is to be used, the tube with plugs 45, 47 containing the

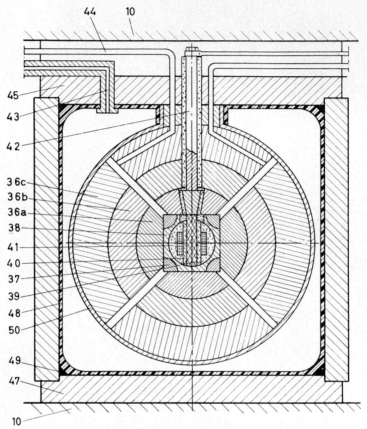

Figure 3. Diagrammatic cross section of a multiple piston high pressure apparatus. The high pressure zone, 41, is compressed by the pistons 36, which are driven by the hydraulic pressure acting on the exterior of the plastic shell 50

high-pressure component is fitted into the mounting. The geometrical axis of the tube and the longest axis of symmetry of the mounting will then coincide.

This briefly is how the machine is constructed. It will now be described in closer detail from both the structural and theoretical viewpoints.

We turn once more to *Figure 3*. It can be seen that the high-pressure component may be said to consist of a thick-walled spherical vessel cut into six similar pieces. Each of these is cut into three smaller pieces, top, middle, and base, 36a, 36b, and 36c respectively, so that among other things, the pieces may be tempered as required. (See also *Figure 4*.) Each piece thus composed is numbered 36. The surface of its top-piece, which faces the centre of the sphere, is square. When the six pieces 36 are assembled these surfaces bound a cubic cavity whose centre coincides with that of the sphere. In this cavity there is a cubic body 38 also concentric with the sphere, consisting of a soft shell of copper. (See also *Figure 4*.) This in turn contains a spherical cavity in which there is an electrical resistance rod 39 of graphite and non-conducting material, a tube 40 of electrically insulating material such as bornitride, and on the exterior of this and in contact with it, another tube not numbered in the drawing, made of the mixture of materials from which diamonds can form in conditions of high temperature and pressure. Surrounding this is a heat-insulating material 41, usually soapstone. When

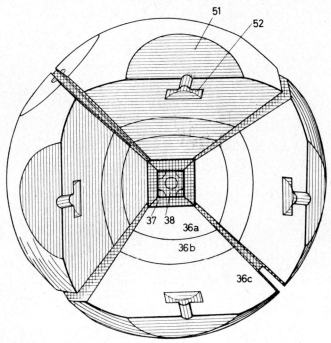

Figure 4. View of high pressure piston assembly, after removal of one piston

the pressure rises inside the copper shell and the parts within it, the shell may squeeze out into the columns between the pieces 36, or more properly, between 36a. To prevent this, there are the ribs 37, which are of hard steel. At their ends are shields which serve to bridge the gaps which occur there. These shields are not specially shown in any of the drawings because their form is a purely geometrical consideration. Both ribs and shields are leaded, and this thin layer serves as a lubricant between shields, ribs and the plane surfaces of the pieces 36a. This is an important detail, because while the pressure is rising, relative movement occurs between these parts. With further reference to the diagrammatic *Figure 3*, we may assume that the copper shell 50 is not squeezed into the columns between pieces 36c. How this is prevented in practice will be described a little further on with reference to *Figure 4*. The pressure in the low-pressure chamber is achieved by pumping a suitable liquid such as water into it, through the diagrammatically represented channel 43 in *Figure 3*. When the pressure in this chamber rises, the pressure will be rising faster in the high-pressure chamber. Here the pressure will be equal to that in the low-pressure chamber, or the low pressure, multiplied by the ratio between the base area and the top area of a piece 36. The latter is, of course, the square area of a piece 36a, whilst the former is equal to a perpendicular projection of a piece 36c onto a plane parallel to the square area of 36a.

How the copper shell 50 is prevented from being squeezed into the columns between the pieces 36, or the base-pieces 36c, may be understood from *Figure 4*. The drawing shows the form of the outward-facing surfaces of each base-piece. After first making this area spherical, it is planed in four places. The four plane surfaces 51 thus formed are symmetrically placed in relation to the corners of the base-piece. The perpendicular bisector of this plane surface's only straight edge runs through the centre of the sphere. One surface 51 of any base-piece is then obviously in the same plane as the neighbouring surface 51 of the base-piece next to it. Two such surfaces together form a circular plane surface, if one disregards the column between the pieces. Each of these circular surfaces is now covered with a shield, which we will call the large shield. This shield is spherical on the outside and plane on the inside. The plane surface lies in contact with the two surfaces 51, apart from a lubricant, consisting of a thin lead plate, which separates them. 52 designates a slot in the steel for assembling the high-pressure component. We now imagine this component assembled, with the large shields, twelve in number, lying on the surfaces 51. There still remain eight small places where the copper shell 50 might be squeezed into the columns. These are at the corners of the base-pieces. The sphere is also planed at these points. The new plane surfaces thus formed extend over the edges of the above large shields. These smaller surfaces are now covered with shields, called small shields. Friction here will be reduced as before. This method of preventing the copper shell from being squeezed into the columns works most effectively, and no other is used. The friction is only very slight. An added advantage of this method is that the pieces 36 are held very strongly in position. Those forces which during an experiment tend to displace a piece 36 from its natural position, emanate from irregularities in the cube in the centre of the sphere. They are generally not so great that they cannot be held by the large shields.

When the pressure rises in the low-pressure chamber and therewith also in the high-pressure chamber, the columns between the pieces 36 diminish. The width of column must be so calculated that at maximum pressure it is about two-tenths of a millimetre at the ribs 37.

Before reaching maximum pressure, the whole sphere has been cooled to some 40 or 50°C below zero, using a coolant of boiling or non-boiling liquid. This is pumped in through a channel 44 and out again through a corresponding channel on the other side of the centre. At maximum pressure the electric current flows through the lead 42, which is in contact with the copper shell 38 and the mounting. The current flowing through it develops heat in the resistance rod 39, wherewith diamonds form in the tube surrounding the insulating tube 40.

It should be mentioned that the low-pressure chamber is sealed from the outside atmosphere by means of the rubber container 48. The rings 49 prevent the rubber from being squeezed out into the tiny columns or crevices between the plugs (45, 47) and the tube. These rings should not be of tempered steel, for they will break. Soft, weak iron has proved to be excellent. It yields back and forth with each experiment, but this is of no importance.

As we have said, *Figure 3* is diagrammatic and not representational. This applies especially to the appearance of the high-pressure chamber in the region about the centre where the diamonds are formed, and to the electric lead. Thus, in reality, all insulating layers are much thinner than can be indicated on this diagram. Also not shown is a device to prevent the insulating material from being squeezed out by the high pressure. The electric lead has, in general, caused very little difficulty, and its construction has therefore not been altered much during the last 20 years. This however is not the case with that part of the chamber where the diamonds form, that is, the centre. The construction of this part has been altered many times and still varies constantly in appearance. The construction shown must therefore only be taken as one diagrammatic example among many. There are still great difficulties to be overcome in this part of the machine. But for a long time I have had reason to believe that these difficulties will be less, the larger are the diamond machine and the high-pressure chamber.

Another difficulty has been to concentrate the high pressure on the centre, or at least on that place where the diamonds are formed. The best way to solve this problem is as follows. Six holes are drilled in the copper shell 38. They are geometrically coaxial with the pieces 36. Into these holes are mounted truncated cones of, say, steatite, which break up the curvature in the heat-insulating material 41—the feature which does most to prevent the pressure concentrating in the centre.

IV. Description of the Mounting Yoke

We shall now describe the mounting in greater detail. As we have said, it consists mainly of two semicircular pieces 10, between them and in contact with their plane surfaces the mainly rectangular pieces 11, and around the said four pieces, the binding-mantle 12. (See *Figure 5*.) Between the binding mantle 12 and the circular surfaces of the pieces 10 there is a smooth plate 16, and outside the binding-mantle a shield plate 17. The flanges 18 and 19, which are held together by the bolts 20, support and protect the mantle from the sides. The dimensions of the mounting are: overall height, 280 cm; overall width, 250 cm; thickness of the pieces 10, 60 cm; length of the pieces 11, 80 cm; shortest distance between the pieces 11, 92 cm. As stated, the maximum load on the mounting is 13,200 metric tons.

We shall now assume that all the pieces 10, 11, 12, 15 and 16 are joined together by welding, for instance, to form an integral piece of steel. It has been found that the mounting will then break after it has been used a couple of times under a load of several thousand metric tons. The pieces 10 (or more properly the former pieces 10, for they are now all joined into a single component) will break near the rectangular corners between them and the former pieces 11. Even if these corners were heavily rounded and the dimensions of the mounting increased to the extent this would require,

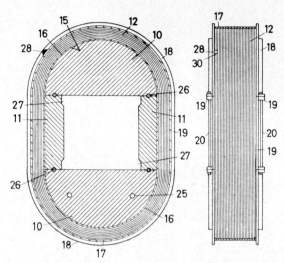

Figure 5. The mounting yoke which carries the axial thrust of the plugs for the tube

a fracture could not in practice be avoided. In theory, it is undoubtedly possible to overcome this weakness by increasing the dimensions considerably, but this is just the solution we do not want, since it cannot be achieved practically. We therefore return to considering the mounting divided up into pieces, as shown in *Figure 5.*

We have already mentioned that a tube could be strengthened in that certain tensions were eliminated from a certain region so that the steel could concentrate on withstanding other forces which were more dangerous in that particular region. We also said that the pieces into which the tube was divided maintained a slight but sufficient freedom of movement relative to each other, in the direction of the removed force. In the divided mounting we have the same phenomenon but differently expressed, since both the shape of the pieces and the way the forces act are different from those of the tube. An important difference in detail must therefore be described before we go further. In the tube the pieces could, without resistance, move a little in relation to each other in the direction of the removed force. In the mounting, on the other hand, there always occurs one, and at high loads two, corresponding relative movements, of which the first and most important is hindered by friction. This latter must therefore be reduced as much as possible by usual means of lubrication, if the mounting is to function as intended.

When there is no load on the mounting—that is, when the pressure in the tube is nil—the tension in the mantle 12 is such that the pieces 10 are drawn towards each other and against the pieces 11 with a force which for practical reasons is somewhat greater than the mounting's maximum load. The latter was 13,200 metric tons, so the former has been set at 15,000 metric tons. The curved surfaces of the pieces 10 are smooth, as are the surfaces of the steel plates 16. Between the pieces 10 and the plates 16 there is a solid lubricant, in this case graphite, so that the friction here will be as little as possible. To facilitate assembly, the graphite is pressed into a piece of thin cloth. The steel bands of the binding-mantle 12 are 3 mm wide and 1 mm thick. Between the layers of binding in the mantle and between its innermost layer and the outer surfaces of the plates 16 there is no lubricant. On the contrary, these surfaces are very carefully cleaned so that the friction here, for reasons which will shortly be explained, may be as great as possible.

In order to explain the mounting's *modus operandi*, let us make a mental experiment and assume that the friction between the plates 16 and the pieces 10 is nil. If one then assumes the right to overlook a very small unevenness in distribution caused by high friction between layers of the mantle, it can be said that the specific pressure against the circular surfaces of the pieces 10 is the same at all points. The effect is as though the mantle exercised a hydraulic pressure on these surfaces.

Suppose that the pressure in the tube, and with it the load on the mounting, is slowly increased. The pieces 10 move away from each other, whilst the pieces 11, which in the beginning were compressed with a force totalling 15,000 metric tons, lengthen elastically. The mantle, of course, also lengthens and together with the plates 16 it then slides frictionlessly on the circular surfaces of the pieces 10. The tension in the mantle increases by only a negligible amount, whereas the load on the rectangular pieces falls very quickly. A fairly simple calculation shows that a mounting such as this will hold in spite of the large maximum load of 13,200 metric tons, and in spite of the small dimensions just mentioned. However, this was only a mental experiment, for we assumed that the friction, or the coefficient of friction, between the plates 16 and the pieces 10 was nil, which in reality it is not. We should therefore see what happens when we give it its real value. This is quite simple.

The movement between binding-mantle 12 and pieces 10 is, of course, greatest in the neighbourhood of the contact surfaces between pieces 10 and pieces 11, whilst 90° from there—that is to say, at the crown of pieces 10— it is nil.

When the load on the mounting changes with the pressure in the tube, tangential forces are transferred to the pieces 10 through friction between these and the plates 16. Suppose the pressure is rising. The tangential forces on a piece 10 are then directed from its crown. They try to break the piece into three. If the coefficient of friction is equal to that between two unlubricated metal surfaces, the pieces 10 will be bent. When the pressure in the tube then sinks they will be bent in the opposite direction, so that after a few variations of load they break. However, if a lubricant is introduced between the plates 16 and the pieces 10, the coefficient of friction falls to a fully acceptable value. In fact, it falls so much that in practice the mounting functions as though the coefficient were nil. Therefore we can say that in practice the mounting does function in accordance with the mental experiment we have described. A great number of real experiments have confirmed this.

As we have said, friction between different layers of the binding-mantle is great. Thus, when the pressure in the tube rises, all the layers are forced to stretch an equal amount. If friction were small it could happen that in some layers only the straight lengths along the pieces would be stretched. The specific increase in length would thus be greater, and an unnecessary additional tension would arise.

We naturally wish to be able to construct a mounting which is as small as possible. That is to say, the thickness of the pieces 11, and therefore the diameter of the pieces 10, should be a minimum. However, the pieces 11 may not be too thin, since for practical reasons the tension in the binding-mantle 12, or the force exerted by it, must be somewhat greater than the maximum force on the plugs 45 and 47. This tension in its turn, however, should not be unnecessarily large. If the pieces 11 are as thin as possible given the above considerations, then it follows that when the mounting is not under load they will be loaded to near the limit of elasticity, which in this case clearly involves no risk. Their length is approximately fixed by the diameter of the sphere that forms the greater part of the high-pressure component. We obtain, from the above considerations, the value of the maximum increase in length of the pieces 11, that is to say the increase in the distance between pieces 10, when the pressure in the tube rises to its maximum value. Clearly the increase in length of the pieces 11 will be greatest when their cross-sectional area is least; that is to say, when the steel is near the limit of elasticity when the mounting is not under load.

If the movement or increase in length is too great, then practical difficulties will arise with the sealing of the tube by its two plugs 45 and 47. This might lead to the conclusion that the pieces 11 should be thicker and therewith the whole mounting more massive, but it has been shown in a great number of tests that it is perfectly permissible to have the pieces thin enough for the steel to be at the limit of elasticity when the mounting is not under load, without the increase in length being so great as to cause sealing difficulties. It would be very different if the pieces 11 were left out altogether. The maximum increase in the distance between the pieces 10 would then equal half the total increase in the length of the mantle when the tension in it is raised from nil to its maximum value. This increase, to judge from results so far obtained, seems to be so great that the sealing difficulties can scarcely be overcome. This is one reason why the pieces 11 are essential; another is that they greatly facilitate the construction of the mounting, in particular its assembly.

We will now assume that the pressure between the pieces 10 and 11 is constant everywhere when the mounting is not under load. We further assume that the tension in the mantle 12 is as little as possible, leaving aside all practical considerations. This means that the absolute force of the contact between the pieces 10 and 11, disregarding weights, is nil when the pressure in the tube is maximum. Finally we will make another mental experiment and assume that these pieces 10 are completely rigid or inelastic. If such steel existed, the specific pressure would diminish evenly so that it was the same at all points, as the load on the mounting increased. This specific pressure and the above absolute force of contact would become nil simultaneously with the pressure in the tube reaching its maximum value. In this case it would not matter whether or not the pieces 10 and 11 formed an integral piece. But because no completely rigid bodies exist, conditions will be otherwise, as we will now show.

When the mounting is not under load, the plane surfaces of the bodies 10 which face its centre of gravity are slightly convex, due to the force exerted by the mantle 12. They are slightly concave when the pressure in the tube is maximum. Since the tension in the mantle is assumed to be minimum, a crevice or column must arise between the pieces 10 and 11. When a certain pressure has been reached in the tube, this crevice begins to form in the corner between one piece 10 and another 11. As the pressure rises further, the crevice widens and at the same time lengthens towards the mantle 12. The crevice is thus wedge-shaped. The area of contact between a piece 10 and another 11 is thus reduced more and more as the pressure increases, to the point where it is nil at maximum pressure. The wedge-shaped crevice has then reached as far as the plate 16, and the pieces are touching each other along a single line only, located where these pieces and the plate 16 all make contact. Let us assume that the load on the pieces 10 is the best that can be practically achieved, from the point of view of durability. The plane—or now slightly concave—surface of a piece 10 is met by the force from a plug 45 or 47, and the circular surface of the piece is met by the force from the mantle 12, which may now be likened to a hydraulic pressure. Suppose that in some way we can now introduce a tensile force between these pieces, so that the pieces 11 are lengthened and cling fast to the pieces 10 as if they were welded together. The pieces 10 will then bend still further, in spite of the fact that the tension in the mantle will have diminished slightly. The bending of pieces 10 means that an additional tension has been introduced. If before bending they were at breaking point or at the limit of elasticity, they will now either break or become deformed. Even if they were not at these limits, their efficiency will nonetheless deteriorate in that they will be loaded less advantageously.

We now see why it is important that this part of the mounting should be divided up into pieces too; in other words, that pieces 10 and 11 are separate units. It is clear that they move relative to each other without friction. However, the most important factor continues to be that the mantle 12 is independent of the pieces 10 and moves over them with the least possible friction, as described.

There now arises the question of how large a mounting can be built. This depends on the possibilities which exist for producing the pieces 10. In the existing machine they are forged. The weight of each is about $3 \cdot 6$ metric tons and the tensile strength of the steel is 60 kg/mm². If they are to be considerably larger, they must be steel castings. Assuming the linear dimensions to be quadrupled, the weight of a piece 10 would then be $3 \cdot 6 \times 4^3$ $= 230$ metric tons. If the strength of the material is assumed to be the same, which may be possible now, the maximum load on such a mounting would be $13,200 \times 4^2$, that is, about 210,000 metric tons. The total volume of the high-pressure chamber in the existing machine is about 400 cm³. This chamber in the larger machine could thus be 400×4^3 or about 25,000 cm³.

131

At present, however, such an expensive diamond machine is not likely to be built—at least not before an idea to which I have long subscribed has been shown to be highly probable; namely, that the great difficulties which beset the actual forming of the diamonds will automatically diminish as the size of the machine and the high-pressure chamber is increased.

V. Description of Cylindrical Enclosing Tube

As we have seen, the hypothesis has been applied to two of the three main parts of the machine; namely, the high-pressure component and the mounting. It has not, however, been applied to the tube. We can deduce from the mathematical analysis that for theoretical reasons it is pointless to use the hypothesis in constructing a tube where $a > c/\sqrt{3}$, but the purely practical reasons against it are immediately obvious. On the other hand, if the pressure is to be greater than 6,000 kg/cm², then the tube must be divided up into pieces in the way already described. This should never be necessary, however, since as far as we can see, a higher pressure than 6,000 kg/cm² in the low-pressure chamber is not feasible enough in practice to be worthwhile. This applies even more to larger machines. We shall now describe the construction of the tube, and refer to *Figures 6* and *7*.

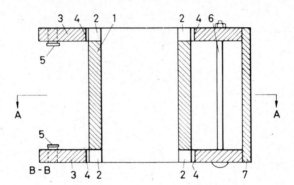

Figure 6. Cross section of the cylindrical enclosing tube before wrapping it with steel bands

The inner diameter of the tube is 53 cm, as we said. A tube this size that will withstand a positive pressure of 6,000 atmospheres is not difficult to build using known methods. The difficulties lie, or lay, in finding any cause for building it. There was no point in doing this before the problem of the mounting had been solved, before one had managed to build a mounting which could absorb the enormous forces exerted by the plugs. Then suddenly this problem was solved through the hypothesis, and the cause we had needed to build the tube became a reality.

Simple mathematical calculations show that the tube could be constructed by the well-known method of fitting two or more fairly thin tubes around each other. A warm tube is fitted over a cold one, the dimensions having been carefully calculated. A tube assembled in this way is extremely strong, provided there are no faults in the material whatsoever. It needs only a single hardening fault to cause an explosion. Partly because of this and partly to reduce the outer diameter of the tube, and thereby the distance between the pieces 11 and the weight of the whole mounting, it was necessary

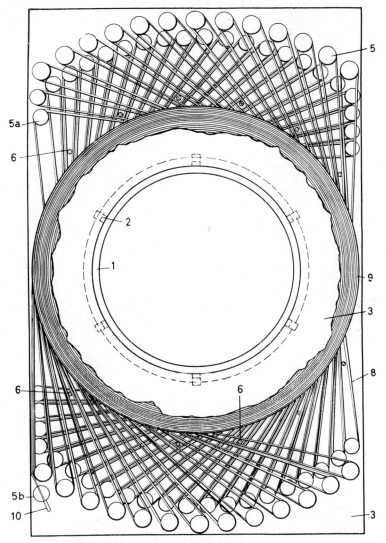

Figure 7. Plan view of the tube (cross section A–A of *Figure 6*), showing the method of wrapping the steel bands

to choose the method of winding the tube round with steel bands. That there could be faults in a large number of turns in the winding is unthinkable, thus the risk of explosion is eliminated. Known methods of winding would not have proved adequate in this particular case, so the winding is carried out in a special way. Here too there were problems, the solutions of which will now be described.

The tube in *Figures 6* and *7* is numbered 1. Two thick plane plates are numbered 3. In each of these plates there is a large central hole whose diameter is the same as that of the tube, or slightly greater. Slots 4, directed radially and preferably six in number, are taken out of the cylindrical surfaces of the holes. Corresponding keys 2 on the tube fit into these slots 4. The tube is thus prevented from turning relative to the plates 3. On the other hand, it is free to widen and to narrow with alterations of the pressure inside it. The tube and large holes will thus be geometrically coaxial, independent of the pressure. It should be mentioned now, however, that in the existing machine this detail has been somewhat altered. In each of the large holes is fitted a ring, and the slots 4 are taken out of this. As before, tube and holes are coaxial, but no moment can be transferred from the tube through the keys 2 to the rings, since these can turn relative to plates 3.

The tube 1 and the two plates 3 are mounted into a special winding machine, with which the band 9 (*Figure 7*) will be wound into the tube. There are a number of holes in the plates 3, into which short pegs or staves 5 may be fitted. One end of the band 9 is fixed into one of these to begin the winding, and the other end is fixed into another, when the winding is completed. The latter is marked 5b. The former is not shown in the drawing, but is identical to 5b. A cap of soft iron with a certain carbon content is pressed hydraulically into the ends of the band, which passes through a slot in these two pegs, i.e. the first and last. The bands are joined together by similar caps in the straight parts of the winding, and a large number of experiments has shown that the joints are just as strong as the band itself. When one layer has been wound, say, in the direction of a right-hand thread, i.e. right-hand pitch, the band is turned round one such peg 5 on the other plate, and then wound back again still in right-hand pitch. When x layers have been wound in this way, one begins to wind the remaining y layers in the opposite direction, i.e. left-hand pitch. This is done by letting the band pass over a peg and continue in the same direction instead of turning the band round it. This one peg is marked 5a. The band thus continues over the peg 5a in the same direction, wherewith the winding is converted to the opposite pitch, in this case left-hand.

From *Figure 7* it can be seen that because of the tension in the band, the x layers exert a turning moment on the plate 3. The moment may be called M_x. The y layers exert a moment in the opposite direction, which may be called M_y. Each layer is wound with a certain tension, which is so calculated that the shearing stress will be the same everywhere in the winding when the pressure in the tube is maximum. The ratio between x and y is so chosen that the moment transferred to a plate is nil when the pressure is maximum. Thus $M_x + M_y = 0$. At all other pressures a moment is transferred to one plate 3, and an equal but opposite moment to the other plate 3. The moment in one plate must therefore be transferred to the other. The tube and the slots 4 and keys 2 should not be used for this, nor can they be, when the slots are in a loose ring as described above. The moment is therefore transferred through the two plates 7 (see *Figures 6* and *8*). These should be fairly massive so that their elastic deformation may be small. They are therefore reinforced from the inside, as we see from *Figure 8*. This deformation, which cannot be entirely avoided, causes a fault to occur in the tension of the straight parts of the band 9. This fault must be so slight that it may be disregarded in practice. When the winding is complete, some bolts 6 are mounted, which hold the various parts of this structure together.

Figure 8. Photograph of the entire apparatus, showing the mounting yoke and the frame for the bands enclosing the tube

VI. Concluding Remarks

ASEA's diamond machine and its theoretical background have been summarily described. Many thoughts came to me while writing this essay. I reflected that I write now as I should have written perhaps twenty years ago. Then, it was the high pressure and the great volume of the high pressure chamber which were the prime considerations. They were the goal which had for so long slipped away like a mirage into the seemingly impossible. Yet when these things were finally achieved one found that there were new difficulties to be overcome. I intimated their nature earlier by saying that they lay in that part of the high-pressure chamber where the diamonds form.

However, I have not been working on these problems for the last ten years. This is partly because I had to turn my attention to other matters, and partly because I came to the conclusion that at least a good part of the remaining problems would only be solved by building a larger machine. It may be optimistic to expect that such a machine will be built, for it will be an expensive and therefore daring experiment.

There is someone I should especially like to thank for the extremely useful assistance he gave me in the construction of the diamond machine and in a large number of experiments over the course of the years. He has given perhaps twenty-five years of his life to the diamond machine. His name is Fritz Wallin. He was foreman of my laboratory, and is now with ASEA.

It is a great pleasure for me to be able to thank ASEA's former technical director Ragnar Liljeblad and the present technical director Halvard Liander. They have contributed greatly to overcoming the problems I have just described. Without Ragnar Liljeblad there would have been no collaboration between ASEA and myself and no diamonds would have been produced by this machine.

Reference

[1]LIANDER, L. and LUNDBLAD, E., *Ark. Kemi*, **16,** No. 9, 1960, pp. 139–149

7

SYNTHESIS OF MINERALS AT HIGH PRESSURES

LORING COES, JR.

The Norton Co., Worcester, Mass.

I. Introduction

THIS chapter deals with some preliminary studies of the synthesis of minerals at high pressures. The main motive in this work was to study the conditions attendant on the formation of natural diamond. A further objective was an exploration of the whole field of silicates in order to find substances having sufficient hardness for abrasive purposes. The field of study embraced pressures up to about 45,000 kilobars (the compressive strength of sintered tungsten carbides) and temperatures up to about 1,000°C.

At the time this study was begun, there were about 40 'hard' minerals which could not be synthesized by dry melt techniques. The distinction 'hard' is included to separate this field from the large number of hydrated minerals of the mica, amphibole, clay, and zeolite groups. The latter are 'pressure minerals' but form in a distinctly different pressure range, apparently below a few hundreds of atmospheres, and are all hydrated minerals. The class of 'hard' minerals referred to above also includes some hydrated minerals, but these, as well as the rest of the group, require pressures of the order of a few thousand of kg/cm^2 for their synthesis.

The most important natural concentrations of these minerals are in the eclogite rocks, and the pressure apparatus described below was first turned to a synthetic study of these.

Eclogite is essentially a garnetiferous pyroxenite in which the pyroxene is omphacite or chrome diopside. The rock usually contains 50 per cent or more of garnet, but this constituent may be so small that the rock grades into the pyroxenites. The pyroxene which is present, omphacite, is a diopside rich in a jadeite component and also contains chromium. The garnet is a magnesium-rich variety.

In addition to the garnet and pyroxene, several accessory minerals are also found in eclogite. These are: kyanite, sillimanite, epidote, zoisite, lawsonite, chloritoid, plagioclase, white mica, magnetite, corundum, rutile, ilmenite, chromite, pyrite, titanite and spinel.

The unusual mineral assemblage in the rock gives it a density and average packing index which distinguishes it from all other rocks.

The primary silicates present, i.e. garnet, pyroxene (var. omphacite), kyanite, epidote, zoisite, sillimanite and chloritoid, are silicates with high packing indices and cannot be formed at atmospheric pressure.

The low-density silicates—the micas, and plagioclase—are secondary products present in kelyphite formed by alteration of the pyrope. These are considered to have been formed after the crystallization of the primary silicates.

In addition to the substances enumerated above, the eclogite usually contains carbon in small amounts, usually as graphite and occasionally as diamond. It is remarkable that the silicates represented in the list, with the exception of sillimanite and omphacite, all are found in nature enclosing carbon. In fact, the only silicates found in nature enclosing carbon and which are not also found in eclogite are tourmaline and staurolite. Still more remarkable, in view of the experimental work, is the absence of staurolite from eclogite.

Much has been written concerning the origin of eclogite. Some authorities maintain that it is of igneous origin, while others class it as metamorphic. The weight of evidence seems to favour the metamorphic origin since many of the accessory minerals (kyanite, jadeite, epidote, zoisite, and chloritoid) are not found in igneous rocks. The garnet would be equally at home in either environment. In the diamond-bearing pipes the eclogite occurs as xenoliths (foreign rocks) in the kimberlite.

No syntheses had been reported for dyanite, andalusite, jadeite, lawsonite, epidote, zoisite, chloritoid, or staurolite. Diopside had been repeatedly synthesized at atmospheric pressure. The many reported syntheses of sillimanite were made before mullite was recognized as a distinct species. Bridgman[1] (1938–39) failed to produce kyanite by shearing andalusite under pressure. Foster[2] (1942) and others had reported failure to produce jadeite.

In the garnet group many claims had been made. The early claims, however, are of doubtful authenticity because the work was done in dry melts. According to Clark[3], Shepard and Rankin[4] mentioned, without details, the formation of grossularite under pressure but no mention is made of grossularite in the paper referred to, nor in other papers by the same authors.

While it can be said that most eclogite contains no diamond and most diamonds are not found in eclogite, it has been well demonstrated that diamond does occur in some eclogite, apparently as a primary mineral.

Although data are lacking to prove that all diamond originated in eclogite, it is well known that diamond from any source is always accompanied by omphacite, magnesian ilmenite, and chromian pyrope, which are normal constituents of eclogite.

The conclusion reached by Trovimov[5] (1939) that diamond is more common than usually supposed and is found as inclusions in all types of rock from the very acid to the very basic, is entirely without foundation. After a survey of all known occurrences, he presents no more than ten, other than kimberlite. No fewer than five of these are well known to be unsubstantiated claims; two are meteorites, two are not definitely proven, and the last is the Brazilian occurrence which most authorities believe to be of secondary origin.

II. Apparatus

The pressure apparatus used for this study was essentially a double-ended piston and cylinder device employing sintered tungsten carbide pistons and a cylinder of special sintered alumina supported by a steel sleeve. A cross section of the apparatus is shown in *Figure 1*.

The alumina cylinder had an outside diameter of about 1·250 in., a height of 1·250 in., and contained a central hole 0·250 in. in diameter. Parallel with the axis of the cylinder and 0·281 in. from its centre-line was

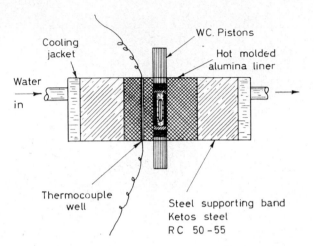

Figure 1. Schematic cross section of high pressure, high temperature apparatus. The sintered tungsten carbide pistons carry the heating current and are driven into a special alumina cylinder

a hole 0·040 in. in diameter which carried a thermocouple. The cylinder was fabricated from a special high-strength aluminium oxide which contained 1 per cent cobalt oxide to inhibit grain growth during the hot pressing operation. After pressing, a taper of one inch per foot was ground on the outside of the cylinder.

The alumina cylinder was then pressed into a steel sleeve which had a similar taper on its inside surface. The interference between the two cylinders was 0·002 in. on the diameter. This interference produced about 150,000 lb./in². hoop tension in the steel sleeve and 150,000 lb./in². inner fibre stress in the alumina cylinder. The steel sleeve had an outside diameter of 3 in. and was made of 'Ketos' hardened to Rockwell C 50–54. A water-cooling jacket surrounded the sleeve.

Force was applied to the pistons by hydraulic presses constructed with accurately parallel working faces. These faces bore cemented tungsten carbide anvils which in turn pushed on the cemented tungsten carbide pistons through 0·001 in. thick aluminium foil.

The capsule containing the reactants was placed inside a carbon heater tube and electrically insulated from it by magnesium oxide. The heater tube was capped on each end by 0·250 in. long solid graphite cylinders which connected the pistons with the heater tube. Sometimes a concave hardened steel sealing ring was interposed between the piston and the graphite plug, as shown in *Figure 2*. The capsule was heated by passing

an alternating electric current through the heater tube via the pistons. A
typical input of 200 amperes at 4 volts heated the capsule to 800°C.

The temperature of the capsule was measured indirectly by the external
thermocouple in the 0·040 ir hole by the following method. A dummy

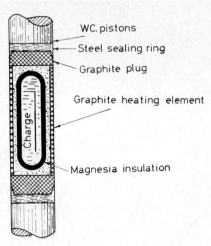

Figure 2. Detailed drawing of the
heated sample region of the
apparatus of Figure 1

WC. pistons
Steel sealing ring
Graphite plug
Graphite heating element
Charge
Magnesia insulation

capsule containing a Pt–Pt 10 per cent Rh thermocouple temporarily
replaced the regular capsule, and at a series of power inputs the temperature of the external thermocouple was plotted against the temperature of
the thermocouple in the dummy capsule. Thus correction factors were
obtained for each cylinder assembly which permitted the capsule tempera-

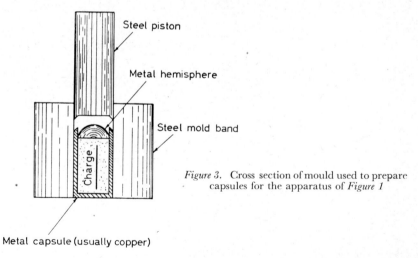

Steel piston
Metal hemisphere
Steel mold band
Charge

Figure 3. Cross section of mould used to prepare
capsules for the apparatus of Figure 1

Metal capsule (usually copper)

ture to be estimated to within about 10°C using the external thermocouple
temperature.

The capsules themselves were 0·187 in. outside diameter and 0·500
in. long. They were made from various materials, usually copper, and were
assembled in a separate mould shown in Figure 3. A capsule consisted of a

deep cup loaded with reactants. The open end was closed with a hemi-spherical plug and the wall protruding above the capsule was closed down on the plug by a piston with a concave end. After being sealed, the capsule was rolled in magnesium oxide paste and inserted in the carbon heater tube.

The pressure inside the apparatus was calculated from the forces and areas involved. Observations on the phase transitions of bismuth estab-lished that such calculated pressures were accurate to within about 2 kilobars. The principal error in pressure measurement arose from friction; friction absorbed about 15 per cent of the force on the pistons. However, the actual capsule pressure may have been lower than 85 per cent of the calculated pressure if the reaction in the capsule were one which produced a substantial volume decrease. By the same token, the actual pressure inside the capsule may have been somewhat higher than 85 per cent of the calculated pressure if the reaction produced a substantial increase in volume, particularly when the pistons were forced outward by the reaction chamber, or during long runs. For these reasons the pressures reported in the syntheses which follow are those calculated on the basis of force and area, neglecting friction.

An apparatus such as that described above operated without failure and was able to contain gases at least as light as water vapour. The following limits of operation were possible for periods of several hours:

Kilobars	Temperature, °C
30	1,000
40	900
45	800

III. Details of Mineral Syntheses

The actual stability regions of each of the minerals were not always determined because one species may grade into another as the synthesis pressure or temperature changes, presumably because of overlapping sta-bility zones. Most of the minerals, except pyrope garnet, could be synthe-sized at pressures of 25,000 atm or less. Subsequent investigations by other workers, in particular F. A. Hummel, H. S. Yoder, G. D. Kennedy, and F. R. Boyd, have more clearly defined the regions of stability of many of these minerals, often with the result that the pressure required for stability was much less than that used in the synthesis described here.

(i) Omphacite

Omphacite is a pyroxene consisting essentially of diopside which holds in solid solution appreciable amounts of jadeite and a chromium silicate, presumably analogous to jadeite, and having the formula $NaCr(SiO_3)_2$, hitherto unknown in the pure state.

In the experimental work it was assumed that the conditions necessary for the formation of omphacite would depend wholly on the conditions necessary to form jadeite and the analogous chromium silicate. This assumption seems reasonable because diopside itself can be synthesized at atmospheric pressure while jadeite cannot.

Diopside, jadeite and omphacite are not found enclosing carbon in nature and none of the synthetic materials enclosed carbon either.

141

Jadeite was made by the following reaction

$$Na_2SO_4 + Al_2O_3 \cdot 2SiO_2 \cdot 2H_2O + 2SiC \rightarrow$$
$$2NaAl(SiO_3)_2 + 2C + H_2O + H_2S$$

The carbon was deposited as graphite at all temperatures above 600°C and pressures from 35,000–45,000 atmospheres. No carbon was ever included in the jadeite crystals. Jadeite can be formed by the same reaction at 900°C and 20,000 atmospheres.

Jadeite and spessartite garnet can be formed simultaneously as follows

$$6NaMnO_4 + 5Al_2O_3 \cdot 2SiO_2 \cdot 2H_2O + 8SiC \rightarrow$$
$$6NaAl(SiO_3)_2 + 2Mn_3Al_2(SiO_4)_3 + H_2 + 9H_2O + 8C$$

This reaction can also be carried out at 900°C and 20,000 atmospheres. In this case the carbon is included in the garnet with none in the jadeite.

The chromium present in diopside is probably present as $NaCr(SiO_3)_2$, which belongs to the jadeite–acmite series, but this substance does not occur in nature in the pure state, nor had it been previously synthesized. By the action of sodium dichromate on silicon carbide according to

$$2Na_2Cr_2O_7 + 2H_2O + 3SiO_2 + SiC \rightarrow 4NaCr(SiO_3)_2 + 4H_2 + C$$

a silicate has been obtained which has the optical properties of a pyroxene of the jadeite–acmite series. These properties are:

Ref: Index $\alpha = 1 \cdot 67$, $\beta = 1 \cdot 74$, $\gamma = 1 \cdot 76 +$
extinction 44°
Biaxial negative, $2V = 40°$ (app.)
Insoluble in HF, soluble in NH_4HF_2

The silicate was a deep chrome green and crystallized in short monoclinic prisms.

The carbon produced in the reaction was not included in the silicate. The reaction can be carried out at 600–900°C and 25–45,000 atmospheres with no change in results except crystal size.

Diopside itself does not form readily under pressure and has been formed only occasionally as a by-product in other reactions. Reactions designed to produce diopside usually result in enstatite and dense silica. Only systems in which the magnesium content is low and the calcium high produce diopside. However, the existence of a solid solution series from diopside to clinoenstatite obscures the results.

(ii) Garnets

The garnet present in eclogite is an impure pyrope consisting of a solid solution of the molecules $Mg_3Al_2(SiO_4)_3$, $Fe_3Al_2(SiO_4)_3$, $Mn_3Al_2(SiO_4)_3$, $Ca_3Al_2(SiO_4)_3$, $Ca_3Fe_2(SiO_4)_3$, and $Ca_3Cr_2(SiO_4)_3$. The pyrope molecule makes up 60–70 per cent of the whole and almandite (Fe,Al) 12–20 per cent, the other molecules being present in amounts up to 10 per cent.

The constituents of the garnet were studied individually and some important differences were noted in the conditions necessary for their formation and their ability to hold carbon.

(*a*) *Spessartite*—The pressures necessary for formation of spessartite are not greater than 20,000 atmospheres in the range 600–900°C. Hummel[11] has since shown that spessartite can be synthesized at one atmosphere. This garnet forms small, well-developed crystals, pale green in colour. Carbon formed during crystallization of the garnet is included in the crystal up to the point of complete opacity. This garnet has been formed by the reactions

$$3MnO_2 + Al_2O_3 \cdot 2SiO_2 \cdot 2H_2O + 2SiC \rightarrow$$
$$Mn_3Al_2(SiO_4)_3 + 2H_2O + C + CO$$

$$6NaMnO_4 + 5Al_2O_3 \cdot 2SiO_2 \cdot 2H_2O + 8SiC \rightarrow$$
$$6NaAl(SiO_3)_2 + 2Mn_3Al_2(SiO_4)_3 + 9H_2O + H_2 + 8C$$

(*b*) *Andradite*—The pressures necessary for formation of andradite are not greater than 20,000 atmospheres at temperatures of 600–900°C. The garnet crystallizes in small dodecahedra having a reddish brown colour. Carbon formed during crystallization of the garnet is included in the crystal, arranged radially and concentrated at the centre. This garnet has a greater tendency to be accompanied by the corresponding pyroxene, hedenbergite, than any other garnet. This is probably due to the fact that it resembles the pyroxenes more closely than the other members.

Many reactions have produced andradite; the most important are

$$Fe_2O_3 + 3Ca(OH)_2 + 2KClO_3 + 3SiC \rightarrow$$
$$Ca_3Fe_2(SiO_4)_3 + 3H_2O + 2KCl + 3C$$

$$2Fe + 3CaSO_4 \cdot 2H_2O + 3SiC \rightarrow$$
$$Ca_3Fe_2(SiO_4)_3 + 6H_2O + 3S + 3C$$

$$2Fe(PO_4) \cdot 2H_2O + 3Ca(OH)_2 + 3SiC \rightarrow$$
$$Ca_3Fe_2(SiO_4)_3 + P_2O_3 + 3H_2O + H_2 + 3C$$

(*c*) *Almandite*—The pressure necessary to form almandite is not greater than 20,000 atmospheres in the temperature range 600–900°C. This garnet crystallizes most readily of all the garnets and often this builds crystals whose form can be recognized with the naked eye. The crystals are always rhombic dodecahedra tending to become modified by the tetragonal trisoctahedron as the crystal size increases. The small crystals are usually clear pink.

Carbon formed during the crystallization of the garnet is included in the crystal, concentrated at the centre. This garnet is often formed as a by-product in reactions carried out in iron capsules. It has been made by the reactions

$$3Fe_2O_3 + 2Al_2O_3 \cdot 2SiO_2 \cdot 2H_2O + 2SiC \rightarrow$$
$$2Fe_3Al_2(SiO_4)_3 + 2C + 3H_2O + H_2$$

$$3Fe + 2Al(NO_3)_3 \cdot 9H_2O + 3SiC \rightarrow$$
$$Fe_3Al_2(SiO_4)_3 + 3CO + 9H_2O + 3N_2O$$

(*d*) *Grossularite*—The pressure necessary to form grossularite is not greater than 20,000 atmospheres in the temperature range 600–900°C. This garnet crystallizes in small, colourless dodecahedra and has much less tendency to include carbon than other garnets. The phenomenon of radially arranged carbon concentrated at the centre of the crystal has never been produced in this garnet. The crystal size produced under the conditions used is the smallest of all the garnets except uvarovite.

Grossularite has been produced by the following reactions

$$3Ca(OH)_2 + Al_2O_3 \cdot 2SiO_2 \cdot 2H_2O + SiC \rightarrow$$
$$Ca_3Al_2(SiO_4)_3 + 2H_2 + 3H_2O + C$$

$$2CaO + Ca(NO_3)_2 \cdot 4H_2O + 2Al(OH)_3 + 3SiC \rightarrow$$
$$Ca_3Al_2(SiO_4)_3 + 3C + 6H_2O + N_2 + H_2$$

In the latter reaction the grossularite is always accompanied by zoisite, and if the alumina is increased, zoisite becomes the main product but is always accompanied by considerable grossularite The zoisite shows a greater tendency to include carbon formed in the reaction than does grossularite.

(e) *Uvarovite*—Uvarovite is definitely a garnet which must be formed at a higher temperature than the others.   It is classed as 'infusible' (in the blowpipe) whereas the other members melt incongruently at temperatures in the neighbourhood of 1,000°C. Uvarovite was not produced synthetically in well-defined crystals although it was produced in ill-defined, minute, rounded grains which have the optical properties of uvarovite.   Hummel[7] has shown that uvarovite can be synthesized at one atmosphere.

The best method used was based on the reaction

$$3CaCO_3 + 2CrO_3 + 3SiC \rightarrow Ca_3Cr_2(SiO_4)_3 + 3CO$$

Carbon is also formed, but does not seem to be included in the garnet.

(f) *Pyrope*—Pyrope is the most important constituent of the eclogite garnets and proved to be the most difficult to synthesize.

The minimum pressure for formation lies in the range 25—30,000 atmospheres at 800–900°C.   The formation is very sensitive to chemical and physical conditions and unless these are carefully controlled, enstatite is formed instead.   The enstatite is always accompanied by kyanite, staurolite, and mica.   When the optimum conditions are maintained, the pyrope is formed nearly pure with only traces of staurolite as a by-product. Pyrope crystallizes in colourless crystals which have a much greater tendency to develop as the tetragonal trisoctahedron than any of the other garnets.

Its behaviour toward carbon is especially characteristic. Carbon formed during the crystallization of the garnet is included in the crystal and concentrated at the centre, but only to a certain extent. Unlike almandite, spessartite, and andradite, which include carbon up to the point of complete opacity, the carbon included in pyrope is small and constant (being about 5 per cent by volume). The amount of included carbon seems to be independent of the total amount of carbon formed.

Two reactions which have been found to produce pyrope are

$$2MgO + Mg(NO_3)_2 \cdot 6H_2O + 2Al(OH)_3 + 3SiC \rightarrow$$
$$Mg_3Al_2(SiO_4)_3 + 8H_2O + 3C + N_2 + H_2$$

$$(MgO)_3 \cdot 2SiO_2 \cdot 2H_2O + Al_2O_3 \cdot 2SiO_2 \cdot 2H_2O \rightarrow$$
$$Mg_3Al_2(SiO_4)_3 + SiO_2 + 4H_2O$$

The second reaction is an instructive one as it represents a metamorphic process which could take place in nature in clay slates in contact zones.

Pyrope produced by this reaction is always accompanied by kyanite, which encrusts and penetrates the pyrope crystals.

In spite of the difference in chemistry involved in the above reactions, the optimum physical conditions are the same: 30,000 atmospheres, 900°C.

The sensitivity of the pyrope synthesis to chemical and physical conditions is greatly reduced by the presence of small amounts of iron. This is probably due to the much greater crystallizing power of the almandite garnet, and also explains why pyrope is never found pure in nature.

The addition of small amounts of calcium and chromium hydroxide to reactants of the first reaction produces a pyrope which contains chromium, judging by the development of a green colour and increase in refractive index. The amount actually taken up is not known. The relationship of pyrope to carbon is not changed by the presence of chromium.

(g) $Mg_3Fe_2(SiO_4)_3$—The compound $Mg_3Fe_2(SiO_4)_3$ is not found in nature and its existence need not be postulated to explain the composition of any known natural garnet.

The suggestion by Fermor[6] (1938) that the composition and texture of certain enstatite chondrules indicate their formation by the pressure inversion of such a garnet, is not supported by the experimental evidence. Fermor believed he had found evidence of the existence of such a garnet in a South African diamond pipe, but the exact nature of the evidence is not clear. It was found possible to synthesize this garnet by the reaction

$$2MgO + Mg(NO_3)_2 \cdot 6H_2O + Fe_2O_3 + 3SiC \rightarrow$$
$$Mg_3Fe_2(SiO_4)_3 + 8H_2O + N_2 + H_2$$

(iii) Staurolite

Staurolite is not found as a constituent of eclogite, but its absence entitles t to some consideration here. Staurolite combines a high packing index with a comparatively low formation pressure. In the synthetic work it appears as a by-product in many reactions, particularly those in which pyrope, kyanite or corundum are also formed.

Its frequent association with pyrope in nature has led to the belief that it has been derived from pyrope, and this derivation has been accomplished synthetically.

Using natural garnet (Cedar Creek, New York) containing 38 per cent of the pyrope component, staurolite can be synthesized by alkaline attack at pressures of 30,000 atmospheres and 900°C. The base used can be sodium bicarbonate.

In view of these facts, the absence of staurolite from eclogite is difficult to explain. Synthetically, staurolite is best prepared by the reaction

$$2Fe + 4Al(OH)_3 + Al(NO_3)_3 \cdot 9H_2O + 4SiC \rightarrow$$
$$2FeO \cdot 5Al_2O_3 \cdot 4SiO_2 \cdot H_2O + 4H_2O + 10H_2 + 4C + 1\tfrac{1}{2}N_2$$

The staurolite is produced in prisms showing 60° and 90° twinning and in parallel intergrowth with kyanite. The reaction takes place at pressures of 20–45,000 atmospheres and 600°–900°C. The carbon formed is partly included in the crystal.

Replacing Fe by Fe_2O_3 in the above reaction greatly reduces the yield of staurolite and results in considerable almandite formation.

145

(iv) Kyanite

Kyanite is a typical metamorphic mineral apparently produced under high pressure. It is not found in igneous rocks. In nature it is associated with quartz, mica, tourmaline and especially staurolite, with which it forms parallel intergrowths. Kyanite is found containing graphite in the variety rhaetizite, in which the carbon particles show no orientation as they do in chiastolite.

Experimentally, kyanite is the easiest of the three silicates to produce and frequently occurs as a by-product in reactions where its formation is not anticipated. The pressure necessary for the formation of kyanite lies below 25,000 atmospheres at 800°C and its stability range overlaps that of both sillimanite and andalusite. As in nature, its most frequent companion is staurolite, even in systems substantially free from iron or magnesium. As would be expected, the tendency for kyanite to form as a by-product is greatly increased by higher pressure.

In reactions designed to produce topaz, kyanite is never found as a by-product, but is either absent or is the principal product with no topaz formation. The close chemical similarity between topaz and kyanite and their equal packing indices indicate that the course of the reaction is determined by factors unknown at present.

The simplest method for formation of kyanite makes use of the reaction

$$6Al(OH)_3 + 2Al(NO_3)_3 \cdot 9H_2O + 4SiC \rightarrow$$
$$4Al_2SiO_5 + 27H_2O + 4CO + 3N_2O$$
$$4CO \rightarrow 2CO_2 + 2C$$

Kyanite is produced in good yield, in crystals containing carbon inclusions, at pressures of 25—45,000 atmospheres and temperatures of 600–900°C. The carbon is nodular in form and has a graphite lustre. The particles are arranged at random in the kyanite crystal.

By decreasing the $Al(OH)_3$ and increasing the $Al(NO_3)_3 \cdot 9H_2O$ in the above reaction, and keeping Al : Si constant, the amount of C formation can be gradually reduced to the vanishing point, but no diamond formation took place at any carbon concentration under the most favourable conditions (45,000 atmospheres, 600°C) under which the reaction could be carried out.

IV. New Silicate Phases

(i) Dense Silica

In the course of these experiments at high pressure, a new dense form of crystalline silica was discovered. The new silica had not previously been described as the product of synthesis nor had it been discovered in nature as a rock constituent.

The conditions needed for the formation of the new dense silica, together with its great stability, may provide a means by which the conditions attendant on the crystallization of some deep-seated rocks can be more closely estimated. Its absence from these rocks may provide a maximum pressure above which they could not have been formed.

The information on rock-forming conditions is made more valuable by the variety of chemical environments from which the dense silica can crystallize and to the wide temperature range over which it can form, above a critical pressure.

The possibility exists that the existence of this form of silica in nature may have been overlooked. In some cases it may have passed for a mica which it resembles in form, refractive index, and double refraction. It is easily distinguished from the micas, however, by its hardness and insolubility in hydrofluoric acid. So far it has been found in the Canyon Diablo, Arizona, meteorite crater[8].

The best reaction mixture found for the dense silica formation consisted of equal parts of dry sodium metasilicate and diammonium phosphate. 0·2 gm of this mixture was charged into the mould and sealed. The capsule was heated at a temperature of 750°C under a pressure of 35,000 atmospheres for a period of 15 hours. The yield was about 20–30 mg of dense silica in colourless tabular hexagonal crystals up to 50μ in diameter.

Mineralizing agents other than the diammonium phosphate were used with almost equally satisfactory results, the better ones being boric acid, ammonium chloride, ammonium vanadate, and potassium fluoborate. Potassium silicate may be substituted for the sodium silicate with good results. Boric acid and powdered flint give about one half the yield of the sodium silicate–diammonium phosphate system and somewhat poorer crystallization of the product. This process is interesting, however, in that it shows that the metal ions are not necessary for the dense silica formation. The use of tantalum capsules in place of iron does not change the results.

The dense silica can also be produced, in good yield, under the same pressure and temperature conditions by the oxidation of silicon by silver carbonate, the silver carbonate being reduced to metallic silver. This experiment shows that hydrogen is not a factor in the dense silica formation.

The various syntheses described above establish without question that the new substance is a compound of silicon and oxygen. It is completely volatilized by heating with ammonium bifluoride. It is transformed, without change in weight, into silica glass and cristobalite when heated in platinum at 1,700°C. These experiments establish that the new substance has the composition SiO_2 and is a new crystalline form of silica.

The stability region for the dense silica has been approximately determined by synthesis only. It has been found that dense silica formation rarely takes place below about 30,000 atmospheres pressure and that at 35,000 atmospheres dense silica is formed at any temperature between 500–800°C. Formation probably takes place below 500°C, but is too slow to be observed experimentally.

Below about 30,000 atmospheres in the above temperature range, normal quartz is produced by the same chemical reactions. Occasionally, near 30,000 atmospheres, mixtures of dense and normal silica have been produced, though it is not clear whether the formation was simultaneous or was the result of pressure variation in the system. Above 800°C, at 30,000 atmospheres, only normal quartz is produced.

The dense silica crystallizes in hexagonal plates with unsymmetrical extinction. It is biaxial and optically positive with an optic axial angle of 54°.

The refractive indices are: $a = 1·599$, $y = 1·604$, $y-a = 0·005$. The

147

crystals belong to the monodinic system and the following x-ray data have been obtained

d-value	Intensity	d-value	Intensity	d-value	Intensity
6·20	W	2·03	W	1·501	VW
4·38	VW	1·84	VW	1·418	VW
3·43	M	1·79	W	1·409	VW
3·09	VS	1·71	W	1·345	W
2·76	W	1·70	W	1·321	VW
2·69	W	1·66	VW	1·285	W
2·33	W	1·58	VW	1·236	VW
2·29	W	1·545	W	1·171	VW
2·18	W				

The density is 3·01. The density–refractive index relation correlates well with other forms of silica, as is shown in *Figure 4*.

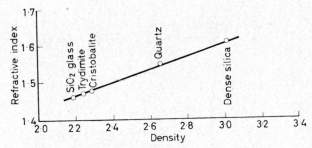

Figure 4. The relationship between the refractive index and the density for various forms of silica

Chemically the dense silica is very inert and shows less chemical reactivity than normal quartz. It is not attacked by long heating in hydrofluoric acid. In view of the density, this fact correlates well with the data collected by Schwarz on the rates of solution of other forms of silica in hydrofluoric acid of various concentrations. *Figure 5* shows solution rates for the different forms plotted against the density.

(ii) $Al_2O_3 \cdot 3SiO_2$

Another interesting substance discovered was a 1 : 3 aluminium silicate, $Al_2O_3 \cdot 3SiO_2$, which has not been found in nature.

This substance requires a higher pressure for its synthesis than any other silicate. It has not been formed at any pressure less than about 40,000 atm.

The name 'piezotite' has been suggested for this new mineral, which has the following properties:

Composition: $Al_2O_3 \cdot 3SiO_2$
Triclinic $\alpha = 1 \cdot 67,$ $\beta = 1 \cdot 675$
Biaxial pos. $2x = 90°$

It crystallizes usually in 60° cruciform twins resembling kyanite but which cleave into 5 side plates. It is insoluble in hydrofluoric acid, but dissolves slowly in fused ammonium bifluoride. It is stable on heating to at least 1,000°C, but at 1,500°C decomposes slowly into mullite and glass. It can be formed from a variety of systems containing silica and alumina at about 700°C in the pressure range of 40–45,000 atm.

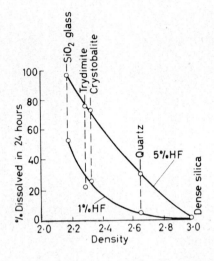

Figure 5. The solubility rates in hydrofluoric acid of the various forms of silica

It is interesting to note that systems designed to produce spessartite (see page 143) will, in this pressure range, produce only piezotite.

The x-ray data for $Al_2O_3 \cdot 3SiO_2$ are:

Piezotite Powder Data

d-value			Intensity
7·020	..	..	..	Weak
4·360	..	..	..	Very faint
4·139	..	..	..	Very faint
3·953	..	..	..	Faint
3·418	..	..	..	Medium
3·271	..	..	..	Medium-strong
3·031	..	..	..	Strong
2·780	..	..	..	Medium
2·660	..	..	..	Faint
2·466	..	..	..	Medium-weak
2·382	..	..	..	Weak
2·302	..	..	..	Very faint
2·189	..	..	..	Very faint
2·130	..	..	..	Very faint
2·077	..	..	..	Very faint
1·992	..	..	..	Very faint
1·924	..	..	..	Very faint
1·734	..	..	..	Very faint
1·484	..	..	..	Faint
1·452	..	..	..	Faint
1·429	..	..	..	Faint
1·405	..	..	..	Faint
1·350	..	..	..	Faint

(iii) *Single Crystal Data*

There were no back-reflections and the film was therefore uncorrected for shrinkage. The scale of the data may be in error by as much as $0 \cdot 5$ per cent.

Approximate (± 2 per cent) values for the (triclinic) unit-cell parameters are:

$$a = 7 \cdot 46 \text{ Å}$$
$$b = 4 \cdot 63 \text{ Å}$$
$$c = 4 \cdot 89 \text{ Å}$$
$$a = 95° \ 20'$$
$$\beta = 99° \ 10'$$
$$\gamma = 106° \ 48'$$
$$V = 158 \cdot 5 \ R3$$

References

[1] BRIDGMAN, P. W., *Amer. J. Sci.*, **237**, 1959, p. 7
[2] FOSTER, W. R., *J. Geol.*, **50**, 1942, p. 152
[3] CLARK, F. W., *Data of Geochemistry*, p. 400
[4] SHEPARD, E. S. and RANKIN, G. A., *Amer. J. Sci.*, **28**, 1909, p. 305
[5] TROVIMOV, V. S., *Soviet Geol.*, **4**, 1940, p. 73
[6] FERMOR, L. L., *Rec. geol. surv. India*, **73**, 1938, p. 145
[7] HUMMEL, F. A., *Amer. Min.*, **35**, 1950, p. 324
[8] CHAO, E. C. T., SHOEMAKER, E. M. and MADSEN, B. M., *Science*, **132**, 1960, p. 220

PHASE EQUILIBRIA IN SILICATE SYSTEMS AT HIGH PRESSURES AND TEMPERATURES: APPARATUS AND SELECTED RESULTS

F. R. BOYD

Geophysical Laboratory
Carnegie Institution of Washington
Washington, D.C.

I. Introduction

MINERAL assemblages in many kinds of rock reflect the conditions of temperature and pressure under which they formed. Laboratory studies of the equilibrium relations among silicates combined with study of natural mineral assemblages provide quantitative information about these genetic conditions. Reactions which occur among minerals range in complexity from simple polymorphic inversions to transitions involving four or five phases in a system of eight or nine essential components. For example, quartz, the stable form of SiO_2 under normal conditions in the earth's crust, is converted to a denser polymorph (coesite) by pressures in excess of 20–40 kilobars. The common lava, basalt, is composed principally of iron-magnesium pyroxene and feldspar, but at high pressure it is transformed in a complex reaction to a sodic pyroxene and garnet rock (eclogite).

Phase-equilibria studies in silicate systems can also provide information about the internal structure of the earth. It is now possible to reproduce in the laboratory the combined conditions of high temperature and pressure equivalent to depths as great as 400 kilometres. Two major discontinuities in the observed velocities of earthquake waves have been found in this depth range. The shallowest of these, the Mohorovicic discontinuity, which marks the base of the earth's crust, is found at an average depth of 5–10 kilometres in oceanic areas and 35 kilometres in continental areas. The pressure at the Mohorovicic discontinuity ranges from 2 to 10 kilobars. At greater depth, beginning at about 200 kilometres and extending to 900 kilometres, is another discontinuity formerly called the 20° discontinuity. The pressure range at this discontinuity is from 70 to 300 kilobars. Many geologists believe that these seismic discontinuities are due to phase changes induced by high pressure.

Most silicate reactions are sufficiently sluggish so that they may be studied by a quenching technique. Mixtures of crystalline phases or glasses are held at a particular temperature and pressure, rapidly quenched, and the products removed and identified by optical means or by x-ray diffraction. The sluggish nature of these reactions is an advantage in that the physical properties of phases formed at high pressures and temperatures are easily studied. However, a large number of runs must be made to determine the location of a phase boundary. Hence, the pressure equipment used must be capable of routine and convenient operation. The single-stage apparatus described below permits measurements to be made up to 50 kilobars with relative ease. The two-stage apparatus has been used successfully at pressures up to about 100 kilobars at high temperature, but is currently in the course of further development.

II. Single-Stage Apparatus

Apparatus for use in the range 10–50 kilobars at temperatures up to 1,750°C is shown in *Figure 1*. The pressure vessel is a cylinder of cemented

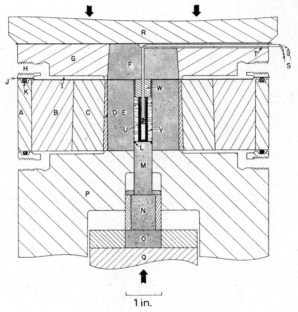

1 in.

Figure 1. **A**, soft steel safety ring; **B**, steel retaining ring, E4340 R_c 42; **C**, steel retaining ring, E4340 R_c 55; **D**, steel shim, R_c 60; **E**, cemented carbide core, 6 per cent binder; **F**, cemented carbide end plate, 6 per cent binder; **G**, steel retaining ring for end plate, R_c 42; **H**, water jacket connection; **J**, water jacket; **K**, 0·010 in. plastic insulation (Mylar); **K**, O-ring seal for water jacket; **L**, steel sealing ring, R_c 40–50; **M**, cemented carbide piston, 6 per cent binder; **N**, cemented carbide piston, 6 per cent binder; **O**, cemented carbide piston, 6 per cent binder; **P**, bridge, NuDie V R_c 50; **Q**, 100-ton capacity hydraulic ram; **R**, 800-ton capacity hydraulic ram; **S**, thermocouple leads in $\frac{1}{16}$ in. diam. ceramic tube; **T**, slot milled in end plate to admit thermocouple tube; **U**, sample; **V**, talc cell with graphite heating element; **W**, stainless steel power lead with $\frac{1}{32}$ in. thick lavastone insulating sleeve. Power leads are connected to **G** and **P**. Interference **F/G**= ·006 in. on the diameter; interference **D/C**= ·023 in. on the diameter; interference **B/C**=0·040 in. on the diameter. See *Figure 2* for details of sample and furnace assembly

carbide (E) supported on the circumference by steel retaining rings (B and C) and on the ends by loading with a large-capacity hydraulic ram (R). The sample is heated electrically by a graphite tube embedded in talc (V). Pressure is transmitted to the sample and furnace assembly by a cemented carbide piston (*M*) actuated by a second hydraulic press. The pressure vessel is patterned after a design by Hall[1]. The construction and calibration of this apparatus have been described in a previous paper[2] and will only be summarized here. The drawings in *Figures 1* and *2* include improvements made in the apparatus since the original description.

The life of the carbide core of the pressure vessel is greatly extended by obtaining maximum possible support from the steel retaining rings and by concentrating 100–200 tons load on the ends of the core. The interferences used for the retaining rings are given in the legend for *Figure 1*. Water cooling the retaining rings is desirable since if they become hot they expand away from the carbide core and the support given to the carbide is reduced. Up to a hundred runs can be obtained from a carbide core.

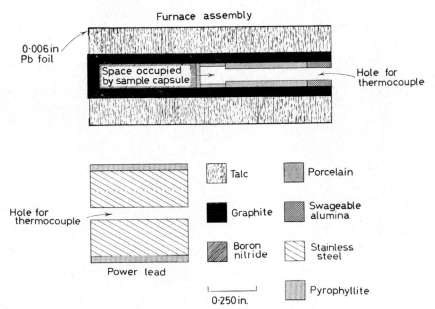

Figure 2. Detail of furnace and power-lead assembly used in the single-stage apparatus shown in *Figure 1*. The assembly is not recoverable, and a new unit is used for each run

The piston is ground to fit the core with a clearance of 0·0005 in.–0·0010 in. on the diameter. The ends of a piston tend to chip with use unless they are jacketed with steel.

A sample and furnace assembly is shown in *Figure 2*. Talc has been found to be superior to pyrophyllite and boron nitride as a pressure medium for high-temperature use. Values of friction measured at room temperature on the bismuth and thallium transitions are about half as large in talc as in pyrophyllite. At high temperature this difference is somewhat reduced. Since talc is a hydrate, boron nitride and ceramic inserts are used inside the graphite furnace to reduce the possibility of the sample being contaminated with H_2O. The boron nitride and graphite must be prevented from coming into contact with the thermocouple and platinum capsule containing the sample. Boron nitride will dissolve in platinum and may lower its melting point by as much as 400°C. Hence, ceramic inserts are used around the capsule and thermocouple.

The thermocouple is introduced in a ceramic tube through a hole in the stainless steel power lead. It is in contact with the sample capsule and is kept from extruding by friction. Difficulties with the thermocouple wires pinching off or extruding are eliminated if an insert of low-strength ceramic (swageable alumina, *Figure 2*) is used around the thermocouple tube.

Approximately 2 kilowatts are needed to heat the graphite furnace to 1,750°C. Power is most satisfactorily supplied by a low-voltage transformer with a variac on the input. Temperature can be controlled using the thermocouple as a sensing element.

Experience has shown that the electrical resistance of the graphite heating element increases markedly during a run over the course of a few hours. It was first suspected that this increase was only apparent and that the thermocouples were being contaminated. Calibration of couples after a run has nevertheless not revealed significant contamination and the resistance change must be due to recrystallization of the graphite.

Pressure is determined by measuring the oil pressure acting on the hydraulic ram and computing the load pressure on the furnace assembly from the areas of the ram and piston. The load pressure is then corrected for friction. The friction is determined by calibration on the bismuth I–II and thallium II–III transitions which at 30°C are at $25 \cdot 2$ and $37 \cdot 1$ kilobars[2]. The friction with the piston advancing on a talc cell of the type shown in *Figure 2* is 13 per cent at both transitions. The bulk of this friction is due to the shear strength of the talc rather than to the mechanical friction in the piston or ram assemblies. At high temperature the shear strength of the talc is reduced and the friction is taken to be 8 ± 5 per cent of the load pressure.

III. Two-Stage Apparatus

The pressure range of the single-stage apparatus described above is limited by fracture of the piston at load pressures of 50–55 kilobars. Fracture usually occurs within the bridge where the piston is not supported by the walls of the pressure vessel. However, pressures up to approximately 100 kilobars can be obtained by adding a second stage which supports the piston.

Apparatus of this type is shown in *Figure 3*. A preliminary description of the design has previously been published[3]. Apparatus which employs a similar type of piston support has also been described by Giardini, Tydings and Levin[4].

The high-pressure stage, end-plate, and furnace assembly are similar to the single-stage design except that the bore is reduced from $0 \cdot 500$ in. to $0 \cdot 375$ in. The high-pressure piston (H, *Figure 3*) is loaded by a tapered piston of larger diameter which is advanced through a second pressure vessel, henceforth called the supporting stage. The volume (B, *Figure 3*) around the high-pressure piston in the supporting stage is packed with a highly compressible material such as KBr. As the large-diameter piston is loaded by a hydraulic ram, a part of the load is communicated to the sample and furnace assembly (in E, *Figure 3*) and the remainder supports the high-pressure piston through compression of the KBr. It is possible to design the dimensions of the furnace assembly and of the KBr cell so that a load pressure of 75–100 kilobars is brought to bear on the furnace assembly while a supporting pressure of about 20 kilobars is developed in the KBr.

A number of materials have been tried as pressure media in the supporting stage. AgCl has been found to be satisfactory if only a limited length of stroke is needed. Teflon is highly compressible and should be ideal. In practice its use led to excessive piston breakage, for reasons that are not

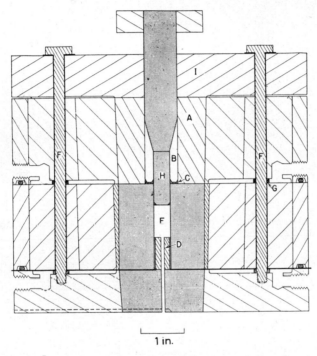

1 in.

Figure 3. **A**, steel supporting stage core, LaBelle HT R_c 55; **B**, volume filled with KBr cell wrapped in indium foil; **C**, sealing ring, R_c 50; **D**, steel power lead, R_c 60, with $\frac{1}{32}$ in. thick pyrophyllite insulating sleeve; **E**, volume filled by sample and furnace assembly similar to that shown in *Figure 2*; **F**, steel bolts (6), R_c 30, insulated with tape; **G**, neoprene washers; **H**, cemented carbide piston, 1 per cent binder; **I**, end plate, 4340 R_c 50. Other parts are similar to those shown in the single-stage apparatus in *Figure 1*. All carbide parts are stippled and with the exception of **H** are 6 per cent binder

understood. KBr works well. In addition to a high plasticity and compressibility, it has a phase transition at about 18 kilobars (*Figure 4*) with a volume change of about 10 per cent. An adequate stroke is thus obtained at maximum supporting pressure. The friction in the supporting stage can be greatly reduced by pre-forming the KBr cell with a film of indium or lead coating the inner and outer surfaces.

The length of stroke needed is minimized by pre-compressing the sample and furnace assembly after it is placed in the high-pressure stage, and by machining the high-pressure piston so that a stroke of $0\cdot020$–$0\cdot040$ in. is taken on the furnace assembly before contact is made with the KBr.

The high-pressure stage and the supporting stage must be bolted together to prevent extrusion of the KBr as the pressure is released. If the bolts are extended through to the end-plate, extrusion of the power lead at the termination of a run is also prevented.

The method of introducing thermocouple leads into the furnace assembly used in the single-stage apparatus (see above) is also used in the two-stage and has been found to work well up to at least 80 kilobars. The stainless steel power lead used in the single stage is replaced with a tool steel power

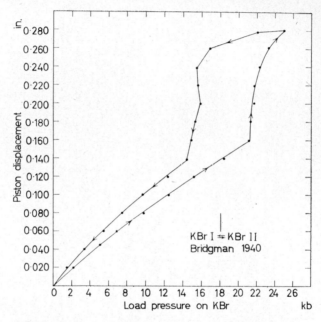

Figure 4. Compression of a KBr cell wrapped in lead foil in the supporting stage apparatus (*Figure 3*). Comparison with Bridgman's data indicates a friction of about 17 per cent. This friction can be reduced to about 14 per cent if indium foil is used in place of lead

lead (*D, Figure 3*) hardened to R_c 60–65 to reduce stress on the edge of the bore.

A procedure has been developed for determining the load pressure on the sample and furnace assembly which is independent of calibration points. The supporting stage is loaded with a KBr cell and the apparatus is placed in the hydraulic press with a second press yoking the high-pressure piston and the tapered main piston together. As the pressure on the KBr is increased the piston displacement is measured with a dial gauge. A typical compression curve for a KBr cell is shown in *Figure 4*. Experience has shown that the curve with increasing pressure is reproducible to a few per cent. The curve with decreasing pressure characteristically shows a considerable scatter of points in the transition zone, but in practice this portion of the curve is not needed.

After obtaining a compression curve for the KBr cell, the apparatus is removed from the press and a sample and furnace assembly is placed in the high-pressure stage. As pressure is then increased on the run the piston displacement is measured and the load on the supporting stage is read from the KBr compression curve. This load is subtracted from the total load to give the load pressure on the sample and furnace assembly. The partition of load between the high-pressure stage and the supporting stage is about 1 : 1. To reduce error in determining the load pressure on the furnace assembly, attempts are made to stay within the displacement interval at the start of the KBr transition $(0 \cdot 160 – 0 \cdot 240$ in. in *Figure 4*).

The load pressure determined by the procedure outlined above must be corrected for friction in the furnace assembly. Measurements with the single-stage apparatus have indicated that this friction is 13 per cent at room temperature and is taken to be 8 ± 5 per cent at high temperature. The calibration procedure outlined has been checked at the Bi I–II transition and found to be accurate within 5 per cent. Further calibration checks at higher pressures are in progress.

The principal type of failure with the two-stage apparatus has been fracture of the carbide core of the high-pressure stage. Both lateral and radial fractures develop. Radial fractures do not seem to impair the usefulness of a core but the lateral fractures lead to spalling at the end of the core containing the power lead. Such spalling renders a core unusable after a few runs. A similar problem with the single stage was solved by end-loading. The two-stage design is self end-loaded but this is evidently not sufficient and loading the ends of the core with a separate press seems desirable.

Difficulty is also caused by plastic flow in the high-pressure piston. A cemented carbide piston with 6 per cent binder will begin to deform plastically at a load pressure of 70–75 kilobars when supported with a pressure of 20 kilobars. This deformation takes place slowly and considerably higher pressures can be maintained for 5–10 minutes. Pistons have been shortened by as much as 5 per cent of their length with corresponding bulging of the piston in the supporting stage. This difficulty has been cured for the range up to at least 80 kilobars by use of pistons with 1 per cent binder. These show no significant deformation in runs up to an hour in length. The high-pressure limit of the pistons with 1 per cent binder is not yet known.

IV. Geochemical Results

Considerable data on phase equilibria in silicate systems at pressures in the range 10–50 kilobars have been obtained with the single-stage apparatus and by investigators using other types of equipment[5,6]. Some general aspects of this research are reviewed below. Data thus far obtained with the two-stage apparatus in the range 50–100 kilobars are principally of a reconnaissance nature. The apparatus has been used to synthesize diamonds by the method of nucleation on nickel described by Bovenkerk and others[7]. The stability field of the spinel form of iron olivine (Fe_2SiO_4) is currently being investigated, and this work is briefly described.

(i) Subsolidus Transitions

The most abundant minerals in the earth's crust have crystal structures in which the atoms are arranged in relatively open networks. These include quartz, and the alkali feldspars albite ($NaAlSi_3O_8$) and orthoclase ($KAlSi_3O_8$), together with a number of less common minerals. It has been found that these minerals transform in the pressure range 10–30

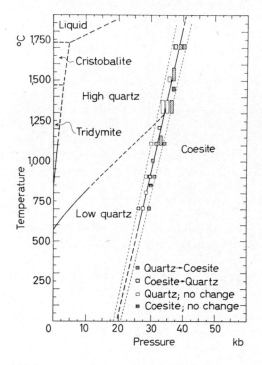

Figure 5. The quartz–coesite transition with the fields for other polymorphs of SiO_2. The light, dashed lines on either side of the transition curve represent the uncertainty in correcting the pressure measurements for friction. Details of this determination are given by Boyd and England[21]. The high–low quartz inversion is from the data of Yoder[22], and the fields of stability of tridymite and cristobalite are from Tuttle and Bowen[23]

kilobars to denser polymorphs or assemblages of denser phases. Since the pressure at the base of the crust in continental areas is about 10 kilobars, the minerals which form the bulk of the crust are not stable under the pressure and temperature conditions prevailing at depths equal to or a little greater than the base of the crust.

A chemically simple example, the inversion of quartz to coesite, is shown in *Figure 5*. Coesite, the dense form of SiO_2 stable at high pressures, was discovered by Coes[8]. The inversion of quartz to coesite proceeds readily in the temperature range 700°–1,700°C and can be reversed over a narrow pressure interval which is within the precision of the single-stage apparatus. The data in *Figure 5* were obtained by holding samples consisting of quartz or coesite at the indicated pressure-temperature conditions for lengths of time of the order of an hour. This time is sufficient partially or wholly to change quartz to coesite to the right of the curve and to change coesite to quartz to the left of the curve. Runs at temperatures below 1,200°C were fluxed with H_2O. These results show that quartz is unstable at pressures greater than 20–40 kilobars (depending on the temperature), which corresponds to a depth range in the earth of roughly 50–100 kilometres.

Reactions involving the feldspars have also been studied. Birch and LeComte[9] have shown that albite breaks down in the pressure range 15–25 kilobars at temperatures between 600° and 1,000°C to the assemblage jadeite ($NaAlSi_2O_6$) and quartz. Jadeite, a relatively dense pyroxene, is stable only at high pressure. Kennedy (personal communication) has also found evidence that orthoclase undergoes a phase transformation at pressures somewhat in excess of 10 kilobars.

The discovery that many of the minerals which make up the earth's crust are unstable at pressures equivalent to those present in the region below the crust lends support to the hypothesis that the Mohorovicic seismic discontinuity is a phase transition. This transition is probably not chemically as simple as those described above. It might involve the transformation of basalt to eclogite, in which the feldspar and iron-magnesium pyroxene present in basalt are replaced by a denser garnet and jadeitic pyroxene in eclogite. This hypothesis has been discussed in the light of recent high-pressure data by Kennedy[10]. Natural basalt can be converted to eclogite at high pressures and temperatures in the laboratory[10,11]. Presently available data indicate that the reaction takes place at temperatures and pressures approximately equivalent to those expected at the base of the crust, but more data are needed.

Some minerals, such as olivines [$(Mg,Fe)_2SiO_4$] and pyroxenes [$(Mg,Fe,Ca)SiO_3$] have crystal structures in which the atoms are more densely packed than quartz and the feldspars. These minerals are stable in the forms in which they are found in the crust to pressures considerably in excess of 30 kilobars. Bernal[12] has suggested that the seismic discontinuity formerly called the 20° discontinuity might be due to the inversion of olivine to a denser form having the structure of spinel. There is now thought to be a transition zone, commencing at a depth of 200–300 km and extending to a depth of 800–900 km, rather than a sharp discontinuity[13]. Natural olivines form a solid solution series between Mg_2SiO_4 and Fe_2SiO_4, and a transition zone might be explained by a phase transition in a binary (or more complex) solid solution series.

Bernal's hypothesis has received support from the experiments of Ringwood[14], who synthesized a spinel form of the iron-end member of the olivine series (Fe_2SiO_4) in a squeezer apparatus and found that the reaction took place in the range 35–40 kb at 600°C. The author and J. L. England have confirmed Ringwood's experiment using the two-stage apparatus. Fe_2SiO_4 spinel has been obtained both from mixtures of oxides and metallic Fe and from Fe_2SiO_4 crystallized hydrothermally as an olivine. The cell size was found to be 8·234 Å, in good agreement with Ringwood's value of 8·235 Å. A preliminary location of a point on the transition curve was found to be 60 kb at 1,500°C. These and Ringwood's data indicate that the transition curve has a positive slope concordant with the slopes of most other silicate transitions and that the curve lies in about the same P–T range as the graphite–diamond transition.

The probable composition of olivines at depth in the earth, however, is about 80 per cent Mg_2SiO_4–20 per cent Fe_2SiO_4. Hence, information is required about the spinel transition in pure Mg_2SiO_4 and along the join between the end members as well as the data currently being obtained on Fe_2SiO_4. A spinel form of Mg_2SiO_4 has not yet been synthesized, but Ringwood[14], and Dachille and Roy[15] have predicted that it should be stable in the pressure range above 100–150 kilobars.

(ii) Melting Relations

A few data on the effect of pressures over 10 kilobars on the melting of silicates have been obtained. Practically all of these data are for the melting

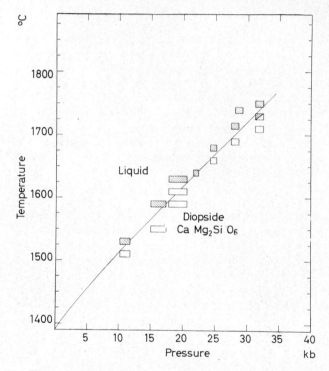

Figure 6. The melting curve of diopside. The curve is drawn from the data of Yoder[16] in the range 0–5 kb, and Boyd and England[3] in the range 10–30 kb

of pure compounds. Study of the melting relations in multi-component systems is practical and has important geologic applications, but has not yet been systematically undertaken.

The melting curve of diopside ($CaMgSi_2O_6$) is shown in *Figure 6*. Runs in the pressure range 10–30 kilobars are from Boyd and England[3]. The curve in the range 0–5 kilobars is drawn from the data of Yoder[16]. Diopside liquid is easily quenched to a glass at atmospheric pressure but cannot be quenched at pressures above about 15 kilobars. This may seem anomalous since pressure increases the viscosity of a liquid. Increased temperature, however, decreases the viscosity and the net effect is for the fluidity of the melt to increase as the melting curve is traced to higher pressures and temperatures. In the case of diopside the texture of the crystal aggregates which form from liquid during the quench is different from that obtained by growth in the solid state. Hence, melting can be detected at high pressure in spite of the fact that liquid diopside cannot be quenched. The initial slope of the melting curve, in the range 0–5 kilobars, is $13\cdot0°$/kb. In the range 10–30 kilobars, the slope flattens to about $10°$/kb, in agreement with the expected form of a melting curve.

Other silicate melting curves have similar slopes. The slope of the melting curve of the garnet pyrope ($Mg_3Al_2Si_3O_{12}$) has been found to be $14°$/kb in the range 20–40 kilobars[11]. Birch and LeComte[9] have found the slope of the albite ($NaAlSi_3O_8$) melting curve to be $11°$/kb out to 15 kilobars. The similarity in slopes of these curves is surprising in view of the differences in chemical composition and crystal structure of these minerals.

These slopes are much greater than the $2–4°$/kb range found for most metals[17,18]. In a gross way this is consistent with the fact that the earth's outer core, believed to be a Ni–Fe alloy, is liquid while the lower mantle, believed to be of silicate composition, is crystalline. Nevertheless, if the mantle has been molten in the past, temperatures at great depth would be expected to approach the melting curve. Estimates of the temperature of the mantle-core boundary based on melting curves for pure silicates are higher by a factor of about 5 than those based on the melting of iron and nickel[19].

S. P. Clark (personal communication) has suggested that the effect of pressure on the beginning of melting in multi-component silicate systems may be appreciably less than that on pure silicates. Studies on a number of systems will have to be made to evaluate the effect, but it may help to reduce the difference between the expected melting temperatures of rocks and Fe–Ni alloys at depth in the earth.

Acknowledgments

The apparatus development and phase-equilibria studies described in this paper are the products of the joint research of the author and J. L. England. The author is indebted to him and to Hugh J. Greenwood and Brian Skinner for critically reading the manuscript.

References

[1]HALL, H. T., *Rev. Sci. Instrum.*, **29**, 1958, p. 267

[2]BOYD, F. R. and ENGLAND, J. L., *J. Geophys. Res.*, **65**, 1960, p. 741

[3]BOYD, F. R. and ENGLAND, J. L., *Yearb. Carnegie Instn.*, **57**, 1958, p. 170

[4]GIARDINI, A. A., TYDINGS, J. E. and LEVIN, S. B., *Amer. Min.*, **45**, 1960, p. 217

[5]GRIGGS, D. T. and KENNEDY, G. C., *Amer. J. Sci.*, **254**, 1956, p. 722

[6]ROBERTSON, E. C., BIRCH, F. and MACDONALD, G. J. F., *Amer. J. Sci.*, **255**, 1957, p. 255

[7]BOVENKERK, H. P., BUNDY, F. P., HALL, H. T., STRONG, H. M. and WENTORF, R. H., Jr., *Nature, Lond.*, **184**, 1959, p. 1,094

[8]COES, L., Jr., *Science*, **118**, 1953, p. 131

[9] BIRCH, F. and LeCOMTE, P., *Amer. J. Sci.*, **258**, 1960, p. 209
[10] KENNEDY, G. C., *Amer. Sci.*, **47**, 1959, p. 491
[11] BOYD, F. R. and ENGLAND, J. L., *Yearb. Carnegie Instn.*, **58**, 1959, p. 82
[12] BERNAL, J. D., *Observatory*, **59**, 1936, p. 268
[13] BIRCH, F., *J. Geophys. Res.*, **57**, 1952, p. 227
[14] RINGWOOD, A. E., *Geochim. et Cosmochim. Acta*, **15**, 1958, p. 18
[15] DACHILLE, F. and ROY, R., *Amer. J. Sci.*, **258**, 1960, p. 225
[16] YODER, H. S., *J. Geol.*, **60**, 1952, p. 364
[17] STRONG, H. M. and BUNDY, F. P., *Phys. Rev.*, **115**, 1959, p. 278
[18] BUTUSOV, V. P., *Soviet Physics—Crystallography*, **2**, 1957, p. 533. (A translation of the journal *Crystallography* of the Acad. Sci. U.S.S.R., published by Amer. Inst. of Physics.)
[19] STRONG, H. M., *J. Geophys. Res.*, **64**, 1959, p. 653
[20] BRIDGMAN, P. W., *Proc. Amer. Acad. Arts Sci.*, **74**, 1940, p. 21
[21] BOYD, F. R. and ENGLAND, J. L., *J. Geophys. Res.*, **65**, 1960, p. 749
[22] YODER, H. S., Jr., *Trans. Amer. Geophys. Union*, **31**, 1950, p. 827
[23] TUTTLE, O. F. and BOWEN, N. L., *Mem. Geol. Soc. Amer.*, **74**, 1958

9

OPPOSED-ANVIL PRESSURE DEVICES

FRANK DACHILLE and RUSTUM ROY

Department of Geophysics and Geochemistry
College of Mineral Industries
The Pennsylvania State University
University Park, Pennsylvania

I. Introduction

HIGH pressures are produced today in one of three general types of apparatus: shock-wave, piston-and-cylinder, and 'opposed-anvil'. The highest pressures so far reached, of the order of one million bars, are generated by shock waves produced by explosives. It is clear that major chemical or structural changes would be difficult to achieve in the very short time, of the order of microseconds, during which the pressure is actually applied in such shock-wave experiments. This has been demonstrated by the failure to obtain in shock-wave experiments dense forms of certain phases which can be obtained by other means, and only recently has the shock-wave synthesis of diamond been reported. (The finding of natural coesite in the meteor craters of Arizona and Ries-Kessel, Bavaria, suggests that the combination of shock

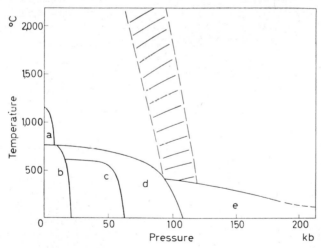

Figure 1. Diagram illustrating useful *p–t* regions of various anvil materials and design. The cross-hatched region is the approximate corrected limit of published results obtained with internally heated piston-and-cylinder or tetrahedral devices. The overlap of some areas is not shown. Also not shown is the limit of shockwave pressures (approximately 1,000 kb at unknown concurrent temperatures). The regions are labelled for anvils of the following types: **a**, sintered polycrystalline alumina or mullite; **b**, René 41; **c**, tool steels of type HS-66 or Speed Star; **d**, carbide inserts in René 41; **e**, carbide inserts in the tool steels of type HS-66 or TK. Area **e** also includes at room temperatures diamond anvils, and the graded support carbide anvils (Drickamer type) reported to approach the 500 kb range

163

pressures and shearing action on such a scale is sufficient.) In the second type of apparatus, generally referred to as piston-and-cylinder devices, relatively large working volumes can be contained at high pressures and high temperatures.

This chapter is concerned with the third type of apparatus, which is characterized by the application of uniaxial pressure in the absence of a conventional cylinder. The relative simplicity of the device gives the names 'simple anvil', 'Bridgman anvils', and 'simple squeezer' their currency and their appeal. Due to the successful application of the piston-and-cylinder devices in diamond synthesis, the simple anvil devices have recently been overshadowed. However, it is clear that at this writing the highest static pressures so far produced have been in elaborations of these cylinderless uniaxial devices. Pressures of nearly 200 kb appear to be regularly attainable in various laboratories, while the claims of the maximum pressure attainable range from 400–500 kb.

The pressure–temperature areas of effective use of several of these devices are shown in *Figure 1* (solid lines). For comparison, the area available to piston and cylinder devices is roughly limited to the area to the left of the striped band. The important variable of length of time of run has not been included.

II. Historical Development

A study of the literature discloses little previous work along these lines. In a way, the needle is the prototype of this family of apparatuses in that a high pressure is developed at the end of a solid tool by utilizing the difference in the area over which the force is applied. Perhaps the earliest significant work is that of Carey Lea[1], who constructed a screw vice with a mechanical advantage of about 1,300 (not correcting for friction) for the specific purpose of studying the influence of pressure on chemical reactions in solids. The pressure was brought to bear through small steel jaws on an envelope of platinum containing the sample folded into a bit of copper. The whole packet, with an area of 0·5 in. by 0·25 in., was subjected to a total force estimated at 135,000 pounds, giving a pressure of 70 kb. In this manner the behaviour of a number of compounds of Ag, Hg, Pt and other metals was studied under pressure applied for appreciable times. The results were not too interesting in themselves, but when compared with his later experiments[2], in which compounds of the same type were simply ground in a hand mortar for only 15 minutes, they served to emphasize the importance of shearing forces and strains in the speed of solid state reactions.

Basset[3] has mentioned briefly the attainment of pressures of about 300 kb and presents schematically a probable mode of pressure distribution on the anvil faces.

Bridgman[4] made use of an anvil design in a large number of experiments on the effects of high shearing and pressure stresses on many classes of substances. Later he used modified anvils and a shallow cylinder with a 1,000-ton press to study the graphite–diamond stability on sample discs 1·5 in. in diameter[5]. The major step forward in the design of these anvil devices is described by Bridgman and Simon[6]. They reported room-temperature runs of a few minutes duration at pressures up to 200 kb. Bridgman[7] had earlier reported that he had attained pressures in the order of 425 kb by using opposed anvils completely surrounded by liquid isopentane at 30 kb.

Griggs and Kennedy[8] first extended the useful temperature range of the simpler (one-stage) type of device to about 600°C, while also modifying the design. In our laboratory several different types have been developed since 1955, which extend the temperature, pressure and/or time rating by the use of different designs and new materials. In the Soviet Union Vereschagin[9] has mentioned the use of such opposed anvils up to 300 and 500 kb, although no details were given.

Dachille and Roy[10] described the use of an additional shear component superimposed on the sample wafer at pressures of up to 120 kb and temperatures of a few hundred degrees centigrade. In the laboratory of Professor Vereschagin at the University of Moscow, one of us, Rustum Roy, was shown an apparatus almost identical in conception, although much superior in execution. Griggs *et al.*[11] have also described something similar for use in the study of deformations of petrological interest.

Apparatus for x-ray diffraction under high pressure using boron carbide pistons was constructed by us in 1957[12], while Jamieson *et al.*[13] have successfully used single crystal diamonds for data up to about 35 kb (see Chapter 4). Weir, Lippincott *et al.*[14-16], have used supported diamond pistons for infra-red absorption work (see Chapter 3). The ingenious stepped-piston design of Drickamer[17] for optical measurements up to 200 kb, and the very recently[18] described anvil design used by him in resistance measurements up to estimated pressures of 500 kb (see Chapter 2), are in reality very similar to simple anvil devices.

III. Present Design of Apparatus

A description of the more successful types of opposed anvil apparatus in use in our laboratory will be made to illustrate the most important features of the design of these devices and the state of the art as developed in various laboratories, including our own.

(i) Over-all Apparatus Design

Figure 2 shows a schematic representation of a typical assembly for laboratory-scale research. Oil pressure is generated in a reciprocating piston pump and drives a 20–100 ton hydraulic ram contained in a suitable frame about three feet high and 12 to 18 in. in diameter. The line hydraulic pressure, which is indicated by Heise bourdon gauges, is controlled to within about 3–5 per cent by the use of appropriate electrical contacts on the bourdon gauge. The pressure is transmitted to the sample area by means of two thrust bars. The sample area is heated by a set of split semi-cylindrical furnaces about six inches long. The temperature at the sample can very easily be controlled to within $\pm 5°C$ or less for periods of a week or two by a thermocouple-signalled controller. The use of small hollow stainless steel cylinders to surround the actual piston area eliminates much furnace repair and some danger to personnel from catastrophically failing

165

pistons. A similar, somewhat looser, shield can be used to introduce an inert atmosphere around sintered tungsten carbide or other pistons to prevent their oxidation.

With a '20-ton' ram and 10,000 psi line pressure, maximum pressures of about 72 kb can be obtained on a 0·25 in. diameter sample (only 18 kb on a 0·50 in. diameter sample). On 0·375 in. and 0·50 in. diameter samples, '50-ton' and '100-ton' rams respectively give approximately the same maximum pressure (70 kb), which is convenient for use with simple pistons.

(ii) Piston Design: Simple Pistons

A simple piston design is limited by the ultimate compressive strength of the material. In the form of unsupported cylinders, no materials appear able to withstand compressive stresses much over about 60–65 kb or about

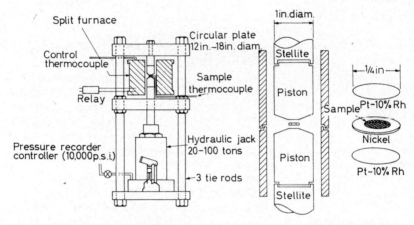

Figure 2. Schematic layout of a complete opposed-anvil apparatus used with a 20-ton hydraulic jack. The head plate is of 2 in. thick steel plate and the tie rods are threaded from 1 in. diameter bar. For 100 tons total thrust, 3 in. head thickness and 1½ in. diameter bars are necessary. The hand-operated jack is useful in the positioning and starting of individual runs

one million psi. This limit can be approached very closely in practice. The pressure–temperature limits reported in this section apply for the relatively long periods of several hours to a few days.

The design of our most widely used simple piston is shown as part of Figure 2. The piston materials used in these laboratories were special tool steels such as Carpenter's Speed Star or Bethlehem HS-66, hardened to Rockwell C 65–66. These steels have proved to be very much more satisfactory, both in terms of cost as well as life, than tungsten carbide inserts or anvils. The simple design, moreover, is more convenient and also appears to give better performance than the use of lightly supported cemented carbide pistons described by Griggs and Kennedy[8]. The main advantage of carbide pistons is that unlike steel, which is limited to about 625°C at 50 kb, carbide pistons may be used at 50 kb at temperatures as high as 750°C if protected by a nitrogen atmosphere. Other materials

166

which may be used to great advantage for large samples are the high-temperature, high-strength nickel-based alloys, such as René 41, which permit the attainment of about 20 kb at up to 750°C in relatively short turns of less than one hour's duration. Their advantages are their relative ease of machining and the absence of hardening or grinding procedures. For higher temperatures in our laboratories we have used sets of pistons approximately four inches long of the same shape as shown in *Figure 2*, made of polycrystalline ceramic-process alumina, mullite, or dense, fine-grained silicon carbide. There are several difficulties associated with these materials, chiefly due to their poor thermal shock characteristics, so that 7 kb at 100–1,200°C is the maximum that we have been able to achieve consistently. Temperature quenching of the samples is much more difficult with these pistons than with metal pistons.

(iii) Piston Design: Supported Pistons

No basic improvements have been made over the design originally conceived by Bridgman. A diagram showing the present design used in

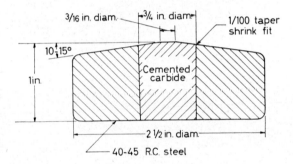

Figure 3. The supported anvil modelled after the design of Bridgman and Simon. Useful runs have been made by substituting for the carbide an insert of high-speed tool steel hardened to Rockwell C 66. In use these anvils are backed by a 1 in. thick disc of tool steel hardened to R_c66

many of our pistons is given in *Figure 3*. It will be noted that the lateral support for the carbide is derived not only from shrinkage interference but also from the slight taper. A successful combination has been a 1 per cent taper and a 0·5 per cent interference, using steel with a Rockwell C hardness of 45.

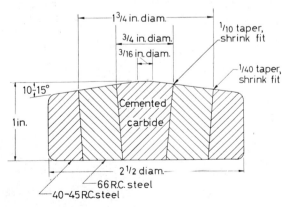

Figure 4. Details of a doubly-supported anvil which attempts to provide a graded support for the carbide

Hardnesses of over 50 on the Rockwell C scale should be avoided on the outermost ring. A cemented tungsten carbide containing about 6 per cent cobalt seems to be the most satisfactory for general use. The choosing of the taper, shrinkage and hardness has been on a trial and error basis to date, although only a few trials could be afforded. Two opposed pistons of this design reliably give pressures up to 150 kb, with a maximum of just below 200 kb. A high percentage of failures may be expected in the 150–200 kb range. These pressures can be maintained for a few minutes to about one hour at temperatures up to 400°C.

A doubly-supported piston in use in our laboratories is illustrated in *Figure 4*, although it has not been demonstrated statistically that these are really superior to the singly-supported pistons. We have also made use of a steel-in-steel combination with the inside piston at a hardness of Rockwell

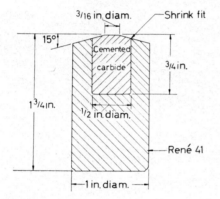

Figure 5. A variant of a supported piston useful in area **d** (*Figure 1*) with and without continuously applied displacive shear

C 65–66. This design has been useful up to 100 kb, almost doubling the range of the simple steel anvils. One additional advantage is that even should the insert split under high stresses, it is often possible to grind new surfaces for further use.

Another design used with success has been one which consists of an untapered carbide cylinder completely inset in the high-temperature, high-strength alloy, René 41. (See *Figure 5*.) This design, in the size shown, is measurably less expensive and more convenient than the usual singly-supported designs. Moreover, it is the most appropriate design for the pressure–temperature range just above 450°C and 60 kb.

IV. Sample Preparation and Holders

In the course of some thousands of runs, the best method found for handling powdered samples is to compress the sample into a soft metal (usually nickel) ring with the use of a four-piece pellet mould (shown in *Figure 6*) so that there results a 0·010 in. thick wafer having the outer diameter of the ring equal to that of the piston face. The inner diameter of the ring may be 0·5 to 0·8 times the outer diameter. At times the use of piston faces larger than the sample assembly is effective in working with samples which cannot be compacted easily or which are essentially fluid or plastic. A pressure of approximately 10 kb is used (if tolerable) in the pellet-forming step; the sample then remains porous enough to absorb 5–20 per cent of its volume of water or any other catalyst solution. For chemical studies the sample wafer is sandwiched between two discs of Pt–10 per cent Rh, 0·001 in. thick. Of course, it is not essential to use the ring at all; in many runs in the higher pressure range the rings are forced

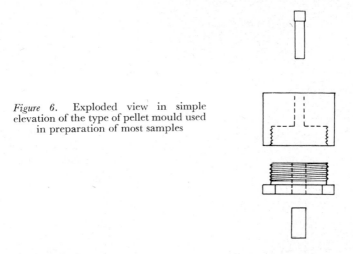

Figure 6. Exploded view in simple elevation of the type of pellet mould used in preparation of most samples

out from between the piston faces and no longer bear any of the applied load. If no ring is used, powder may be spread uniformly on the piston face, or a thin sheet of the material, such as glass, metal, or single crystal, may be simply inserted between the pistons. In general, thicknesses of 0·010 in. to 0·020 in. for diameters from 0·25 in. to 0·50 in. are most suitable. Greater amounts are extruded and appear to give less uniform pressure within the sample.

V. Modifications for Measurements *in situ*

(i) X-ray Diffraction

Polycrystalline, cylindrical, opposed pistons of boron carbide 0·25 in. in diameter have been used in our laboratory in a simple scaled-down version of the apparatus shown in *Figure 2*, mounted horizontally on a GE x-ray diffractometer (see *Figure 7*). Due to Compton scattering, the intensity loss with the polycrystalline boron carbide was very much greater than that calculated from the simple absorption coefficients for Mo radiation. Hence, such pistons gave useful data only on single crystals of mica and the alkali halides; the precision of the apparatus was not sufficient to use the data for reliable compressibility measurements. Pressures up to about 15 kb were applied without damage to the pistons, but we could not observe the transitions in RbCl, $AgNO_3$ and others in this range.

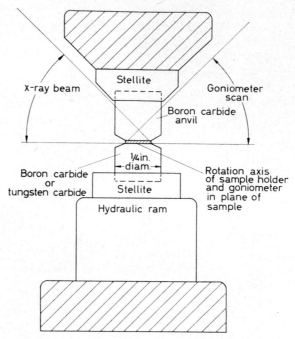

Figure 7. An early model of anvil apparatus for x-ray diffraction studies at high pressures. Two tie rods, above and below the central column, are not shown

(ii) Electrical Measurements

Bridgman[19] first made electrical measurements on the wafer-thin samples used in the opposed anvil design. His method was to use an annular ring of pyrophyllite to insulate the two pistons from each other. The metal samples, in the form of wire, were embedded in the very plastic AgCl with each end making contact with one of the pistons. The difficulty with this arrangement is that the pyrophyllite ring does not deform elastically and plastically in the same manner as the sample and AgCl. Bridgman estimated that in his apparatus the real pressure was about 50 per cent lower than that calculated from the bearing area.

VI. Modification for Introduction of Additional Shear Components

Although much of the effectiveness (in terms of rates of reaction) of opposed-anvil apparatus is due to the enormous shearing stresses at the edges of grains, quite significant improvements in the rates of solid phase reactions have been achieved by the modification of the simple uniaxial apparatus shown schematically in *Figure 8*. Shearing stresses are applied continuously to the sample by rotating one anvil relative to the other back and forth through a maximum of two degrees of arc every 15 seconds. The anvils so used have been the high-speed steels, René 41, and carbide-in-René, so as to include pressure limits of 110 kb and temperatures to 500°C. The most effective procedure is to have the sample wafer in direct contact with anvil faces. When it is necessary to avoid or minimize contamination, Pt–10 per cent Rh discs may be used to enclose the sample, and the amplitude of motion is reduced to $\frac{1}{2}$ degree of arc or less. In almost all runs a portion of the sample is extruded out from between the faces but sufficient

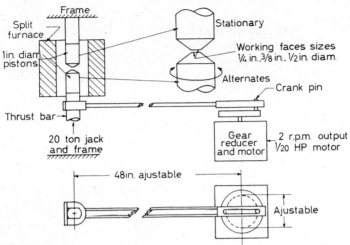

Figure 8.   Modification of the apparatus shown in *Figure 2* to provide a very slow, alternating shearing stress to the specimen

material remains for x-ray and microscopic examination.   Almost invariably the retained sample disc is in the form of two distinct concentric zones, the central one compact and lenticular and the outer one, obviously more highly sheared, readily breaking into circular areas.

VII. The Nature and the Calibration of the Pressure Stresses on the Sample

It is evident that the pressure is not the same in all portions of a thin wafer compressed between anvils, but that instead the pressure near the periphery of the sample must be somewhat lower than the pressure in its centre. The precise calculation of the pressure distribution would be quite lengthy even if all the relevant physical properties of the sample and the anvils were known.   However, by using suitable experimental methods and comparisons, to be described below, it is possible to place rather narrow limits upon the non-uniformity of the pressure distribution and upon the possible effects of non-hydrostatic uniaxial compression, as well as the change of these factors with time.

To begin with, in a particular run close to the equilibrium pressure and temperature for a given phase, one can observe the abundance of the phase in various portions of the sample. From such observations it seems likely that in runs of several hours' duration at pressures over 10 kb at temperatures of a few hundred degrees centigrade, the pressure distribution in a sample is essentially uniform when the sample is surrounded by a metal ring which has about 0·6 of the total bearing area. Perhaps in shorter runs or in runs at lower pressures and temperatures the sample may not flow plastically enough to develop highly uniform pressures in it, but such runs are rarely used to obtain equilibrium data.

Assuming then that the pressure is uniformly distributed across the sample, one may determine the pressure simply by dividing the piston force by the total bearing area. The piston force can be calibrated rather accurately, within 0·5 per cent, by using a Morehouse ring and dead-weight gauge to determine the press ram area and the hydraulic pressure. The bearing area between the pistons is easily determined to less than 1 per cent from measurement of several different diameters of the piston working faces with a microscope.

In this way the actual mean pressure could easily be duplicated within ±500 bars of a mean value in the region above 10 kb. For example, in the

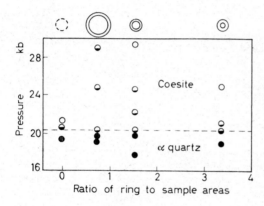

Figure 9. Some data obtained to evaluate the influence of metal ring and sample size on the distribution and reproducibility of pressure. The temperature was held constant at 500°C while the sample size and metal ring to sample area ratio was varied as shown

quartz–coesite transition with aqueous NH_4Cl as mineralizer, it was found that the reproducibility was within ±400 bars at 20 kb and 500°C.

The accuracy of this method of determining the pressure as well as the uniformity of the pressure on the sample were investigated in a quartz-coesite study by altering the sample wafer geometry. The sample was confined within metal rings which had different ratios of inner to outer diameter; the sample was also used with no outer metal ring at all. Thus the ratio of ring area to sample area was varied from over 3 down to 0. The results are shown in *Figure 9*, and indicate that no great error is involved in taking the sample pressure to be the piston force divided by the area.

One may compare equilibrium studies made either in hydrothermal apparatus or in apparatus using gas or fluids as hydrostatic pressure media with studies made in opposed-anvil apparatus. One finds that the calculated pressures in the opposed-anvil apparatus produce the same effects whether or not the pressures are truly hydrostatic. Thus, in the olivine–spinel transition in Mg_2GeO_4, a portion of the *p–t* curve was determined to the limits of the capacity of the hydrothermal apparatus[20]. Then the reaction was studied in the opposed-anvil apparatus, using sintered alumina pistons, from conditions within the range of the hydrothermal apparatus out to the practical limits of the pistons. In this manner hydrothermal results up to 870°C and 2·7 kb agreed well with the results of the opposed-anvil runs up to 1,000°C and 7 kb. In the same manner a close agreement of phase boundaries in the system Mg_2GeO_4–Mg_2SiO_4 was obtained using the two types of apparatus[21].

The stability relations found for jadeite by Robertson *et al.*[22] above 600°C to pressures of 25 kb in nitrogen-pressured, hydrostatic apparatus are only about 1 kb higher than the later results found by Hoffer *et al.*[23] at temperatures of 300–600°C in the opposed-anvil apparatus. The *p–t* relation of the reconstructive polymorphic transition calcite–aragonite was established by MacDonald[24] from work with the opposed anvils, but the results of Clark[25], using the nitrogen-pressure apparatus in the same temperature range, would place the transition pressure about 1 kb higher.

In a fluid-pressured apparatus Bridgman[26] found that CS_2 changed to a brown, waxy material at pressures of 42 kb and above. At the same temperature and calculated pressures—that is, total thrust divided by piston area—we have found the same effect in the opposed-anvil apparatus. When the pressure is below this figure, the CS_2 remains unchanged, and will, of course, immediately evaporate away when the sample is exposed to the atmosphere.

The above examples certainly indicate a reasonable agreement in results obtained in both fluid-pressured and opposed-anvil apparatus. The agreement, however, is not good with results from piston-and-cylinder devices using solid pressure transfer media. Thus, we find that Hall[27] concluded from his experiments in such apparatus that the minimum pressure of formation of coesite was 32 kb at 450°C. Later Boyd and England[28] reported results obtained in their modification of an internally-heated piston-and-cylinder apparatus, using talc as a pressure-transmitting medium, which place the quartz–coesite transition at 500°C and 25·1 kb. These results are higher than the 20·4 kb value at 500°C found by MacDonald[29] and by Dachille and Roy[30] in opposed-anvil apparatus.

The problem of pressure calibration at high temperature remains a serious one, principally because of the difficulties of ascertaining high pressures accurately at high temperatures. There is, however, one way in which pressure calibration above 30 kb may be achieved: the assignation of certain values to certain pressure-dependent functions after their determination in several laboratories. At high temperatures it appears that certain relationships, such as reconstructive transformations in one-component systems, e.g. diamond-graphite, will best serve as bases for calibration.

Two other calibration methods have been suggested. Dachille and Roy[31] measured the pressure-composition section at 500°C in the system SiO_2–GeO_2, and suggested that the solubility of GeO_2 in SiO_2-quartz (readable as an x-ray spacing) could serve as a piezometer in the range up to 32 kb. More recently the remarkable behaviours of SiO_2-glass and other glasses at high pressure observed by Roy and Cohen[32] have provided a continuous function (refractive index) dependent upon the pressure and the temperature up to 150 kb. If a reproducible pressure–temperature grid of the values of refractive index could be found and agreed upon by different laboratories, one would have an excellent piezometer and calibration method.

VIII. Some Results Obtained with the Opposed-Anvil Apparatus

(i) Synthesis of New Phases

A number of new dense forms have been discovered and prepared in our laboratory with this apparatus. From both the glassy and hexagonal forms of B_2O_3 a new form[33] was readily obtained at pressures above 22 kb in the temperature range 350–600°C. BeF_2, the almost perfect weakened model of SiO_2, was found to crystallize in the coesite structure in essentially the same pressure–temperature region as does silica. Another silica analogue first found and reported by us is the quartz form of BPO_4[34], which required pressures of the order of 50 kb for its synthesis. The $BAsO_4$ quartz analogue was first correctly described as such on the basis of results obtained in our opposed-anvil apparatus although the phase itself had been made earlier[35] in a piston and cylinder unit. PbO_2, with a rutile structure, was found to form a denser orthorhombic phase above 10 kb[36]. In a similar pressure region the analogous transformation was also found in MnF_2 and its pressure–temperature dependence was determined[37]. The Ga–Si and Al–Ge analogues of jadeite ($NaAlSi_2O_6$) have been synthesized in this apparatus at minimum pressures of 9 and 12 kb respectively, compared with $11\cdot2$ kb at 600°C for the parent compound[22]. The Cr Si and Ga–Ge jadeite analogues were first made in this apparatus, but later work showed that they could be formed at lower pressures in the hydrothermal apparatus. More recently the high pressure polymorphism in the zircon–monazite–scheelite phases of rare earth phosphates and arsenates has been studied in this apparatus[38].

(ii) Phase Equilibrium Studies

The majority of simple phase diagrams determined above 10 kb have also been studied in the opposed-anvil type of apparatus. Griggs and Kennedy[8], in their first paper on the application of this type of apparatus to mineralogical problems, presented several preliminary p–t curves or extensions of p–t curves to higher p–t regions than attained before. One of the first studied, which gives an example of the reproducibility attainable, is shown in Figure 10, where the univariant curves for the quartz–coesite inversion first determined by MacDonald and later by Dachille and Roy are superimposed. These studies were carried out by very different techniques (see latter paper) and yet gave reasonably close agreement, especially in the temperature region 400–550°C. Examples of a similar type are the equilibrium studies in our laboratory on BeF_2, MnF_2, PbO_2, BPO_4, As_2O_3, Sb_2O_3, B_2O_3, Nb_2O_5 and PbO. Some of the results are also summarized in Figure 10 to show the spread of the transition pressures and also the uncommon nature of the p–t relations, especially for the reconstructive transition in As_2O_3, Sb_2O_3 and PbO. Other studies are represented by those in the system Mg_2SiO_4–Mg_2GeO_4[21], the data at one temperature being summarized in Figure 11, and in the reaction $Pb_3O_4 \rightleftharpoons Pb_2O_3 + PbO$, wherein the influence of pressure on solid solutions and a dissociation reaction is demonstrated. The first study of the pressure dependence of the calcite–aragonite equilibrium was done in opposed-anvil apparatus[24] and was found to agree within about 1 kb with earlier thermochemical results at lower temperatures[39] and with subsequent work[25] in hydrostatic nitrogen-pressured apparatus.

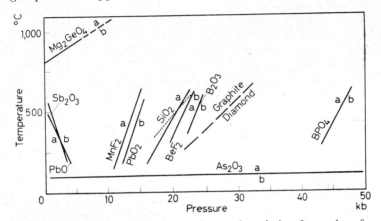

Figure 10. Representative equilibrium univariant *p–t* boundaries of a number of compounds as determined in this laboratory (with two exceptions: the dotted line for SiO₂ quartz–coesite[29] and the thermodynamic data for the graphite–diamond equilibrium[40]). The symbols **a** and **b** refer to the phases in equilibrium along each line and are listed in the order a,b for each compound: Mg_2GeO_4, olivine–spinel; PbO, litharge–massicot; Sb_2O_3, senarmontite–valentinite; MnF_2 and PbO_2, rutile–orthorhombic; SiO_2 and BeF_2, quartz–coesite; B_2O_3, hexagonal–monoclinic; As_2O_3, arsenolite–claudetite, BPO_4, cristobalite–quartz

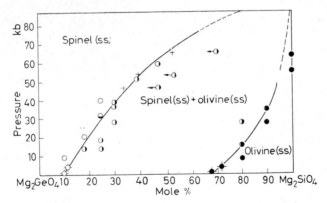

Figure 11. Isothermal section at 542° in the *p–t–x* of the system Mg_2GeO_4–Mg_2SiO_4. The symbols used are: open circles, spinel s.s.; filled circles, olivine s.s.; crossed circles, boundaries determined in hydrothermal apparatus; crosses, boundary position as determined from calibrated solid-solution x-ray spacing data[21]

(iii) *Kinetic Studies of High Pressure Reactions, Including the Addition of a Continuous Shear Component*

A number of comparative kinetic studies of solid state reactions have been made with the opposed-anvil apparatus in this laboratory. The influence of temperature and of hydrothermal conditions on solid–solid reactions is relatively well known, but not so that of pressure or that of an added displacive shearing action.

A convenient example for the study of these effects[10] is that of the PbO_2 I⇌II polymorphism. The II form was discovered separately in a phase equilibrium study in our laboratory[36] and the pressure dependence of the temperature of transition worked out. Other workers earlier had found that what we have called the II form (orthorhombic) could be produced by the mechanical working by ball milling of the stable I (rutile) form. The suggestive fact that a shear and a pressure component were present in the grinding process which also produced a high pressure form recalled

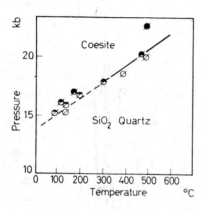

Figure 12. The solid line is the equilibrium SiO_2 quartz–coesite boundary determined in this laboratory and the dashed portion is its extension to room temperature. The barred circles are runs made with the addition of displacive shearing action in the apparatus of *Figure 8,* and show plainly that equilibrium is not noticeably displaced but that reaction rates are greatly accelerated at lower temperatures by added shearing stresses

the old questions on the possible influences of shear on the displacement of equilibrium and on the rate of reaction.

The experimental studies on this problem have been aimed at determining the effects of shearing stresses on the equilibrium between two phases from the effects on the kinetics of the reaction. Several studies have been made which show that the addition of a displacive shearing component to samples in an opposed-anvil apparatus does not change the absolute stability fields of various phases, at least within the experimental error of the method. It has also been shown that these reactions proceed at appreciable rates at temperatures 100–300°C below the minimum temperatures necessary under 'static' conditions. Thus, it was found that SiO_2-coesite could be formed at 100–150°C (see *Figure 12*) and reactions like $PbO_{litharge} \rightleftharpoons PbO_{massicot}$, $PbO_2I \rightleftharpoons PbO_2II$, $MnF_2I \rightleftharpoons MnF_2II$, $CaCO_{3calcite} \rightleftharpoons CaCO_{3aragonite}$ were possible at room temperatures at the appropriate pressures. To change natural aragonite to calcite required a temperature of 200°C with shear; at least 450–500°C is necessary under static conditions.

The influence of pressure, shear and temperature on the PbO_2I–PbO_2II reaction is shown in *Figure 13*. The linear dependence on pressure of both static and shear runs is clearly indicated by the four curves, although the initial slope of the 400°C static series may be due to shearing stresses during the first stages of compaction. The effect of displacive shear may be approximately evaluated by comparing the slopes of the static runs at 25°

176

and 400°C, 0·17 and 0·33 per cent conversion per kb in 10 minutes, with those of the 25° and 300° 'shear' runs, 1·1 and 3·1 per cent, an increase of 6–10 times. The increase for a 400° shear series has been found to be even greater. In all these series there is the possibility that some of the increased conversion noted with increased pressure may in fact be due to the increased inter- and intra-granular stresses on going to the higher pressures.

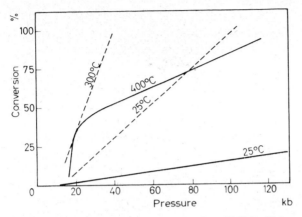

Figure 13. The rate of conversion from $PbO_2 I \rightarrow II$ in opposed-anvil apparatus. The reaction time was constant at ten minutes for different pressures at selected temperatures. The solid lines are for 'static' pressure runs, and the dashed lines are for those runs made with the addition of displacive shearing action

A direct comparison in this system to illustrate the influence of shearing stresses may be made by referring to the conversion-time plot of *Figure 14.* The course of the reaction at 25°C and 40 kb with shear would be equivalent to that of 200–250°C at the same pressure without shear. Also, the conditions of 25°C at 90 kb with shear match closely the results at 400°C and 40 kb without shear.

Figure 14. Additional data on the $PbO_2 I \rightarrow II$ conversion, showing the course of reaction with time. The solid lines are for 'static' runs and the dashed lines are for 'shearing' runs

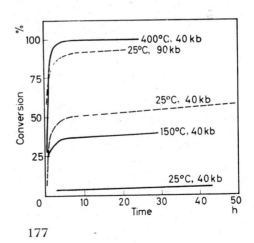

This polymorphic transition in PbO_2 is crystallographically simple and very fast when compared with the network silicate rearrangement in albite+nepheline→jadeite, and even more so with that of quartz→coesite under study in this laboratory. *Figure 15* summarizes our results[23] for a constant time study of the jadeite reaction starting with a dry albite+nepheline mixture equivalent to a $1 : 1 : 5$ ratio of $Na_2O \cdot Al_2O_3 \cdot SiO_2$. This was used because the stoichiometric mixture for jadeite $(1 : 1 : 4)$ did not give measurable rates of reaction in the range of the equipment available at the time. Hence, in almost all of the results some free silica in the form of quartz or coesite could be detected. The fractional conversion to jadeite was determined by the use of the ratios of selected integrated

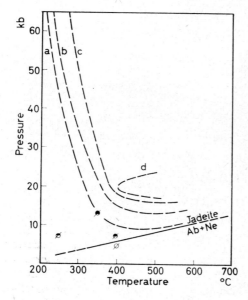

Figure 15. One study of the kinetics of the reaction albite + nepheline → 2 jadeite based on the results of nearly 200 runs in the opposed-anvil apparatus. The solid straight line is the equilibrium $p–t$ univariant boundary for the reaction as re-determined in this study, and the dashed curved lines are contours of equal reaction of standard 40-hour runs. Contours **a**, **b**, **c**, and **d**, are for 20, 30, 65 and 90 per cent conversion to jadeite, respectively. The acute closure of the 90 per cent contour coincides closely with the SiO_2 quartz–coesite transition and may be an indication of a 'Hedvall effect'. The barred circles represent experiments with the addition of displacive shear

x-ray diffraction intensities and an appropriate calibration curve. The curved lines in *Figure 15* above the equilibrium lines are approximate contours of equal forward reaction in 40 hours at various conditions of pressure and temperature. Isothermal or isobaric 'sections' taken from *Figure 15* will reveal the effect of these variables in different regions. The two most obvious are that (1) a kinetic barrier associated with temperature exists, so that even pressures as high as 90 kb are not sufficient to give measurable reaction below 200°C, and (2) a second barrier is evident as a pressure band above the equilibrium $p–t$ line for the reaction. An analogous situation has, of course, been known for a long time in connection with the study of rapid transitions by Bridgman, who refers to this band as a 'zone of indifference'. Reactions of this type apparently cannot be made to 'run' very easily or in a short time unless conditions are well beyond both the pressure and temperature barriers. It is apparent that these results are in marked contrast with a remark of Pistorius and Kennedy[41], who state in connection with a similar silicate reaction,' . . . It has been our experience in this device that runs of one half-hour or several days give essentially the same results. . . .' The influence of an additional displacive shearing component in this reaction is indicated on the plot by a few barred circles. Thus, at about 350°C and 13 kb, ordinarily a region of 20 per cent conversion, the addition of shearing resulted in 60 per cent conversion. Some conversion resulted with shear at even lower temperatures and pressures. The reverse reaction is more difficult, so that even at 400°C with shear in the albite+nepheline stability field, the jadeite remains unchanged.

Acknowledgments

The high pressure crystal chemical research in this laboratory is supported financially by the Metallurgy Branch, Office of Naval Research, under Contract No. 656 (20).

References

[1] LEA, M. C., *Amer. J. Sci.*, 3rd Ser., **46**, 1893, p. 241

[2] LEA, M. C., *Amer. J. Sci.*, 3rd Ser., **46**, 1893, p. 413

[3] BASSET, J., *J. Chim. Phys.*, **40**, 1943, p. 181

[4] BRIDGMAN, P. W., *Phys. Rev.*, **48**, 1935, p. 825

[5] BRIDGMAN, P. W., *J. chem. Phys.*, **15**, 1947, p. 92

[6] BRIDGMAN, P. W., *J. appl. Phys.*, **24**, 1953, p. 405

[7] BRIDGMAN, P. W., *J. appl. Phys.*, **12**, 1941, p. 461

[8] GRIGGS, D. T. and KENNEDY, G. C., *Amer. J. Sci.*, **254**, 1956, p. 722

[9] VERESCHAGIN, L. F. and SHAPOCHKIN, V. A., *Physics of Metals and Metallography*, **7**, 1959, p. 478; VERESCHAGIN, L. F., 'Investigations in the area of the physics of high pressures', Proceedings, Lake George Conference, *Progress in Very High Pressure Research*, John Wiley and Sons, New York, 1961

[10] DACHILLE, F. and ROY, R., 'Influence of displacive shearing stresses on the kinetics of reconstructive transformations effected by pressure in the range 0–100,000 bars', *Proceedings of the Fourth International Symposium on Reactivity of Solids*, Amsterdam, Elsevier, 1960

[11] GRIGGS, D. T., TURNER, F. J. and HEARD, H. C., 'Deformation of rocks at 500 to 800°C, Memoir 79, Geol. Soc. Amer., 1960

[12] DACHILLE, F. and ROY, R., Oral Presentation, Geochemistry Session, Geological Society of America, 1957

[13] JAMIESON, J. C., LAWSON, A. W. and NACHTRIEB, N. D., *Rev. Sci. Instrum.*, **30**, 1959, p. 1,016

[14] WEIR, C. E., LIPPINCOTT, E. R., VAN VALKENBURG, A. and BUNTING, E. N., *J. Res. Nat. Bur. Stand.*, **63A**, No. 1, 1959, p. 55

[15] WEIR, C. E., LIPPINCOTT, E. R., VAN VALKENBURG, A. and BUNTING, E. N., *Spectrochim. Acta*, **16**, 1960, p. 58

[16] WEIR, C. E., LIPPINCOTT, E. R. and VAN VALKENBURG, A., *J. chem. Phys.*, **32**, 1960, p. 612

[17] FITCH, R. A., SLYKHOUSE, T. E. and DRICKAMER, H. G., *J. Opt. Soc. Amer.*, **47**, 1957, p. 1,015

[18] BALCHAN, A. S. and DRICKAMER, H. G., *Rev. Sci. Instrum.*, 1961. (In press)

[19] BRIDGMAN, P. W., *Proc. Amer. Acad. Arts Sci.*, **81**, 1952, p. 165

[20] DACHILLE, F. and ROY, R., *Bull. Geol. Soc. Amer.*, **69**, 1958, p. 1,550

[21] DACHILLE, F. and ROY, R., *Amer. J. Sci.*, **258**, 1960, p. 225

[22] ROBERTSON, E. C., BIRCH, F. and MACDONALD, G. J. F., *Amer. J. Sci.*, **255**, 1957, p. 115

[23]Hoffer, A., Dachelle, F. and Roy, R., *J. Amer. Ceram. Soc.*, 1961. (In press)

[24]MacDonald, G. J. F., *Amer. Min.*, **41,** 1956, p. 744

[25]Clark, S. P., Jr., *Amer. Min.*, **42,** 1957, p. 564

[26]Bridgman, P. W., *Proc. Amer. Acad. Arts. Sci,* **74,** 1942, p. 399

[27]Hall, H. T., *High Temperature, a Tool for the Future—Proceedings of Symposium,* Stanford Research Institute, Menlo Park, California, 1956, pp. 161–166

[28]Boyd, F. R. and England, J. L., *J. Geophys. Res.*, **65,** 1960, p. 749

[29]MacDonald, G. J. F., *Amer. J. Sci.*, **254,** 1956, p. 713

[30]Dachille, F. and Roy, R., *Z. Kristallogr.*, **111,** 1959, p. 451

[31]Dachille, F. and Roy, R., *Bull. Geol. Soc. Amer.*, **68,** 1957, p. 1,713

[32]Roy, R. and Cohen, H., *Nature*, **190,** 1961, p. 798

[33]Dachille, F. and Roy, R., *J. Amer. Ceram. Soc.*, **41,** 1959, p. 78

[34]Dachille, F. and Dent Glasser, L. S., *Acta Crystallogr.*, **12,** 1959, p. 820

[35]Mackenzie, J. D., Roth, W. L. and Wentorf, R. H., *Acta Crystallogr.*, **12,** 1959. p. 79

[36]White, W. B., Dachille, F. and Roy, R., *F. Amer. Ceram. Soc.*, **44,** 1961, p. 170

[37]Azzaria, L. and Dachille, F., *J. phys. Chem.*, **65,** 1961, p. 889

[38]Stubican, V. and Roy, R., *Bull. Amer. Ceram. Soc.*, **40,** 1961, p. 193

[39]Jamieson, J. C., *J. chem. Phys.*, **20,** 1953, p. 1,385

[40]Rossini, F. D. and Jessup, R. S., *J. Res. Nat. Bur. Stand.*, **21,** 1938, p. 491

[41]Pistorius, C. W. F. T. and Kennedy, G. C., *Amer. J. Sci.*, **258,** 1960, p. 247

10

HIGH PRESSURE AT LOW TEMPERATURE

JOHN W. STEWART

University of Virginia
Charlottesville, Virginia

I. Introduction

STRICTLY speaking, the pressures considered herein (of the order of 20,000 atm maximum) fail to qualify under the present definition of 'very high pressure'. However, on account of the special interest and difficulties associated with the accompanying low temperature, it was felt that this material should be included. It would be extremely valuable to extend the range of available pressure at low temperature into the very high pressure region. This has not been possible so far and appears to be quite difficult.

Combined high pressure and low temperature investigations can yield a wealth of useful data. The most fundamental are PVT relations for solids, particularly those with low melting points, such as the permanent gases. In these cases compression data can be more readily correlated with theory than is possible at present for most metals at room temperature. For non-metals at sufficiently low temperature the crystal energy, from which the PVT relation can be computed, involves only the lattice potential energy and the zero point energy. These are more readily calculable than is the thermal contribution to the energy which becomes important at higher temperature. With few exceptions (notably the alkali metals), significant progress in calculating equations of state has been made only for the condensed gases. Closely related to PVT data are melting curve data (important from the standpoint of questions such as the existence of solid–liquid critical points), and PT data on solid–solid transitions of first and second order.

The measurement of the effect of pressure on superconducting transitions is necessarily restricted to low temperature. The dependence of parameters of the superconducting state, such as the transition temperature and the critical magnetic field, upon properties of the crystal lattice, first revealed in the isotope effect[1], plays a crucial role in the successful Bardeen–Cooper–Schriefer[2] theory of superconductivity. High pressure affords the simplest and most convenient means for the experimental variation of interatomic spacing in a crystal lattice. Pressure effects on the superconducting parameters have therefore been extensively studied. These effects are generally small, so that one must either be able to make precise measurements of pressure and temperature, or else go to quite high pressure in order to obtain significant results. Much of the motivation for the development of high pressure techniques at low temperature has originated from studies of superconductivity.

Other low temperature phenomena dependent upon lattice spacing, such as electrical resistance of non-superconductors, thermal conductivity of solid helium, and nuclear magnetic resonance in solid hydrogen, have also been studied at elevated pressures.

The definition of 'low' temperature depends upon the phenomenon under investigation. All known superconducting transitions occur below liquid hydrogen temperature (20°K). For PVT work a simple criterion for low temperature is that the thermal expansion of the substance in question must be negligibly small at the high pressure. For many simple solids under a few thousand atmospheres pressure, this condition will be met at liquid nitrogen temperature or above; while for helium at pressures below 10^3 atm, even 4°K is not really 'low'. In the present discussion we shall be concerned with temperatures below about 100°K.

Technical difficulties encountered in the simultaneous application of pressures of the order of 10^4 atm and temperatures in the liquid helium range are in many respects similar to those in the 10^5 atm pressure range at ordinary temperatures, and are at least as great. The most serious problem arises from the lack of suitable fluids for the transmission of hydrostatic pressure. At 4°K there exist no liquids above about 200 atm, the solidification pressure of He^3. At 100°K helium remains gaseous to several times 10^4 atm. However, because of their high compressibilities, gases are not as satisfactory pressure transmitters as liquids. In the low temperature region one must use solids for most applications. In some cases pressure is applied directly by means of a piston, while in others, to be discussed later, various ingenious indirect techniques have been used.

The use of solids as transmitters of hydrostatic pressure is not new. Bridgman[3,4] encountered this problem at room temperature as soon as he exceeded 30,000 atm by his direct piston displacement method. Above this pressure isopentane became too viscous to be used as a fluid transmitter.

A perfect pressure transmitting medium would support no shear whatsoever. A uniaxial compressive stress applied by a piston to such a substance would be transmitted throughout as an isotropic hydrostatic pressure. Thus no solid can be a perfect pressure medium, since, by definition, all solids must permanently support some shear. However, a number of solids do transmit approximately hydrostatic pressure, and these are the ones which must be used. The criteria for a good solid transmitter in a piston apparatus are the following:

(1) It must have low shear strength.

(2) It must yield plastically in shear, rather than merely fracturing. A weak brittle solid is not satisfactory because of the high internal friction which results from the rubbing together of the broken pieces as the applied pressure is changed.

(3) Its compressibility should be small. Otherwise the volume change is excessive when the pressure is varied over wide limits. This can be bothersome at times.

(4) In order to simplify problems which arise with embedded samples, it should be chemically inert and preferably an electrical insulator.

No substance exists which meets all four of these conditions at low temperature. Fortunately the first two, which are the most important, can be met.

At room temperature indium[3] and silver chloride[5] are quite plastic up to pressures at least of the order of 10^5 atm. At elevated temperatures, other materials such as pyrophyllite, talc, and hexagonal boron nitride[6] are more satisfactory. A complete discussion of the high temperature problems is given in Chapter 5.

At low temperature AgCl becomes too brittle. Indium remains relatively soft down to 4°K, but not nearly so soft as it is at room temperature. The heavier alkali metals yield plastically at shear stresses of a few hundred atm at 4°K, but present obvious difficulties in handling. There seem to be no other substances solid at 300°K which remain sufficiently plastic at helium temperatures to be used as pressure transmitters. In this range the most promising pressure media appear to be solid hydrogen and solid helium. These suffer from the disadvantage that they are the most compressible solids known. For hydrogen at 4°K, $\Delta V/V_0$ at 20,000 atm is $0 \cdot 55$, while for helium[7] $(V_{140}-V_{20,000})/V_{140}$ is $0 \cdot 62$. The melting pressure of He[4] at 4°K is 140 atm. Thus in any investigation involving an embedded sample, the volume of the transmitting medium must considerably exceed that of the sample at low pressure. At higher temperature certain other solidified gases are satisfactory pressure media. At 77°K solid argon may be used.

II. Pressure Transmission

The author[7,8] has investigated hydrogen and a number of other solidified gases as pressure transmitters. *Figure 1* shows a sample holder with an axial hole in the bottom such as was used. The hole can be covered with a

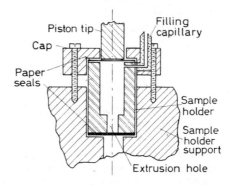

Figure 1. The sample holder used for extrusion experiments with solidified gases

paper seal of low mechanical strength, and a sample of solidified gas condensed in it at low pressure. The applied uniaxial compressive stress required to cause extrusion of the sample through the hole is determined. This is a measure of the ability of the substance to transmit pressure. A good solid should extrude smoothly (like toothpaste from a tube) and at a relatively low pressure. It should not be broken into small pieces. Plastic materials extrude with a gentle hissing noise; brittle ones can be heard to crunch. The extrusion pressure for solid hydrogen at 4°K in a $\frac{1}{4}$-in.

cylinder with a $\frac{1}{8}$-in. hole was found to be less than 200 atm. This is the softest of the solidified gases investigated. The extrusion pressure for helium cannot be measured in this manner because of the elevated melting pressure.

A second major difficulty confronting low temperature work arises from strength of materials. Most steels become brittle at low temperature, and while excellent for pistons which need withstand only compressive stress, they readily fail under tension and are therefore not suitable for pressure cylinders. In recent years many technical data on the low temperature properties of engineering materials have become available so that one now has no major difficulty in finding satisfactory substances for high pressure work at low temperature. In general, steels with low carbon and high nickel content (austenitic stainless steels and nickel steels such as AISI 4615) are sufficiently ductile at low temperature. Beryllium copper (12 atomic per cent Be alloyed with Cu) is also satisfactory up to perhaps 20,000 atm, and has the further advantage that it is non-magnetic. Some grades of stainless steel are also suitable up to about 20,000 atm. These are useful where non-magnetic properties are desired. Carboloy (tungsten carbide cemented with cobalt) has been used with good results.

Since the development of the Collins helium liquefier, the production of the relatively large quantities of liquid helium required for some types of high pressure experiments has not been a serious problem. Helium evaporation rates that would once have been considered prohibitive are, however, often encountered. These can be kept within reasonable limits by careful design of the cryogenic aspects of the equipment[9,10].

We shall discuss the field of combined high pressure and low temperature in two sections. First we shall consider those techniques where the pressure is applied by a variety of methods not involving the motion of a piston in a cylinder at low temperature. Then we shall describe experiments where the pressure is applied directly by means of a piston. In keeping with the emphasis of this book on techniques, we shall discuss equipment and methods rather than results.

III. Methods Other Than Piston Displacement

(i) Electrical Resistance Measurements

The earliest significant work in the combined field of high pressure and low temperature was that of Bridgman[11] about 1932. There had been some previous studies of melting curves of permanent gases up to a few hundred atm which will not be considered here. Bridgman reached 7,500 atm at liquid oxygen temperatures in an investigation of pressure coefficients of electrical resistance of metals. The pressure was applied with gaseous helium. The apparatus consisted of two cylinders connected by a heavy walled tube. The high pressure helium at room temperature was forced into the upper cylinder by conventional means. The lower cylinder, containing the sample, was immersed in a liquid oxygen bath at 90°K. This arrangement had the advantage that the electrical leads to the resistance specimen could be brought out of the pressure system at room temperature. Electrically insulated plugs successful at low temperature have been constructed only recently (see below).

Bridgman encountered serious difficulty from penetration of his steel by the helium gas. Leaks invariably developed at pressures above 8,000 atm, and sometimes below. This system had a relatively large volume, and the danger of explosion, which is always present in gas systems because of the large energy of compression, was particularly great.

Evidently both helium and hydrogen in the gas phase weaken some steels at pressures higher than a few thousand atm. The embrittlement of steel by compressed hydrogen is well known and is apparently unavoidable. The penetration of helium is less serious, and can be reduced by the choice of the proper alloy. Recently pressure in excess of 10^4 atm has been obtained with gaseous helium at liquid nitrogen temperature by Langer and Warschauer[12] in a bomb for optical studies. At lower temperature the helium would, of course, freeze.

Dugdale, with Hulburt[13] and Gugan[14] has made electrical resistance measurements on rubidium and copper up to about 3,000 atm, using gaseous helium. Earlier, Holland, Hugill and Jones[15] had observed the melting curve of helium up to 8,000 atm pressure at temperatures above $50°K$. They employed the 'blocked capillary' technique originated by Keesom[16], and could therefore work with a system of small volume and relatively great safety. They used specially prepared thick-walled stainless steel capillary tubing, and had no difficulty with penetration. The same technique has been used for melting curves of other low melting point gases up to several thousand atmospheres pressure.

(ii) Precompression Techniques

Several interesting indirect techniques using solids as pressure media have been developed. The earliest was the ice bomb of Lasarew and Kan[17] used in superconductivity investigations. A thick-walled beryllium copper chamber containing the sample was filled completely full of water at room temperature. It was then sealed and frozen. The expansion of the ice resulted in a pressure of about 2,100 atm at $-22°C$ (the water–ice I–ice III triple point). This is the maximum pressure that can be attained by freezing ice; above 2,100 atm the solid form of H_2O is always denser than the liquid. As the bomb was cooled from $-22°C$ to $4°K$, the fact that ice has a greater coefficient of thermal expansion than the beryllium copper resulted in a final pressure about 20 per cent lower than the maximum. As judged by the sharpness of the observed superconducting transitions, the stress within the ice at $4°K$ was quite uniform. Evidently the pressure exerted by the freezing ice is nearly hydrostatic and remains so as the temperature is lowered. Although it is known from the observed flow of glaciers that ice is somewhat plastic near its melting point, our extrusion experiments have shown[18] that at $4°K$ it is quite brittle when compressed with a piston. Materials which harden at low temperature can retain during cooling a hydrostatic pressure which is originally produced, by freezing or otherwise, at a higher temperature where the substance is plastic.

Lasarew and Kan were unable to vary their pressure continuously or widely. A limited range could be obtained by altering the sample-to-ice volume ratio within the bomb. To accomplish this, the bomb in each instance had to be warmed up to room temperature and refilled.

The ice-bomb technique has more recently been used in a study of the cadmium superconducting transition at temperatures as low as $0 \cdot 06°K$[19]. Here one is in the domain of adiabatic demagnetization, so that the lack of mechanical connection to an external press is essential. This is the only application of high pressure which has yet been made at temperatures below the liquid helium range.

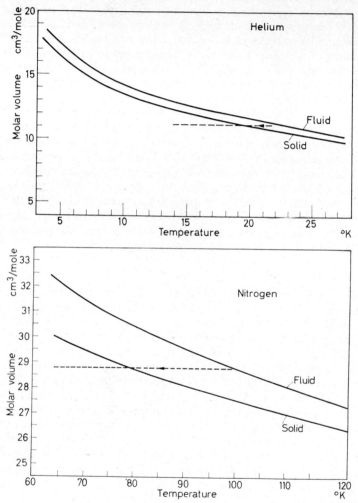

Figure 2. Molar volumes of solid and fluid helium and nitrogen along the solidification curve. The dotted lines represent the cooling process described in the text

Other substances which expand upon freezing are gallium, bismuth (and some of its alloys, such as printers' type metal), antimony, and germanium. These could all in principle be used to generate high pressure. However, their higher melting points and, in some, phase transitions in the solid, make these substances of doubtful value at low temperature. While the melting curve of germanium is known[20] to have an anomalous slope up to at least 120,000 atm, in this range the melting temperature decreases from about 850°C to 360°C, placing it well outside the low temperature domain.

Dugdale and Simon[21] have shown that even though helium contracts upon freezing, substantial pressures can be retained in the solid by cooling and freezing the compressed gas. This is possible because of the relatively small decrease of volume upon freezing, coupled with the exceptionally high compressibility of solid helium. When other substances are cooled in this manner the pressure is soon lost. There appear to be insufficient data to state whether hydrogen could be used in a similar manner. It would certainly be inferior to helium as a source of high pressure. In *Figure 2* is shown a comparison between the behaviour of helium[21] and nitrogen[22].

If, as an example, one starts with fluid helium on the solidification curve at 2,000 atm and 22°K, and cools at constant volume (11·2 cm³/mole), one finds that when all of the helium has solidified, the pressure corresponds to the freezing pressure at 19·3°K (*Figure 2*). Dugdale and Simon[21] found this to be 1,600 atm. As the solid is cooled further, the drop in pressure can be roughly estimated from $\left(\dfrac{\partial p}{\partial T}\right)_v = \dfrac{\alpha}{K}$. Owing to the rapid decrease of α with T (approximately as T^3), the drop in pressure upon cooling will actually be considerably less than that calculated with our assumption of constant thermal expansion. These authors[21] give the thermal expansion α at a molar volume of 11 cm³/mole as roughly 13×10^{-4} per °K, and the isothermal compressibility K as 13×10^{-5} per atm. Thus the pressure drop in the solid is of the order of 10 atm per degree. If we cool the above sample to 4°K, the pressure would still be about 1,450 atm—a useful value. Experimentally, the pressure turns out to be a bit higher than this[23]. The cooling of the solid at constant volume is almost isobaric.

We now make the corresponding calculation for nitrogen, as an example of a substance for which this method of generating high pressure cannot be used. Starting with fluid just ready to condense at 2,000 atm, 28·8 cm³/mole, and 100°K[22] (*Figure 2*), we find that when the nitrogen has solidified the pressure has fallen to the melting pressure corresponding to 79·5°K, or about 820 atm. Over half the initial pressure is lost during the freezing as contrasted to only 20 per cent for helium. Using the value of Grilly and Mills[22] for α (again assumed constant) of $2·7 \times 10^{-3}$ per °K, and the author's[7] determination of K at 820 atm and 65°K, $5·6 \times 10^{-5}$ per atm, we estimate $\left(\dfrac{\partial p}{\partial T}\right)_v$ as roughly 50 atm per degree. Thus, as the nitrogen is cooled all the pressure will be lost by the time the temperature reaches 63°K. Even with higher starting pressures it would be impossible to cool to 4°K with nitrogen while retaining a substantial pressure in the solid.

The pressure attained in solid helium can be computed from measured thermodynamic parameters. An independent value can be obtained if the transition temperature (in zero magnetic field) of a standard superconductor is determined and compared with previous work. Swenson[24] has found that pressures in solid helium as determined by these two methods agree within a few per cent.

187

The pressure generated by the freezing helium is evidently quite uniform. Swenson[24] reports no deformation of superconducting samples. No direct measurements of the plasticity of solid helium have been made, but on account of the weak interatomic forces one would expect it to be a soft material. This technique of isovolumic cooling of compressed helium gas shows great promise for future high pressure work at liquid helium temperatures.

Up to now this method has been used over a range of temperature in the study of the thermodynamic properties of helium itself[21] and in resistance and superconductivity measurements[13,14,24]. Samples of the superconductors mercury, tin, and tantalum[24] have been embedded in freezing helium and investigated at pressures up to 3,000 atm. The pressure was transmitted by gaseous helium at the lower pressures and higher temperatures, and by the solid at higher pressures and lower temperatures. Unfortunately, on account of the rapid drop of the isothermal compressibility of helium with increasing pressure, substantially higher pressures cannot be produced by cooling gas under greater initial pressure at higher temperature.

The highest pressure yet attained at liquid helium temperature is in the neighbourhood of 44,000 atm. This was achieved by the so-called 'fixed clamp' technique of Chester and Jones[25]. A thin sample of superconducting material was squeezed between two massive truncated cones at room temperature. A clamp was then applied to hold the cones together. The clamped cones were detached from the press and cooled to liquid helium temperature. Approximately 10 per cent of the original pressure was lost to friction in the threads of the clamp. The measurement of pressure was rather uncertain on account of assumptions which had to be made as to the changing elastic constants of the clamp and cones at low temperature. This method is based upon a technique devised by Bridgman for the measurement of shear strengths[26] and electrical resistance[27] at room temperature. Thin wafers of material could be held in place between the cones by friction alone at pressures up to 4×10^5 atm. In their low temperature work Chester and Jones used samples 5 mm in diameter, which, after compression, were only 0·01 mm thick. From the sharpness of the observed superconducting transitions they estimated that the pressure was reasonably uniform over the central three quarters of the area of the disc. In order to preserve the sharpness of the transitions, provision was made for interrupting the supercurrent in the outer portion of the disc which was under non-hydrostatic stress.

A similar technique has been employed by Bowen[28] in which cylindrical samples of superconductor are encased within a capsule of silver chloride, placed in a beryllium copper cylinder, and stressed at room temperature by means of a Carboloy piston. The piston and cylinder are then clamped, detached from the press, and cooled to liquid helium temperature. The silver chloride transmits the pressure satisfactorily at room temperature. At low temperature the hydrostatic quality of the stress was not destroyed even though the silver chloride became brittle. The maximum pressures reached were slightly above 20,000 atm.

All of these methods of producing high pressure suffer from the defect that the pressure either cannot be very high, as with gaseous transmitters, or that it cannot be varied continuously. To change the pressure in an ice bomb or clamp, the sample must be warmed all the way to room temperature and the pressure reapplied. These techniques are therefore useless for volumetric measurements. On the other hand, the absence of heavy external connections means that heat leaks into the experimental cryostat can be kept very small. For some types of measurement a single high pressure is sufficient, and a device such as that of Chester and Jones, which can be pressurized at room temperature, detached from the press, and finally cooled, has distinct advantages from the cryogenic point of view. Pressure in gas systems can be varied continuously up to the freezing pressure of the gas, but these are hazardous to work with. The range of gas systems is quite limited at the lower temperatures of interest. This can be substantially increased through the use of the frozen helium technique of Dugdale and Hulburt[13].

IV. The Direct Piston Displacement Method

(i) General

At room temperature the standard means for continuously varying the pressure on a sample is to embed it in a pressure-transmitting medium within a cylinder, and to push on the medium with a piston. The length of the cylinder contents can be continuously monitored by means of the displacement of the piston. If the cross section is assumed constant, volume changes of isotropic materials can thereby be determined. The pressure can be varied without changing the temperature of the sample. This is the only feasible method for determining volumetric effects over a wide range of pressure. The direct piston displacement method is also superior for the investigation of electrical resistance where an isothermal R v. P relation is desired. Bridgman[29] has perfected this method for the measurement of linear compressibilities of solids up to 10^5 atm. At pressures below 30,000 atm a liquid transmitter such as isopentane was used. At the higher pressures the samples were enclosed in sheaths of plastic solids such as indium or silver chloride.

In order to extend this technique to low temperature, one must have means for applying a continuously variable force to the experimental piston. This can be done with a hydraulic press at room temperature (of course, one must not chill the oil in the press) connected to an intensifier of some sort. The use of an intensifier avoids excessively high pressures in the hydraulic system. The intensifier and accompanying tension member must support the thermal gradient from 4°K to room temperature, or at any rate from 4°K to 77°K, without too large heat conduction. It must have high strength without embrittlement at low temperature. The availability of a suitable material, austenitic stainless steel (AISI Type 304) was a key to the successful application of this method at low temperature.

(ii) Apparatus

Figure 3 is a schematic drawing of the pressure apparatus now in use at the University of Virginia.

The hydraulic system is conventional and need not be described in detail.

A Blackhawk 10,000 psi hand-operated pump designed for automotive body shops is used. The connections to the press and dead weight gauge are Blackhawk flexible pressure tubing rated at 10,000 psi. The standard (home-made) dead weight piston gauge is accurate to 0·5 per cent. One could equally well use a conventional manganin resistance gauge for measuring the pressure in the hydraulic system. The dead weight gauge has the advantage that it holds the pressure in the system constant over a period of time. In any event the area ratio of the intensifier must be used to determine the sample pressure. The hydraulic press piston has a diameter of 1·75 in., and travels about 1 in. The upper end of the stainless steel compression member fits snugly against this.

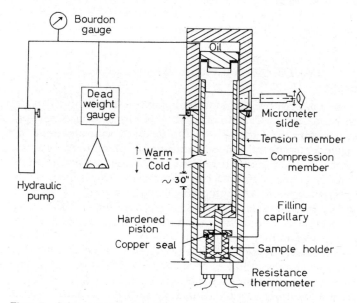

Figure 3. Schematic diagram of the apparatus used at the University of Virginia for producing high pressure at low temperature by the direct piston displacement method. The resistance thermometer, consisting of a coil of indium wire, is used to monitor the temperature of the sample

The length of the compression and tension members used here, 33 in., represents a compromise between strength and thermal factors. The Type 304 (8 per cent Ni, 18 per cent Cr) stainless steel combines very low thermal conductivity with high yield point and ductility at liquid helium temperature. It and related types of stainless steel appear to be the only sufficiently strong materials with both good ductility and low thermal conductivity at these temperatures.

From the cryogenic standpoint, the greater the length of the piston rod, the less is the heat influx. However, a long compression member will buckle at a lower applied load than a short one. Economy of material is achieved by using concentric cylinders for both the tension (2 in. outer diam., 0·13 in. wall) and compression (1·50 in. outer diam., 0·13 in. wall) members. The limitation on maximum allowable load in this press (about 7 tons) is set by the lateral buckling of the compression member acting as a loaded column. The Euler column formula[30]

$$F = \frac{\pi^3}{4l^2} E \ (r_e{}^4 - r_i{}^4)$$

may be applied to such a hollow cylinder of inner radius r_i and outer radius r_e (conservatively assumed to have hinged ends). E is Young's Modulus (30×10^6 psi for the stainless steel), and l is the length of the column. The maximum allowable load F varies as the inverse square of the length while the heat transmitted varies only as the inverse first power of the length. Thus excessive length is not desirable. For a given cross-sectional area of material, a thin-walled hollow cylinder offers the greatest resistance to buckling. For $l=30$ in., $F=7$ tons, approximately. Swenson[31] has found that at 4°K the yield strength of Type 304 stainless steel is roughly 120,000 psi in compression.

The evaporation rate of liquefied gas coolant in the cryostat as calculated from thermal conductivity data alone is always considerably higher than is observed. Wexler[32] has made a study of this problem, and has shown how the very large refrigerative capacity of cold evaporated gas may be taken into account. The heat capacity of helium gas is about $1\cdot25$ cal/g °K over a wide range of low temperature. This is about 25 per cent of the latent heat of vaporization at 4°K. Greatly reduced evaporation rates can be achieved if the pressure apparatus fits rather snugly into the neck of the cryostat so that the flow of escaping gas is turbulent. Clearance of $0\cdot01$ to $0\cdot05$ in. is satisfactory; if less than this, trouble may be experienced at the lowest temperatures from the freezing of atmospheric air around the tension member when the cryostat is opened.

The motion of the piston is followed with a micrometer slide (magnification $32\times$) through which fine scratches milled on the room temperature end of the compression member may be observed. Settings may be made with an accuracy of two or three microns. Backlash is eliminated by always approaching the reading against the spring tension in the slide.

This apparatus has so far been used only for the study of volumetric relations in solidified gases. By modification of the sample holders, next to be described, it could easily be adapted to other types of measurement. *Figure 4* shows a typical piston and cylinder arrangement that has been used.

The intensifier multiplication for a $\frac{1}{4}$ in. piston is 49, so that the 7-ton load corresponds to a maximum sample pressure of approximately 20,000 atm. Larger pistons give correspondingly less multiplication, but larger sample volume. The pistons have been made from oil-hardenable Ketos tool steel (C $0\cdot90$ per cent, Cr $0\cdot50$ per cent, W $0\cdot50$ per cent, Mn 1.30 per cent) heat treated one hour at 1,480°F, oil quenched, and tempered one hour at 450°F. There is no observable plastic deformation of this steel at 20,000 atm at 4°K. Above 150°K we have observed some flow, resulting in seizure of the piston in the cylinder. Type 316 stainless steel and beryllium copper have been successfully used up to 20,000 atm[33]. Unfortunately, however, beryllium copper has a Young's Modulus of the order of only one half that of steel. Furthermore, this varies with both stress and temperature more than is the case with steel. Dilatation of the sample holder from internal pressure is then a large and uncertain correction in volumetric work. This is not serious for electrical measurements, where the non-magnetic properties of beryllium copper and stainless steel may constitute an important advantage. For volumetric work a steel or Carboloy cylinder is much preferable to a BeCu cylinder.

The tensile strength of the Ketos steel is insufficient for it to be used as cylinder material. Several Ketos cylinders of $0·25$ in. internal and 1 in. outer diameter have burst at $4°K$ with brittle fracture at internal pressures in the neighbourhood of 10,000 atm. A suitable cylinder material has

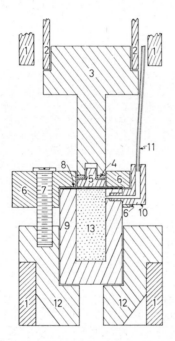

Figure 4. Detail of the high pressure cylinder for use at low temperature

1	Tension member
2	Compression member
3	Piston tip (heated treated Ketos steel)
4	Potassium packing
5	'Mushroom plug'
6, 7	Sample holder cap with screws for attachment
8	Copper sealing foil
9	Pressure cylinder (heat treated AISI 4615 steel). Outer to inner diameter ratio not to s ale
10, 11	Filling capillary and attachment to pressure cylinder
12	Sample holder support (attached to tension member)
13	Solidified gas sample

been found to be case-hardenable AISI 4615 alloy steel (C $0·13–0·18$ per cent, Mn $0·45–0·65$ per cent, Si $0·20–0·35$ per cent, Ni $1·65–2·00$ per cent, Mo $0·20–0·30$ per cent). At the higher temperatures of interest this yields slightly at 20,000 atm so that after several runs the bore of the cylinder becomes stretched and the cylinder must be discarded. Before final machining the cylinders are heated one hour at $1,575°F$, oil quenched, and then tempered one hour at $300°F$. Since surface hardness is of no advantage in the present application, case hardening is not carried out. On account of the sealing difficulties with solidified gas samples, these cylinders are made with a blind hole. Fabrication of open-ended cylinders is simpler, and these are preferred in most applications. Stress concentration at the bottom corner of the hole may lead to failure of the cylinder at a pressure lower than would be the case for an open-ended cylinder. The fit of piston to cylinder is made as close as possible at room temperature (by careful lapping). The thermal expansions of the Ketos piston and 4615 cylinder do not appear to be significantly different.

The solidified gas samples are prepared by condensation through a capillary tube from a supply at room temperature. The capillary is connected to a small hole leading into the side of the cylinder near the top. Once pressure is applied the piston covers the hole so that there can be no extrusion of the solidified sample up the capillary. To prevent leakage during condensation, several sheets of $0 \cdot 004$ in. copper foil seal the top of the cylinder. These are easily punched by the piston when pressure is applied and do not interfere with subsequent measurements.

A similar apparatus has been constructed by Swenson[34] (*Figure 5*) at Iowa State University. His press has a capacity of ten tons with maximum

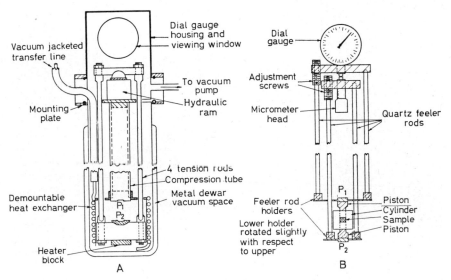

Figure 5. Swenson's piston displacement apparatus for reaching 27,000 atm at liquid helium temperature. In A is shown an exterior view of the apparatus, and in B the connection of the dial gauge to the experimental piston and cylinder

sample pressure 27,000 atm. Carboloy pistons and cylinders are used. Four tie rods take the place of the cylindrical tension member connecting the Blackhawk ram to the low temperature cylinder. Piston displacements are measured by a commercial dial gauge readable to 10^{-5} in. For much of his volumetric work (not connected with solidified gases) Swenson has used double-ended cylinders with two closely fitting pistons. He has found that Carboloy is the best material for volumetric measurements because of its high Young's Modulus (90×10^6 psi) and consequent small dilatation under internal pressure. The grades of Carboloy used were 779 for pistons and 55B for cylinders[34]. He has not employed blind-ended Carboloy cylinders. He has reported difficulty from flow and cracking of Carboloy pistons only near his upper limit of pressure above 20,000 atm.

In contrast, we have observed the bursting strength of a blind-ended Kennametal, grade K96, cylinder to be only 5,000 atm at 4°K and about

15,000 atm at 77°K. Evidently stress concentration set up at the slightly rounded corner at the bottom of the hole led to failure of the cylinders. The same may have been true for the Ketos cylinders. However, for the solidified gas work, the blind-ended design considerably simplifies the problem of sealing.

(iii) Solidified Gas Pressure Media

Where solid pressure transmitters are used, one does not always need packing on the moving piston. Extrusion of the solid between the piston and cylinder wall can often be prevented by the use of extrusion rings of triangular cross section ahead of the piston (or pistons, if the cylinder is double ended). These rings may be made of brass, steel, or hardened beryllium copper. However, solid hydrogen readily extrudes past the most closely fitting rings, and when it is used the piston must be sealed. The compressibility of solid hydrogen is so great that the release of elastic energy upon extrusion from 2,000 atm or above is sufficient to melt the extruded material. This results in an almost explosive loss of the whole sample once extrusion starts. Normal packing materials, such as rubber, or even teflon, become brittle at liquid helium temperatures. Alkali metals, particularly potassium, have been used successfully in Bridgman-type unsupported area packings[36]. A mushroom plug, made of the same material as the piston, is used (*Figure 4*). The potassium can be cut in air and quickly placed in position and cooled. An oxide layer does not harm the effectiveness of the seal so long as the metal within remains pure. Potassium seals will also hold helium once it has been solidified[7].

One major problem for which there appears to be no completely satisfactory solution is that of friction within the solid samples. This is always much more serious than when a fluid is used as the transmitting medium. The friction arises from three sources: (1) the rubbing of the piston, extrusion ring, and packing against the wall of the cylinder, (2) the adherence of the sample itself to the walls, and (3) the internal friction of the polycrystalline sample. The friction usually varies approximately exponentially with sample length[37]. Short samples are therefore preferable up to the point where the background stretch of the press overshadows the sample compression. The compression of the sample is the difference between the observed piston displacements with and without a sample in the pressure cylinder, with a small correction for the expansion under internal pressure of the sample holder volume.

Proper design can effectively eliminate the first effect. This requires a good fit of the piston in the cylinder, and extrusion rings of the proper size. Stevenson[38] has shown that lining the cylinder with one or two layers of 0·005 in. indium foil substantially reduces the friction in solidified gas samples, presumably by eliminating effect (2). The third effect is the inevitable one. Bridgman[29,37] has studied this in detail, and concludes that the best procedure is to take data for monotonically increasing and decreasing pressure, and to correct for the friction by computing the average pressure at constant displacement. This assumes that the magnitude of the frictional force is the same for increasing and decreasing pressure. The correction has been made in this manner for all the published volumetric data at low temperature[7,39]. The presence of friction is particularly disturbing in phase transition measurements[10], where it may completely obscure transformations with small volume changes. At best it renders impossible the precise determination of the transition pressure as well as the volume or compressibility discontinuity accompanying the transition.

To some extent this internal friction is a measure of the plasticity of the samples. Unusually large friction may be a sign that the transmitted stress is not uniform. Motion of the piston is then often accompanied by crunching sounds, presumably from the fracturing of the small crystals. For many solidified gases friction increases as the temperature is lowered and the

Figure 6. A typical compressibility run (solid helium, 4°K). The upper set of curves is for the sample, the lower set of curves for the distortion of the press members with no sample in the pressure cylinder. In each case the central curve represents the correction for friction. Owing to friction, the compression of the sample cannot be determined below about 2,000 atm, corresponding to 5 kg on the dead weight gauge pan. In this case the low pressure data were obtained from Dugdale and Simon[21]

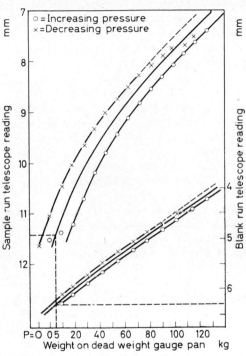

solid becomes more brittle. The observed magnitude of the friction ranges from less than 5 per cent of the maximum pressure in favourable cases, up to more than 15 per cent.

Figure 6 shows a typical set of data for a solid helium sample[7] at 4°K. The central curve is the piston displacement, corrected for friction, plotted as a function of pressure. The lower set of curves represents the correction for background stretch of the tension and compression members. The compression of the sample is the difference between the two central curves. This compression must still be corrected for the dilatation of the sample holder; this is obtained from a separate experiment using a material of known compressibility[7].

The only solidified gases which have so far been used as pressure transmitting media for other types of studies are helium and hydrogen. *PVT* relations have been obtained for a number of other solidified gases[7,10,40,41] and for several other materials[39]. In connection with superconductivity, helium has been used up to more than 10^3 atm by Swenson[24] and Mapother[39], employing the same technique as Dugdale and Hulburt[13]. Fiske[42] and his coworkers at the General Electric Research Laboratory, and Swenson[39,43] have used hydrogen. For precise work solid hydrogen frozen from the normal gas is not satisfactory because of temperature uncertainties arising from the heat liberated in the spontaneous ortho–para conversion. Normal hydrogen at room temperature consists of 75 per cent ortho-hydrogen and 25 per cent para-hydrogen. At low temperature (below 20°K) the equilibrium state is essentially 100 per cent para-hydrogen. The heat liberated in the transition from normal to equilibrium hydrogen at low temperature is 253 cal/mole, which is greater than the heat of vaporization of the liquid. If this transition is allowed to run in the solid transmitter, appreciable heating results. McCormick and Fairbank[44] have found from nuclear magnetic resonance studies at 4°K that the rate of conversion from ortho-hydrogen to para-hydrogen in the normal solid is not appreciably accelerated by pressure up to 5,000 atm. To obtain sharp superconducting transitions, the temperature within the solid hydrogen pressure transmitter must remain constant, and so one must use solid para-hydrogen, or else solid HD, which has only the one modification. The former is easier to prepare. Normal H_2 gas passed over activated charcoal or other catalysts near 20°K rapidly converts to essentially pure para-hydrogen. This can then be condensed into the sample holder without allowing it to warm up.

The plasticity of solid hydrogen at high pressure has not been studied directly. The fact that fairly sharp transitions have been observed up to 10,000 atm for embedded superconductors show that hydrostatic pressure is transmitted reasonably well. Further evidence of this is afforded by the very low friction exhibited by hydrogen samples. In this connection Swenson[43] has noted that while pressure gradients of several hundred atmospheres existed in the para-hydrogen immediately after a substantial change in sample pressure, these 'annealed' out after a half hour or so. This was shown by the sharpness of the observed superconducting transition. Fiske[42] had earlier observed the same effect in normal hydrogen. One might expect similar annealing effects in helium, which, however, has not yet been used at such high pressure.

In all of this superconducting work with helium and hydrogen, the transitions have been detected magnetically, so that no electrical leads into the pressure chamber at low temperature have been required. Non-magnetic beryllium copper was used. The large compressibilities of helium and hydrogen do not constitute a serious drawback for purely electrical and magnetic measurements.

Hatton[45,46] has measured the change of resistance of several non-superconductors between 1·6°K and 4°K at pressures up to 5,000 atm. He also investigated some superconductors in the same pressure range. In order to avoid the ortho–para heating, solid HD was used as the transmitter for some of this work. Resistances were measured by a standard potentiometric technique which required the use of four insulated leads, two for current and two for potential. The copper leads within the pressure cylinder were soft-soldered to the resistance specimens. Solid hydrogen or HD was condensed around the samples after they had been positioned in the cylinder. Pipestone seals of the type designed by Bridgman[47] were used to bring the leads out of the pressure cylinder with completely satisfactory results. There was no leakage of hydrogen past the pipestone cones. It can reasonably be hoped that these seals will prove satisfactory mechanically and electrically at higher pressures.

The same technique for insulated leads has been used successfully in connection with resistance measurements on superconductors at liquid nitrogen temperature by Paul and Warschauer[48]. In their apparatus the pressure was transmitted by gaseous helium.

McCormick and Fairbank[44] have studied nuclear magnetic resonance of solid hydrogen up to 5,000 atm pressure. The main requirement for this work is non-magnetic material for the pressure apparatus. Beryllium copper was used. The extension of magnetic measurements beyond the 10^4 atm range will require the development of stronger non-magnetic materials than are now available.

V. The Future

The practical limit of pressure at low temperature for the present piston displacement technique appears to be in the neighbourhood of 25,000 atm. The limiting factor is the strength of the pressure cylinders. One does not gain appreciably by increasing the outside to inside diameter ratio beyond about 4. The strongest available materials yield or burst at about this pressure. Presumably Carboloy has the highest yield point at 4 °K, but the author's experience with brittle fracture of similar Kennametal and his desire for blind-ended cylinders has led him to continue with the AISI 4615 steel. At room temperature the maximum pressure that can be retained in a single-stage conventional piston displacement apparatus is in the neighbourhood of 30,000 atm. To go higher Bridgman[49] has used two stages with external pressure reducing the stress in the walls of the high pressure inner cylinder containing the sample. In this manner he was able to reach 10^5 atm. A similar technique might be feasible at low temperature, but there one would expect the problems of friction to be enormously greater. Solid transmitters would have to be used in both stages, instead of merely the inner stage as at room temperature. At present, friction in the 20,000 atm range at low temperature seriously limits the accuracy of pressure measurement that can be attained. Furthermore there is no assurance as yet that solid hydrogen and helium remain sufficiently plastic above 20,000 atm to be of any value as transmitters.

The recent high temperature techniques of Hall[6,50] and others[51], using tetrahedral anvils and the set-ups known as the 'Belt' and the 'Girdle', possibly offer an alternative approach. With these, pressures of the order of 10^5 atm can be attained in a single stage at room temperature and above. However, the use of these at low temperature will involve very severe problems of refrigeration. In addition, some means will have to be devised to condense and retain the solidified gas in the high pressure space. This appears to be much more difficult than is the case with a conventional cylinder.

197

Even if the pressure range above 20,000 atm at low temperature is for the present inaccessible, there is a great deal of valuable research to be carried out merely by exploiting presently available techniques. This interdisciplinary field is being pursued by an increasing number of laboratories. It is hoped that this account of the present 'state of the art' will prove useful to others who wish to make additional studies.

References

[1]MAXWELL, E., *Phys. Rev.* **78**, 1950, p. 477

[2]BARDEEN, J., COOPER, L. N. and SCHRIEFER, J. R., *Phys. Rev.*, **106**, 1957, p. 162

[3]BRIDGMAN, P. W., *The Physics of High Pressure*, G. Bell and Sons, London, 1952, p. 399

[4]BRIDGMAN, P. W., *Rev. mod. Phys.*, **18**, 1946, p. 1

[5]BRIDGMAN, P. W., *Proc. Amer. Acad. Arts Sci.*, **72**, 1937, p. 56

[6]HALL, H. T., *Rev. Sci. Instrum.*, **29**, 1958, p. 267

[7]STEWART, J. W., *J. phys. Chem. Solids*, **1**, 1956, p. 146

[8]STEWART, J. W., *Phys. Rev.*, **97**, 1955, p. 578

[9]SWENSON, C. A. and STAHL, R., *Rev. Sci. Instrum.*, **25**, 1954, p. 608

[10]STEWART, J. W., *J. phys. Chem. Solids*, **12**, 1959, p. 122

[11]BRIDGMAN, P. W., *Proc. Amer. Acad. Arts Sci.*, **67**, 1932, p. 305

[12]SWENSON, C. A., Private communication, 1960

[13]DUGDALE, J. S. and HULBURT, J. A., *Canad. J. Phys.*, **35**, 1957, p. 720

[14]DUGDALE, J. S. and GUGAN, D., *Proc. Roy. Soc.*, **A241**, 1957, p. 397

[15]HOLLAND, F. A., HUGILL, J. and JONES, G. O., *Proc. Roy. Soc.*, **A207**, 1951, p. 268

[16]KEESOM, W., *Comm. Phys. Lab. Leiden*, No. 184b, 1926

[17]LASAREW, B. and KAN, L., *J. Phys. USSR*, **8**, 1944, p. 193

[18]STEWART, J. W., Thesis, Harvard University, 1954 (Unpublished)

[19]ALEKSEEVSKII, N. E. and GAIDUKOV, I. P., *J. exp. theor. Phys., Moscow*, **29**, 1955, p. 898; *Soviet Physics JETP*, **2**, 1956, p. 762

[20]HALL, H. T., *J. Phys. Chem.*, **59**, 1955, p. 1,144

[21]DUGDALE, J. S. and SIMON, F., *Proc. Roy. Soc.*, **A218**, 1953, p. 291

[22]GRILLY, E. R. and MILLS, R. L., *Phys. Rev.*, **105**, 1957, p. 1,140

[23]SWENSON, C. A., Private communication, 1960

[24]SWENSON, C. A., *Progress in Very High Pressure Research*, John Wiley and Sons, New York, 1961

[25]CHESTER, P. F. and JONES, G. O., *Phil. Mag.*, **44**, 1953, p. 1,281

[26]BRIDGMAN, P. W., *Proc. Amer. Acad. Arts Sci.*, **71**, 1937, p. 387

[27]BRIDGMAN, P. W., *Proc. Amer. Acad. Arts Sci.*, **81**, 1952, p. 165

[28]BOWEN, D. H., in *Low Temperature Physics and Chemistry*, Proceedings of the Fifth International Conference, J. R. DILLINGER, Ed., University of Wisconsin Press, Madison, 1958, p. 337

[29]BRIDGMAN, P. W., *Proc. Amer. Acad. Arts Sci.*, **76**, 1945, p. 9

[30]TIMOSHENKO, S., *Strength of Materials*, Van Nostrand, New York, 1941, Part II, p. 188

[31]SWENSON, C. A., *Technical Report No. 1, OOR Contract DA-19-020-ORD-1891*, Massachusetts Institute of Technology, 1954

[32]WEXLER, A., *J. appl. Phys.*, **22**, 1951, p. 1,463

[33]PAUL, W., BENEDEK, G. B. and WARSCHAUER, D. M., *Rev. Sci. Instrum.*, **30**, 1959, p. 874

[34]BEECROFT, R. I. and SWENSON, C. A., *J. appl. Phys.*, **30**, 1959, p. 793

[35]SWENSON, C. A., Private communications, 1957, 1959

[36]BRIDGMAN, P. W., *The Physics of High Pressure*, G. Bell and Sons, London, 1952, p. 32

[37]BRIDGMAN, P. W., *Proc. Amer. Acad. Arts Sci.*, **74**, 1942, p. 13

[38]STEVENSON, R., *J. chem. Phys.*, **27,** 1957, p. 656

[39]SWENSON, C. A., *Physics at High Pressure, Solid State Physics*, F. SEITZ and D. TURNBULL, Eds., Academic Press, New York; Vol. 11, 1960, p. 41

[40]STEWART, J. W. and LaROCK, R. I., *J. chem. Phys.*, **28,** 1958, p. 425

[41]STEWART, J. W., *J. chem. Phys.* (to be published)

[42]FISKE, M. D., Private communication, 1957

[43]JENNINGS, L. D. and SWENSON, C. A., *Phys. Rev.*, **112,** 1958, p. 31

[44]McCORMICK, W. D. and FAIRBANK, W., *Bull. Amer. phys. Soc.*, **113,** 1958, p. 166

[5]HATTON, J., *Phys. Rev.*, **100,** 1955, p. 681

[6]HATTON, J., *Phys. Rev.*, **103,** 1956, p. 1,167

[47]BRIDGMAN, P. W., *Proc. Amer. Acad. Arts Sci.*, **74,** 1940, p. 11

[48]WARSCHAUER, D. M. and PAUL, W., *Rev. Sci. Instrum.*, **29,** 1958, p. 675

[49]BRIDGMAN, P. W., *Proc. Amer. Acad. Arts Sci.*, **74,** 1940, p. 21

[50]HALL, H. T., *Rev. Sci. Instrum.*, **31,** 1960, p. 125

[51]WILSON, W. B., *Rev. Sci. Instrum.*, **31,** 1960, p. 331

11

DYNAMIC HIGH-PRESSURE TECHNIQUES

W. E. DEAL, JR.

University of California
Los Alamos Scientific Laboratory
Los Alamos, New Mexico

I. Introduction

AT THE beginning of the twentieth century Bridgman's classic work[1,2] in the field of high-pressure physics was just beginning. Many of the techniques and even materials which enable static high pressure work today in the hundred kilobar (one bar $= 10^6$ dynes/cm$^2 = 0\cdot987$ atmosphere) range were still to be developed. Yet at this same time, several hundred kilobar dynamic pressures were available from explosives (such as TNT) which had already been discovered and used. Dynamic pressures over a hundred kilobars were also available from impact of projectiles with targets. At the same time much of the general mathematical theory of detonation and shock waves had been or was being founded by Chapman, Jouguet, Riemann, Rankine, Lord Rayleigh, and Hugoniot. It was not until during World War II, however, that theoretical and experimental technique developments had progressed sufficiently to allow accurate quantitative measurements of these dynamic high pressures and their effects to be made. Present-day techniques enable precision measurement of dynamic pressures of over five megabars in some heavy materials of high shock impedance. Many interesting physical effects can be studied in this great extension of the pressure range over that attainable statically. The remarkable extension is, however, not without some penalty. The pressures exist only behind rapidly-moving shock waves and their duration at any one spot is measured in microseconds.

Although the description of dynamic high pressure techniques given here is certainly not exhaustive, the most popular and productive of them are included. It should be recognized that no attempt has been made to credit the originators of each technique in the reference list; only a few representative papers are cited.

II. Strong Shock Hydrodynamics

(i) Shock Waves

Shock waves are particularly interesting phenomena of nature brought about by the property of most materials to transmit sound at a speed which increases with pressure beyond an initial linear region. Thus a simple compressional wave of greater amplitude than some minimum amplitude gradually becomes steeper and steeper with travel until it becomes virtually a mathematical discontinuity. Viscosity and heat conductivity tend to smooth out the discontinuity, but in most solids and liquids shock 'thicknesses' are less than can be measured. The velocity of travel of a shock wave can be shown[3] to be always greater than the sound velocity in the unshocked medium ahead of the shock but less than the sound velocity in the shocked medium immediately behind the shock. The particles of matter engulfed by a shock are given a velocity in the direction of travel of the shock which is obviously related to shock velocity and compression.

(ii) The Conservation Relations

This relation and others of some significance in the field of dynamic high pressures can be derived by application of the physical laws of conservation of mass, momentum, and energy across a shock wave. In considering shock waves mathematically, let U_s be shock velocity, U_p particle velocity, ρ density, the reciprocal of specific volume V, P pressure, E specific internal energy, and let a subscript zero refer to conditions ahead of the advancing shock. Consider the mass flux per unit area both into and out of the shock front. This quantity is the product of the material density and the particle velocity relative to the shock front, $\rho_0(U_s - U_{p0})$ ahead of the shock and $\rho(U_s - U_p)$ behind the shock. Thus for the mass conservation relation one has

$$V/V_0 = \rho_0/\rho = (U_s - U_p)/(U_s - U_{p0}) \tag{1}$$

Momentum conservation is expressed by Newton's second law $F = m\,du/dt$. The force per unit area across the shock front is the pressure difference $P - P_0$, the mass flux per unit area is $\rho_0(U_s - U_{p0})$, and the material velocity change is $(U_p - U_{p0})$. Thus one has the momentum conservation relation,

$$P - P_0 = \rho_0(U_s - U_{p0})\ (U_p - U_{p0}) \tag{2}$$

Energy conservation across the shock front can be expressed by equating the work done per unit area per unit time by the pressure forces, $PU_p - P_0 U_{p0}$, to the sum of the kinetic energy change $\frac{1}{2}\rho_0(U_s - U_{p0})\ (U_p^2 - U_{p0}^2)$ and the internal energy change $\rho_0\ (U_s - U_{p0})\ (E - E_0)$

$$PU_p - P_0 U_{p0} = \frac{1}{2}\rho_0(U_s - U_{p0})\ (U_p^2 - U_{p0}^2) + \rho_0(U_s - U_{p0})\ (E - E_0) \tag{3}$$

From the mass and momentum conservation equations one can obtain

$$(U_s - U_{p0}) = V_0(P - P_0)^{\frac{1}{2}}\ (V_0 - V)^{-\frac{1}{2}} \tag{4}$$

and

$$(U_p - U_{p0}) = (P - P_0)^{\frac{1}{2}}\ (V_0 - V)^{\frac{1}{2}} \tag{5}$$

These can then be used to eliminate velocities and thus simplify the energy conservation equation to the more usual form,

$$E - E_0 = \frac{1}{2}(P + P_0)\ (V_0 - V) \tag{6}$$

This was first introduced by Hugoniot and is hence called the Hugoniot equation. The equations (1) to (6) are most commonly used in the slightly simplified form obtained by consideration of a stationary state ahead of the shock with zero U_{p0}. Initial pressure P_0 may also frequently be neglected in dynamic experimentation where P is usually quite a bit larger.

The internal energy of a material at any arbitrary pressure and volume is a function of that pressure and volume. This relationship is the equation of state of the material. Thus if the equation of state is known, the relation between pressure and volume follows from the Hugoniot equation, and shock and particle velocities follow from the other conservation equations.

(iii) Useful Representations

The pressure–volume relation obtained by combination of the equation of state and the Hugoniot equation defines a curve (the Hugoniot) in the P–V plane which is the locus of all possible states which can be attained by shocking the material from the original state P_0, V_0. *Figure 1* illustrates the form of such a Hugoniot curve. The straight line connecting the initial state P_0, V_0 to the state behind a shock P_1, V_1 has a slope of $(\rho_0 U_{s1})^2$ as is seen from equation (4) for zero U_{p0}.

Hugoniot curves can also be plotted in each of the other nine planes

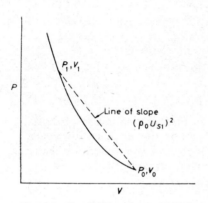

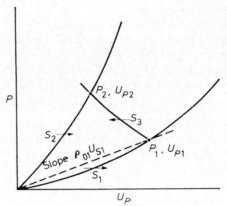

Figure 1. Shock Hugoniot in *P–V* plane   Figure 2. Interaction of a shock at an interface to a second material of higher shock impedance

possible by pairing the five variables of the conservation equations; however, only two of these are of interest—the P–U_p plane and the U_s–U_p plane. The former is particularly useful when considering the traversal of a shock across a boundary between two materials. It is the pressure and particle velocity which are continuous across such interfaces. This continuity is represented in the P–U_p plane as the intersection of two Hugoniot curves. *Figure 2* illustrates such an interaction. A plane shock S_1 of pressure P_1 and particle velocity U_{p1} moving into an undistributed medium of relatively low shock impedance* $(\rho_{01} U_{s1})$ transforms this first material from a pressure $P_0 \ll P_1$ and zero particle velocity to pressure P_1 and U_{p1}. The slope of the straight line connecting the initial state with P_1, U_{p1} is seen to be $\rho_{01} U_{s1}$ from the momentum conservation equation. When this shock strikes an interface to a medium of higher relative shock impedance, a shock S_2 is transmitted forward into the second medium, transforming it from the same low-pressure stationary state as the first material to the state P_2, U_{p2}. Reflected back into the first material, which is now at state P_1, U_{p1}, is a

---

* Shock impedance is defined as initial material density times the shock velocity, and thus varies with pressure.

shock S_3 which slows that material down to U_{p2} and increases its pressure to P_2. The Hugoniot curve labelled S_3 differs from a mirror image of S_1 only slightly. This difference is caused by the difference in initial states. *Figure 3* shows the pressure–distance profiles of the shocks before and after such an interaction. This type of plot is frequently helpful in conjunction with $P–U_p$ curves for visualizing the sequence of events.

The $U_s–U_p$ plane is of interest to the experimentalist in particular because it is these two quantities which are the most amenable to measurement, and it is here that 'raw' data can be plotted. The fact that practically all solids and liquids exhibit a linear U_s versus U_p relationship will be utilized later.

Of equal importance to shock waves in dynamic high-pressure work are the adiabatic pressure release waves. Consider, for example, a plane shock wave of P_1, U_{p1} which impinges upon a free surface. At the instant of

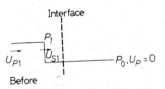

Figure 3. 'Before and after' pressure profiles of the shock waves considered in the interaction of *Figure 2*

arrival of the shock at the surface, one has simply a reservoir of highly-compressed material (moving at velocity U_{p1}) free to expand outward into the unoccupied volume. This expansion is accomplished by an adiabatic rarefaction (sound) wave propagating back through the medium. The first infinitesimal release wave which starts to propagate at sound velocity back into the highly compressed medium a distance Δx reduces the pressure ΔP; the next infinitesimal wave must then travel at a lower velocity than the original one, since the pressure has been reduced. Thus one has a continual stretching out of the originally discontinuous rarefaction. The potential compressional energy released by the rarefaction wave shows up upon complete pressure release as additional particle velocity U_{r1} added to the original shock-induced particle velocity U_{p1}. From solution of the one-dimensional continuous flow equations[4] one has the Riemann integral

$$U_{r1} = \int_{\rho_0}^{P_1} (c/\rho) \, \mathrm{d}\rho = \int_{P_0}^{P_1} -(\partial V/\partial P)_S \, \mathrm{d}P \qquad (7)$$

where c is the sound speed and the subscript S refers to constancy of entropy. The fact that U_{r1} very nearly equals U_{p1} for most solids was established by Walsh and Christian[5]. In fact, in the $P–U_p$ plane the release adiabats from a given pressure are very nearly mirror images across the constant U_p

line corresponding to that pressure on the Hugoniot. The release adiabat from a given shock state is the locus of all possible states which can be achieved by propagation of a rarefaction wave into the high-pressure state. In contrast to the Hugoniot loci, where only the initial and final states are considered significant, these rarefaction loci describe all states between initial and final with a describable time sequence.

Figure 4 illustrates in the P–U_p plane how a shock S of P_1, U_{p1} interacts at a free surface by propagation of a rarefaction R back into the shock: this imparts an additional particle velocity U_{r1} to give the free-surface velocity U_{fs1} at zero pressure. If, instead of a free surface, an interface with a material of lower shock impedance had been present, the same

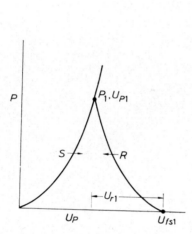

Figure 4. Shock interaction at a free surface

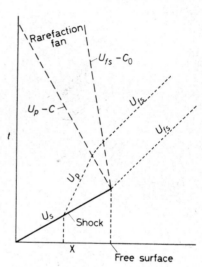

Figure 5. Distance versus time plot for the interaction of *Figure 4*. Short dashed lines are particle paths. Symbols on lines are dx/dt slopes

rarefaction locus would have been used except that its intersection with the Hugoniot of the material of lower shock impedance would then describe the state at the interface.

Omitted in earlier discussion because of its limited usefulness for shocks, the distance–time $(x$–$t)$ plane serves as a very useful tool for visualizing time histories of rarefaction interactions with shocks. *Figure 5* illustrates the interaction of *Figure 4* in the x–t plane.

III. Equation of State from Experimental Data

It was stated above that if the P,V,E equation of state is known, the relations among E, P, V, U_s and U_p for all possible shocks follow from the conservation equations. Conversely, if any two of these quantities can be measured, the other three follow from the conservation equations and one has determined the part of the P,V,E equation of state along the Hugoniot.

Theoretical arguments may then be used to extend this P,V,E equation of state to an area of the $P-V$ plane neighbouring the Hugoniot[6]. Temperatures both along the Hugoniot and at other points in the P,V plane can also be calculated.

Shock velocity is a readily measurable quantity by a number of techniques, but particle velocity cannot be so directly obtained. A quantity which *is* directly measurable, the free-surface velocity U_{fs}, is very close to twice the particle velocity, however. Measurement of U_s and U_{fs} thus give a first approximation to the equation of state along the Hugoniot. With this close approximation and with certain reasonable assumptions, a correction factor (usually about 1 per cent in P and V) can be calculated, and by rapidly convergent successive iteration the slight inaccuracy of the original assumption can be eliminated to yield the equation of state along the Hugoniot, and indeed in a substantial region neighbouring the Hugoniot.

To reiterate, including the equations[6], U_s and U_{fs} are measured in a given experiment. One assumes

$$U_p = U_{fs}/2 \quad \text{or} \quad U_r/U_p = 1 \tag{8}$$

then

$$P = \rho_0 U_s U_p \tag{9}$$

$$V/V_0 = (U_s - U_p)/U_s \tag{10}$$

and

$$E - E_0 = (P/2)(V_0 - V) \tag{11}$$

When this measurement is accomplished for a number of pressures, a first approximation Hugoniot is defined.

Combination of the Mie–Grüneisen equation of state

$$P - P_K = (\gamma/V)(E - E_K) \tag{12}$$

where the subscript K refers to the 0°K isotherm, with the Dugdale–MacDonald modification of a formula by Slater,

$$\gamma = -\frac{V}{2}\left[\frac{\mathrm{d}^2(PV^{2/3})/\mathrm{d}V^2}{\mathrm{d}(PV^{2/3})/\mathrm{d}V}\right] - \frac{1}{3} \tag{13}$$

assumed valid at 0°K only, then yields the following equation for the pressure along the 0°K isotherm $P_K(V)$ in terms of the experimental Hugoniot curve, $P_H(V)$

$$-\frac{V}{2}\left[\frac{\mathrm{d}^2(P_K V^{2/3})/\mathrm{d}V^2}{\mathrm{d}(P_K V^{2/3})/\mathrm{d}V}\right] - \frac{1}{3} = \frac{V(P_H - P_K)}{(P_H/2)(V_{0H} - V) + E_{0H} + \displaystyle\int_{V_{0K}}^{V} P\,\mathrm{d}V} \tag{14}$$

Initial conditions of specific volume, compressibility at zero pressure and 0°K, and specific internal energy at the foot of the Hugoniot E_{0H} (relative to an arbitrary zero energy at zero pressure and 0°K) enable equation (14) to be integrated numerically using a high-speed digital computer to yield 0°K pressure–volume curves. Equation (13) may then be used to establish γ versus V curves. Differentiation of another form of equation (12)

$$P - P_H = (\gamma/V)(E - E_H) \tag{15}$$

where the subscript H refers to the known Hugoniot, gives

$$P_A = -\frac{\mathrm{d}E_H}{\mathrm{d}V} + (P_H - P_A)\frac{\mathrm{d}}{\mathrm{d}V}\left[\frac{V}{\gamma}\right] + \frac{V}{\gamma}\left[\frac{\mathrm{d}P_H}{\mathrm{d}V} - \frac{\mathrm{d}P_A}{\mathrm{d}V}\right] \tag{16}$$

This is a first-order differential equation for an adiabat $P_A(V)$ in terms of the known $P_H(V), E_H(V)$ and $\gamma(V)$. Numerical integration of this equation gives adiabats in the P–V plane. One can now also integrate

$$\frac{U_r}{U_p} = \int_0^{P_H} \frac{(-dV/dP_A)^{\frac{1}{2}} \, dP_A}{[P_H(V_{oH}-V)]^{\frac{1}{2}}} \tag{17}$$

to give a refinement of the original assumption, equation (8). Successive execution of this process beginning at equation (9) not only refines the original assumption but generates a complete P,V,E equation of state from the Hugoniot data, subject to the limitations of the Mie–Grüneisen equation and the Dugdale-MacDonald relation employed at 0°K. In practice, only one cycle of iteration is usually necessary, even for high precision, because of the wide range of validity of equation (8).

Temperatures can be calculated along the adiabats using

$$T = T_i \exp\left[-\int_{V_i}^{V} (\gamma/V) dV \right] \tag{18}$$

where T_i and V_i are obtained from thermal expansion data at zero pressure.

An alternative, simpler scheme for generation of the equation of state uses, instead of the Dugdale-MacDonald formula, the dependence of the Grüneisen gamma on volume alone and an assumed constancy of $(\partial E/\partial P)_V$ in the vicinity of the Hugoniot. This latter assumption can be justified because the resulting equations of state reproduce those of the more complex procedure above well. Differentiation of the Mie–Grüneisen equation gives

$$\gamma = V/(\partial E/\partial P)_V = -[V(\partial P/\partial V)_S(\partial V/\partial T)_P]/C_P \tag{19}$$

The use of experimental data at zero pressure for the bulk modulus, thermal expansion coefficient, and specific heat in the third expression of equation (19) gives a 'thermodynamic' gamma at zero pressure, γ_{oT}. Assumption of constancy of $(\partial E/\partial P)_V$ in the vicinity of the Hugoniot then yields $\gamma(V)$ which may be used in the Mie–Grüneisen equation. Adiabats may be calculated, the ratio U_r/U_p determined, and temperatures obtained as before.

As mentioned earlier, practically all solids and liquids exhibit a linear U_s versus U_p relationship

$$U_s = C + SU_p \tag{20}$$

The limiting value of U_s as $V \to V_0$ and $P \to P_0$ from equation (4) is

$$C = V_0\left[-(\partial P/\partial V)_S \right]^{\frac{1}{2}} \tag{21}$$

a relation which, when evaluated from static compressibility data with slight correction for the difference between isothermal and isentropic derivatives, serves as an additional data point for the linear data fits. Use of equation (20) in conjunction with equations (4) and (5) yields upon insertion in the Dugdale–MacDonald relation an 'experimental' Grüneisen gamma at zero pressure

$$\gamma_{oE} = 2S - 1 \tag{22}$$

206

This may be compared[6] as a consistency check to the γ_{0T} obtained from equation (19).

IV. Generation of High Pressure Shock Waves

(i) Detonation Waves

Detonation of an explosive is accomplished by the propagation through the explosive of a wave of chemical reaction from a point or points of initiation of the reaction. This detonation wave is much like a shock in an inert material, but differs in that the exothermic reaction at or closely behind the front is constantly supplying energy to the wave. It differs also in that the $E(P,V)$ function for the reaction products is different from that for the original explosive. A detonation wave also differs from simple burning (deflagration) in that the pressure and density both increase behind a detonation wave while they both decrease behind a deflagration wave. Let us consider a simplified steady-state detonation wave process in the P–V plane (*Figure 6*). An explosive in state $P=0$, $V=V_0$ is shocked

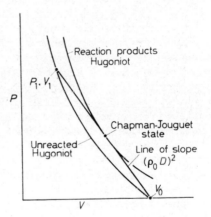

Figure 6. Detonation process in the P–V plane

to state P_1, V_1 by a detonation wave moving at velocity D. In the process of being shocked, the explosive is compressed and heated and begins to react. As it reacts its Hugoniot function changes and the state of the material changes from P_1, V_1 to the Chapman–Jouguet (C-J) state indicated on the Hugoniot of completely reacted products. This change must take place along the line of slope $(\rho_0 D)^2$, the Rayleigh line, because the steady-state reaction profile is moving at constant velocity. The reaction zone thickness is in general very short and there has been some difficulty even in recent times in efforts to measure its thickness. If the explosive considered were infinite in extent, the material behind the C-J state of the wave would remain in this state. In reality, explosives are finite in extent and the C-J state is relieved by a rarefaction wave from the rear of the explosive, the so-called Taylor wave. Thus the generally accepted structure of a plane steady-state detonation wave is a shock followed by a reaction zone of rapidly decreasing pressure (the von Neumann spike[7]) terminating at the

C-J plane. Flow behind this plane of complete reaction is essentially a rarefaction wave (the Taylor wave[8]) centred at the rear of the explosive.

(ii) Specific Explosives

There is a wide variety of chemical compounds which will exhibit the phenomenon of detonation, but only a few of these have the properties of comparative safety, homogeneity, and ease of shape fabrication which make them useful for dynamic high-pressure studies. The same properties are of interest for military applications; hence many of the explosives used are the commonly used military explosives. These explosives are frequently classified (for sensitivity) as initiating, or primary, explosives and high explosives. The difference is not distinct, however, and the division is somewhat arbitrary since there is a complete spectrum of sensitivities and ordering of materials in this spectrum depends upon the type of sensitivity test employed.

The most commonly encountered explosives in dynamic high pressure work are PETN (pentaerythritoltetranitrate), tetryl (trinitrophenylmethylnitramine), TNT (trinitrotoluene), RDX (cyclotrimethylenetrinitramine), and HMX (cyclotetramethylenetetranitramine). In application it is really various mixtures of explosives that are commonly employed. For example, the relatively low melting point of TNT (81°C) makes it a particularly convenient binder for making cast mixtures with other explosives usually of higher performance. A mixture of 60 per cent RDX to 40 per cent TNT by weight is the very common Composition B explosive, while a 75/25 ratio gives the commonly used 75/25 Cyclotol. An 80/20 mixture of HMX/TNT is called Octol, while a 50/50 ratio of PETN/TNT is Pentolite. Various inert materials such as barium nitrate or sodium chloride may also be added to TNT to provide explosives of lower performance. Other binders for these various explosives may be used to satisfy a variety of purposes. The several Composition C explosives, for example, are mixtures with a main explosive component of RDX and are hand-mouldable plastic explosives which can be readily shaped to almost any form desired. Insensitive liquid explosives such as nitromethane are also convenient for some applications.

The TNT binder explosives, when molten, can be poured into moulds and cast to a variety of shapes. Considerable care must be exercised in cooling the moulds so as to yield homogeneous castings. Machining of the better portion of such a casting with appropriate coolant can then yield the large uniform pieces (e.g. 4 in. thick by 10 in. diameter) with plane and parallel faces and high-quality finish which are desirable for dynamic high-pressure work. These pieces can also be made by compacting a suitably prepared explosive moulding powder in a hydrostatic press. Usually it is then desirable to remove the 'skin' of such a pressing by machining.

(iii) Plane-Wave Generators

Detonators of use for dynamic high-pressure techniques are made up of a small quantity of one of the primary explosives in contact with a bridge-wire. This wire is energized by an electric current and initiates detonation

208

in the primary explosive. A small pellet of an explosive of intermediate sensitivity (called a booster, and usually of pressed tetryl) is often necessary between the detonator and the high explosive to assure initiation of high-order detonation. Since the detonator and booster pellet are both small, the wave generated by them when placed on a large block of high explosive is very nearly spherical. Plane waves are quite desirable for most experiments in the dynamic high-pressure field because of the relative ease of analysis of results. These plane waves can be obtained by mounting a detonator-booster combination on a lens-like combination of a fast and slow detonating explosive called a plane-wave generator. *Figure 7* shows a schematic of such a lens. The angle of the cone required is obviously determined by the ratio of the explosive detonation velocities. A typical combination of explosives might be Composition B, with a velocity of 0·8 cm/μsec, and 75 per cent barium nitrate-loaded TNT (Baratol), with a

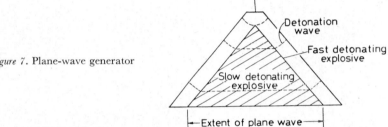

Figure 7. Plane-wave generator

velocity of 0·49 cm/μsec. Other schemes exist for generation of plane detonation waves, but in general they are not as satisfactory for dynamic high-pressure experimentation as the foregoing.

(iv) A Typical Explosive High-Pressure Experiment

The plane-wave generator is usually used in conjunction with a block of high explosive with plane and parallel faces. This block in turn is in contact with a metal plate in which, or on the opposite face of which, the high pressure experiment is performed. A typical experiment at the Los Alamos Scientific Laboratory, for example, might employ a plane-wave generator of 8 in. aperture delivering a detonation wave flat to 0·5 mm or better into a 4 in. thick, 8 in. diameter, uniform cylinder of Composition B. The C-J pressure for this explosive is about 290 kilobars ($4·4 \times 10^6$ psi)[9,10]. The detonation wave in traversing this 4 in. thickness of homogeneous (in composition and density) Composition B loses little in planarity, but the variation of pressure with distance behind the detonation wave is less rapid in the centre than near the edges of the charge, where there is a zone which can be reached by a sonic disturbance from the edge. A 2024 aluminium alloy plate of $\frac{1}{2}$ in. thickness might ordinarily be placed in contact with the plane face of the explosive opposite the plane-wave generator. Shock velocity (0·741 cm/μsec) and free-surface velocity (0·309 cm/μsec) might then be measured at the one-half inch level in this plate. These velocities suffice, along with the known initial plate density, to determine a point on the Hugoniot of 2024 aluminium alloy ($P=319$ kilobars, $V/V_0=0\cdot791$) by use of the conservation relations. In traversing the plate, the shock edges begin to lag back in the region which can be reached by a sonic disturbance from the edge (about one plate thickness along a radius). A lesser effect which contributes curvature to the shock wave is the aforementioned non-uniformity of pressure profile behind the detonation wave. This effect causes little difficulty for relatively thin plates, such as the example considered, when measurements are made before successive shock and rarefaction reverberations can occur.

Control of shock pressure in a plate from shot to shot can be accomplished by use of different explosives; however, one is usually limited in this variation to several conveniently available explosives. Further variation may be accomplished by use of various plate thicknesses to allow Taylor-wave shock attenuation or by use of intermediate 'impedance mismatch' plates which deliver a shock of calculable lower strength to the experimental assembly. Both of these latter techniques have the disadvantage of introduction of more wave curvature (because of the additional plate thickness) arising from both of the aforementioned effects.

(v) The Free-Run Technique

A 'free-run' geometry[11,12] has proved very useful for obtaining even higher pressures than obtainable in plates in contact with explosives. The technique consists of acceleration of a relatively thin projectile plate by a plane-wave explosive system. After an inch or two of run this plate strikes

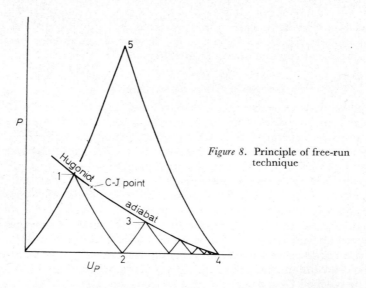

Figure 8. Principle of free-run technique

the target plate on which the experiment is located. Consider the example illustrated in Figure 8, where the target and projectile plate are of the same material and the projectile plate is quite thin relative to the explosive thickness. An explosive at its C-J state shocks the metal projectile plate to state 1, and the free-surface release wave accelerates the plate to state 2. This release wave is reflected at the metal-reaction products interface as a shock to state 3; a rarefaction is also transmitted into the reaction products to bring them to the same state. Successive reflections of this type accelerate the projectile plate to state 4. When this high-velocity plate strikes the target plate, high-pressure state 5 is achieved behind the shock wave, which travels in each plate outward from the plane of contact. The duration of the high pressure is dependent primarily upon the projectile plate thickness. In principle a series of such systems where the target in intermediate stages would be an explosive-projectile plate assembly should enable one to achieve any arbitrarily high pressure. In reality, breakup of the secondary projectile plate and loss of planarity in free-run are so severe as to discourage attempts at even double-free-run experiments. Even higher pressures than for the plane-wave single-free-run geometry are in principle also attainable by more sophisticated wave shaping, employing convergence, but measurements and analysis are rendered more difficult because simple plane-wave shock hydrodynamics is no longer applicable.

(vi) Shock Waves From Projectiles

Plane-wave shocks of reasonably high pressure can also be generated by the impact of rapidly-moving flat-ended projectiles into target plates of interest. Projectiles may be accelerated to high velocity by several means, the most practical being the ancient technique of burning confined propellant and the almost equally simple use of high pressure inert gas. In most uses of the gun for precision dynamic high-pressure work the projectile is allowed to strike the target before it actually leaves the gun, primarily because of the severe difficulty entailed by the tilt of the wave which an unguided projectile generates. As with explosives, there is a loss of useful area of the plane shock in the target because of propagation of sonic release waves from the periphery. In order to have a large area of plane shock adequate for convenient measurement, large diameter guns are used. For example, the Los Alamos Scientific Laboratory uses a $6\frac{1}{2}$ in. diameter smooth-bore cannon to accelerate projectiles up to about $0\cdot1$ cm/μsec for such purposes. Smaller diameters down to perhaps one inch may be used with the advantage of higher conveniently available velocities, but the useful area of measurement is severely limited. Pressures in plane shock waves of appreciable area attainable by gun techniques are not nearly so high as those which one gets by explosive techniques (at least with currently available guns). Gun techniques do have the advantages over explosive techniques, however, that lower-pressure shock waves can be more conveniently obtained and that these pressures can be varied at will from shot to shot simply by using various amounts of propellant.

V. Optical Techniques

Measurement techniques employed in studies of strong shock waves in solids and liquids may be simply classified as optical, electrical, radiographic, and recovery. By far the greater number of measurements has been made by the first two classes of these techniques. A number of the most popular methods of dynamic high-pressure study will be described below in the order listed here. No pretence of completeness of coverage is made; in particular, techniques involving shock waves which are appreciably curved are mostly not mentioned.

(i) The Smear Camera

The simplest measurements to be made for determination of a Hugoniot curve for a material are determinations of shock and free-surface velocities. The optical device used for this is the smear or streak camera, sometimes called a sweeping image chronograph. In its simplest form (*Figure 9*) it consists of an objective lens which focuses an object via a rotating mirror onto a film surface. The brightness of the object and motion parallel to the axis of mirror rotation are thus recorded as a function of the rotating mirror position. If this mirror is rotating at known constant speed and some shuttering mechanism is available to prevent overwrite (multiple exposure),

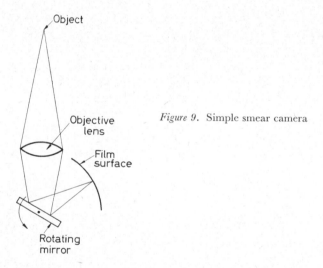

Figure 9. Simple smear camera

the object brightness and motion are recorded as a function of time. If a 50 cm optical lever arm (rotating mirror to film surface distance) and a mirror speed of 1,000 rps are employed, the writing speed of the camera will be $0·63$ cm/μsec—a value comparable to detonation velocities and one which makes possible time resolution of one shake ($0·01$ μsec) or better.

Most objects are not point sources which move parallel to the mirror axis of rotation, so it is desirable to use a slit parallel to the mirror axis in the optical system. This is most frequently placed at a real image formed in the object position of *Figure 9* by another objective lens. The slit can also be placed directly in front of the object. In using a smear camera as a precision interval-measuring device, it is imperative that the writing speed, as well as its variation with position on the film, be measured to high precision and remain unchanged from experiment to experiment.

At 1,000 rps the mirror of a camera will be available for a second exposure in one millisecond. Mechanical shutters operating at times as short as this for the large aperture lenses used in smear cameras are not available, so some explosive-shuttering technique is usually used in conjunction with a slower mechanical shutter. This is done by shattering or spraying with an opaque covering a glass plate through which the light passes, or moving and destroying a turning mirror in the optical path.

(ii) Velocities From Transit Times Using Flash Gaps

Velocity determinations with smear cameras are of a wide variety of types, but may be grouped into two categories: (1) those where only brightness as a function of time is measured from the film record with the relevant distance measured independently; and (2) those where one spatial position as well as time is required to be measured on the film. Each of these types might be further vaguely divided according to whether the event studied is self-luminous or requires external illumination. Let us consider a shock-velocity measurement of the first type where the event is self-luminous. A thin disc of the material of interest of thickness d (*Figure 10*) may be placed

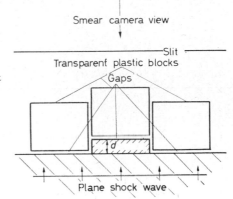

Figure 10. Shock velocity measurement from transit time using flash gaps

on a plate through the opposite face of which an explosive system or a projectile will drive a plane shock wave. When the shock wave reaches the plate surface in the plane of the base of the disc, it will accelerate this surface and close the gaps between the plate and the two lateral plastic blocks. If these gaps are filled with a gas such as air, argon, or xenon (listed in increasing order of potential brightness), this gas will be heated and compressed by the successive gas shock reverberations and become brilliantly luminous for a short time before heating of the plastic effectively cuts off the light. Gaps of $0 \cdot 003$ to $0 \cdot 004$ in. thicknesses are commonly used in conjunction with blocks of Plexiglas (Perspex). Glass blocks have been used, but do not give the clean cut-off or quenching of the light given by plastic.

When a plane shock enters the sample disc of *Figure 10*, peripheral rarefactions will begin to reduce its pressure at the edges, and hence cause the shock wave there to lag back. Care must thus be taken to ensure that the thickness-to-diameter ratio is small enough for an appreciable area of the shock to be left unaffected. When this plane portion of the shock emerges at the top of the disc, the same gap closure mechanism takes place as did at the base. A smear-camera record from such an assembly appears as shown schematically in *Figure 11*. Interpolation between the lateral base reference traces gives the time of entrance of the shock into the disc and the top trace gives the time of arrival at the top. Knowledge of camera writing speed then gives the transit time; and if the pellet thickness is measured beforehand, one has a direct measure of velocity. Care must be taken that the gaps at the base and top of the disc are identical and that

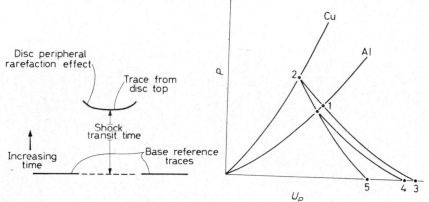

Figure 11. Schematic smear-camera record of shock transit time for assembly of *Figure 10*

Figure 12. Gap closure velocity examples

the velocities of closure are the same. Consider the example of a copper disc on an aluminium plate. *Figure 12* illustrates several possibilities for gap closure velocities. If the aluminium shock is at state 1, the base gaps will be closed at free surface velocity 3. The copper disc will be shocked to state 2 and will close the gap at velocity 5. Time data generated in such a manner requires correction for the difference in gap closure times. However, if a thin copper shim is placed beneath each gap, both gaps are closed at velocity 5 and no correction is necessary. Aluminium shims, on the other hand, would close the gaps at the different velocities 3 and 4; hence aluminium would not be a good choice.

Gap fillings of hollow, microscopic, translucent plastic spheres embedded in a translucent hardening vehicle have been used in some types of experiments. Also, though not often practicable, it is possible with sufficiently high free-surface velocity and enough camera aperture and film speed to delete the clear plastic blocks entirely and use merely the luminosity of the first gas shock generated by free-surface motion for timing information.

Free-surface velocity may be measured by use of an assembly like that of *Figure 10* except that the disc is deleted and free-run of the plate through distance d is allowed. With this arrangement light from the central portion of the assembly would begin as soon as the luminous shock was generated in the gas and would increase in intensity at later times after successive reflections of the gas shock, presumably extinguishing just before arrival of the surface when sufficient heating of the plastic is accomplished. The time of free-surface transit could then be read from beginning of shock light to extinction. A better scheme, which depends upon similar light-generating mechanisms at each plane of interest, would be to use the time difference between extinction of the lateral reference traces and of the central record. A still more convenient and practical technique is to use identical shim-covered gaps at all three positions; comparator reduction of the film record is then much easier and more precise because centres of thin traces are read, rather than edges. In a free-surface velocity measurement of this type the inner edges of the lateral reference blocks propagate a disturbance inward along the free-running surface which slows down this surface; consequently, the thickness to width ratio of this space must be kept small enough to prevent the disturbances from affecting the entire surface before the measurement is accomplished. Care must also be taken in free-surface velocity determinations that free-run distance is kept small enough for measurement to be concluded before the rarefaction from the front surface can have time to be reflected from the rear surface of the plate (as either a shock or rarefaction) and again reach the front surface.

(iii) Velocities From Wedges Using a Flash Gap

A second simple flash-gap technique involves the measurement of distance as well as time from the photographic record. *Figure 13* shows such an arrangement where an inclined plane is cut into a plane-wave shocked plate. A shim-covered gap backed by a clear plastic block is placed as shown. As the shock runs through the last portion of the plate, the gap is closed

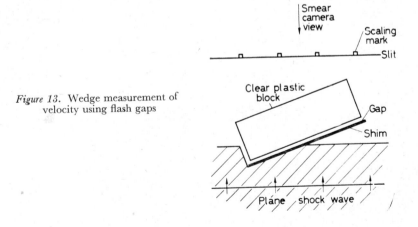

Figure 13. Wedge measurement of velocity using flash gaps

progressively at shock phase velocity up the inclined plane. After the shock reaches the free surface, the gap closure is at free-surface phase velocity. The smear camera records through the slit with scaling markers a spot of light which moves perpendicular to the sweep direction successively at two

215

different constant velocities. The film record is thus a pair of straight-line traces inclined at different angles to the camera sweep direction. Knowledge of the inclined plane angle, the scaling marker spacing, and camera writing speed enable use of the trace slopes to obtain shock and free-surface velocities. Provision for simultaneous determination of wave curvature and tilt must also be included in such an experimental assembly to allow detailed correction of the data for any such effects.

(iv) Impedance Matching

It is sometimes convenient (as in the case of liquids[13,14]) to embed a sample in a plate such that the outer surfaces are coplanar. A flash-gap record across such a surface yields the difference in shock transit time between the plate material and the embedded material. In this case as well as in many simple pellet experiments it is also desirable to use a base plate

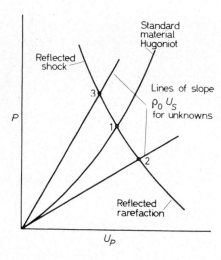

Figure 14. Impedance matching

of a 'standard' material of previously determined Hugoniot and employ the technique of impedance matching so that only one velocity for the unknown sample need be measured. Figure 14 illustrates the technique for two unknown materials, one of lower and one of higher shock impedance than the standard. A velocity is measured in the standard material to establish state 1 on the known Hugoniot. The reflected rarefaction adiabat or the reflected shock Hugoniot from state 1 is constructed. The coordinates of the intersection of the line of slope $\rho_0 U_s$ for the unknown with the applicable curve from state 1 thus suffices to determine a point on the unknown Hugoniot.

(v) Change of Reflectivity as a Shock Detector

When a plane shock wave in a solid arrives at an optically reflective free surface, the reflectivity is almost always considerably reduced. Also, if specular illumination of a highly reflective surface is employed, tilt of the surface by shock acceleration will almost completely eliminate light received by a viewing camera. Either of these effects may be used in conjunction with a smear camera to measure shock velocities in a manner analogous to the flash-gap methods previously described. Free-surface velocity may be determined by the additional use of the change in reflectivity or tilt of thin films (such as aluminized mylar) suspended a known distance from the surface to be studied.

Such techniques require an illuminating source of light of relatively constant intensity usually over an interval of tens of microseconds. This light may be generated by: (1) the explosion of a metallic wire by a condenser discharge (usually in a gas such as argon); (2) an electric discharge through argon or xenon; or (3) propagation of an explosive-generated shock through such a gas. The ease of application of the latter method makes it most appealing where other considerations such as desire for recovery of shot fragments or excess of the explosive limit of the firing site are not overriding. In its simplest form such a 'flash' is comprised of an explosive charge at one end of a tube of argon, the opposite end of which has a transparent or translucent covering. The high-velocity ($0\cdot7$ to $0\cdot8$ cm/μsec) expansion of the detonation products acts as a piston to generate a very brilliant shock wave which traverses the argon-filled tube. Duration of such a flash is, of course, governed by the gas-shock transit time down the tube.

(vi) Other Reflection Techniques

Though there is a reduction in reflectivity of a plate when a shock strikes a free surface, reflectivity is not completely destroyed. Thus if marks are placed on an illuminated surface, the view of such marks through a slit with a smear camera at a known angle (usually about 45°) will yield a free-surface velocity measurement (*Figure 15*). Each of the marks, after its

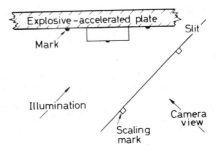

Figure 15. Reflection technique using marks

surface is accelerated, effectively moves along behind the slit at a projection of its velocity. The inclined trace resulting on the smear-camera record yields free-surface velocity, and the interval between beginnings of the inclined traces at the different levels on the plate gives shock velocity. Precision of this technique is not particularly good because of the difficulty of making marks which can be expected to stay on a surface. This drawback may be eliminated by creation of the marks by optical techniques. These may be created in a variety of ways. For example, collimated pencils of light parallel to the direction of plate motion create spots of light at fixed positions on the plate surface. If the plate has a diffusing surface, this may be viewed at an angle to obtain velocities as with fixed marks on the surface. If the surface to be studied has a mirror finish, collimated pencils of light may again be used to create light spots on the surface, but these must be viewed from the angle of reflection with the smear camera to obtain velocities. This variation of the previous technique differs in that the point of light moves across the plate surface as the surface moves; hence, planarity requirements are very strict if appreciable motion is involved. A further modification[15] of this latter technique employs a sharp edge or wire perpendicular to the smear-camera slit, but parallel and close to the plate surface. Illumination by a broad source at the specular angle relative to the viewing direction allows the camera to record position of the edge or wire and its image in the plate as a function of time. Such a record can be used to obtain free-surface velocity. This latter technique is particularly useful in studies where the total motion studied is small; hence relatively high camera magnification is usually employed.

A reflection technique utilizing an optical lever has been devised[16] which is particularly useful for studies of the small free-surface velocities generated by elastic waves[17]. By this technique image displacement on the smear camera record corresponds directly to free-surface velocity. This is accomplished in the refined plane-wave technique[18] by imaging with the camera a point light source via the reflective surface of a wedge mounted on a plane-wave shocked plate. The amount of image displacement at the film plane corresponds directly to the angle of rotation of the wedge surface as the shock traverses the region of the wedge illuminated by the source and defined by the camera limiting aperture. This angle of wedge rotation is defined by the vector addition of the shock velocity moving perpendicular to the base-plate surface and the free-surface velocity assumed normal to the wedge surface. By use of several point sources the time interval between the beginning of wedge tilt at various locations can be determined from the camera record. Thus both shock and free-surface velocities are determinable.

(vii) Two-Dimensional Photographs

A variety of methods is available for obtaining conventional two-dimensional photographs of explosively accelerated assemblies. Most applications of these methods result in primarily qualitative results. Such results, however, can be extremely valuable in that they often enable better understanding of phenomena which can then be attacked quantitatively by other techniques. One of the simplest methods of obtaining several photographs at time intervals of the order of microseconds is to use several short-duration (small gap) flash sources timed at the desired interval in conjunction with a smear camera. The use of an ordinary camera with such illumination results, of course, in multiple exposures, but such exposures are often interpretable and this technique is sometimes used. Several such conventional cameras may also be used with steady illumination to obtain sequential pictures by use of Kerr-cell shutters pulsed at various times. Several electronic image-converter tubes may also be adequately shuttered electronically to obtain a series of high-speed (but usually poorer resolution) pictures. Several techniques exist involving image dissection for obtaining a sequential or even continuous series of two-dimensional pictures. These involve reconstruction of the image by projection of the record back through the same optical system used to dissect the image; such techniques, though often clever, are usually quite complicated and awkward to use.

Probably the most convenient and versatile method of obtaining a set of ultra-high-speed photographs is by use of the Miller framing camera[19] as further developed[20] at the Los Alamos Scientific Laboratory. This type of camera can take a number (usually less than 100) of high-resolution 35 mm photographs at rates up to about eight pictures per microsecond. This is accomplished by forming with an objective lens a real image of the object to be studied on the face of a mirror capable of being rotated at high speeds (up to 24,000 rps). As this mirror rotates, it directs the cone of light defined by the limiting aperture of the objective lens successively into a series of framing lenses which form stationary images on a fixed film surface.

One typical qualitative application of such cameras might be the observation of general surface quality of a developmental projectile plate of the free-run technique. A second example might be the observation of co-ordinates on the plate driving a shock wave into a liquid so as to tell from transparency if any pressure-induced freezing occurred. As a third example involving a more quantitative use of the framing camera, velocities of a number of different points on a plate surface might be determined by viewing the motion of reference marks on the plate relative to a fixed grid. High precision is, however, difficult to achieve. Such a camera with simple auxiliary optics may also be used to obtain stereographic pairs of pictures for even better visualization of qualitative phenomena.

(viii) Smear-Camera Spectroscopy

Of dubious value for application to the equation of state of solids, but somewhat more useful in dynamic high-pressure studies with gases, or possibly transparent liquids, is the technique of using a diffraction grating or prism in conjunction with a smear camera. In this application, the light from a point source is dispersed perpendicular to the camera sweep direction so that a time history of the intensity of each wavelength is obtained. Comparable records can also be obtained using a conventional spectrograph with a number of photomultipliers (recording on cathode-ray oscilloscopes) located behind slits at selected wavelengths along the image surface.

(ix) Temperature Measurements

In principle, the results of either of the above-mentioned techniques of obtaining intensity as a function of wavelength and time could be used to obtain temperature as a function of time by use of the Planck distribution law if the radiating source reasonably approximates a black (or grey) body. In practice the dispersing element is more often deleted and the entire spectrum of radiation emitted (to which a given detector is sensitive) is viewed by either a photomultiplier or smear camera. The photomultiplier (particularly one with infra-red sensitivity) is capable of measuring much lower temperatures than is possible with film; hence the former finds applications in measuring temperatures of shocked solids and liquids (of the order of several hundred degrees centigrade), while the latter is restricted to detonation and gas-shock temperatures (thousands of degrees centigrade). With uniform detector response and emissivity with wavelength, the integral of the Planck distribution law gives a detector response proportional simply to the fourth power of the temperature (the Stefan–Boltzmann law). Under such conditions, only a relatively simple static calibration would be required at one or more temperatures. Detector response and emissivity variation with wavelength are best included, when possible, by static calibration over the temperature range of interest on an object as nearly identical as possible to that to be viewed dynamically. Emissivity is the more difficult to include, for static calibration is virtually impossible in many situations such as for detonation reaction products or shocked high-temperature gases. In such cases some grey-body assumption must be included along with calibrations of detector response using various standard-temperature sources.

On the other hand, in measurements using photomultipliers to determine shock heating of a solid, a static calibration run with a sample may be performed which includes detector response and emissivity variation. This may be done in a vacuum oven with thermocouple temperature determinations, before the dynamic experiment. One has as a result the relation between temperature and photomultiplier output voltage which may be used for interpretation of the dynamic experimental record. In viewing the free surface of a shock-accelerated material with such a system, the state for which temperature is measured is the state at the foot of the adiabat, unless the material is a transparent one for the radiation of interest. In this latter case, shock temperatures may be determined if emissivity uncertainties can be resolved. Temperature measurements for materials with experimentally determined Hugoniots may be compared to the temperatures calculated in the manner described earlier.

Dynamic measurements of shock-generated temperatures have also been attempted with thermocouples, but a number of difficulties, including particularly the necessarily long time of heat conduction to the junction, preclude their use. Microwave noise emitted from shocked high-temperature gases or detonation products has been detected and also used for measurement of temperature; such a technique is not practical at temperatures less than several thousand degrees Kelvin.

VI. Electrical Techniques

(i) Electrical Contactor (Pin) Method

The pin method, ranking in popularity with smear camera optical techniques, is simple in principle, though often elegant in application. It involves the closing of an electrical switch by the shock-wave induced motion of a surface. *Figure 16* shows a typical pin circuit for detecting the motion of a conducting surface. The constant voltage source, E, charges the condenser C through the relatively large resistor R_c to full voltage before firing of the explosive or projectile. When the plate moves and closes the gap, the condenser discharges through the load resistor R. This sharp-rising voltage pulse, along with others like it, is recorded on an oscilloscope trace along with timing markers. The separate pin circuits can be isolated from each other by use of suitable diodes between the condenser load resistor and the oscilloscope input. The shape of the rising portion of the pin pulse is determined both by stray inductances in the circuit and by the manner of closure of the pin switch. For example, a metallic plate preceded by a fine metallic spray of increasing conductivity would present a gradually decreasing resistance across the pin gap and would result in a slow-rising pulse. A clean metallic plate contact with the pin, however, results in a very rapidly rising pulse limited only by stray inductances in the pin circuit.

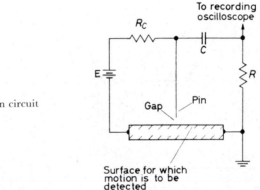

Figure 16. A pin circuit

The shape of the decaying portion of the pulse is largely determined by the RC time constant of the circuit. If this is large, step function pulses will be seen; a small time constant gives a sharp decay of voltage following the initial rise.

The size of the gap beneath the pin, of course, determines the interval between first plate motion and the time of the electrical pulse. Free-surface velocity measurement is accomplished with a number of pins placed at various known distances from a plate. Shock velocity measurement is obtained from pins placed at uniform small gap distances over various thicknesses of a plate. Flat-bottomed holes may be drilled for this purpose. Pins for these types of measurements are usually either fine, flat-ended, stiff wires cemented in an insulating holder, or pointed small-diameter screws threaded and later cemented into the holder. Both types require some detailed measurement of position above the surface before execution of the dynamic experiment. The latter type enable some fine adjustment and are particularly useful for setting small standoff pins by first screwing down until electrical contact is just accomplished and then backing off some small fraction of a turn for a calibrated standoff.

Care must be taken with both shock and free-surface pins that the surface contacting a given pin is not perturbed by a wave in the plate emanating from the point of contact of an earlier pin. When using particularly fine wire for pins, this latter requirement can sometimes be relaxed for free-surface motion pins, but not without caution.

There are probably as many detailed pin designs as there are people who have used them, but they may be classified into three main types: the simple pin already described, the pin pair or coaxial pin, and the covered pin. In the first type the moving conducting plate serves as a substantial part of the circuit. The gap in this type of pin is most frequently filled with a gas, but in small standoff applications a thin layer of insulation is often employed. This insulation is pierced by the motion of the surface involved. A closely spaced pin pair or an insulated wire within a conducting tube (a coaxial pin) may be used in cases where the moving surface is not a good conductor and current paths through it need to be minimized, or where dependable connections through it cannot be established. The covered pin is used where the moving surface is an insulator and usually takes the form of a coaxial pin with the centre electrode very slightly recessed. A thin metallic foil is attached across the end of the outer electrode, so that the moving non-conducting surface pushes the foil against the pin.

When using time differences between pairs of pins, care must be taken that the construction of the pins is quite similar. If not, there may be differences in the closure mechanism which will contribute a timing error. When high free-surface velocities are to be measured, it is necessary to take precautions that an ionized gas shock preceding the plate does not discharge the pin. In such cases the pin assembly can be filled with methane or helium. Where a substantial number of pins is employed in an experiment, there may be some difficulty identifying which pulses on the record correspond to which pins. Coding of the pin signals is often possible by alternating pulses between positive and negative. Various amplitudes or shapes of pulses are sometimes used for identification purposes.

(ii) Condenser Methods

Two types of condenser methods have been used to determine the free-surface velocity of shock-accelerated plates. The first type[21] is illustrated schematically in *Figure 17*. In this circuit a high-frequency (several hundred megacycles) voltage generator is connected across the resistor R in series with the variable condenser of which the moving plate makes one electrode. The signal developed across the variable condenser and recorded by the oscilloscope after rectification and filtration of the 'carrier' frequency is inversely proportional to its capacity. The capacity varies inversely with spacing except for edge effects; thus the signal recorded by the oscilloscope varies approximately directly with spacing. The slope of this distance versus time record is then proportional to the plate velocity. The use of an a.c. generator in this application has the advantage over a d.c. source because static calibration can be accomplished by use of a micrometer adjustment of the condenser spacing along with measurement of oscilloscope response. The several-hundred megacycle frequency is chosen so that the period will be quite small compared with the condenser closure time.

The d.c. condenser circuit (*Figure 18*) is in essence quite similar to that just considered, particularly in applications where R is relatively large and the recorded voltage represents the change in potential across a variable condenser with constant charge. Calibration of such a system is difficult, however, in that the capacity of the small variable condenser must be measured as a function of spacing, much as in the a.c. condenser technique. A clever application has recently been made[22] in which calibration is easier and output voltage is proportional to *velocity* of closure of the condenser gap. This is accomplished by use of a relatively small value of R in the circuit of *Figure 18*. In this case, circuit analysis shows output voltage to be proportional to the product of closure velocity and dC/dx. Calibration

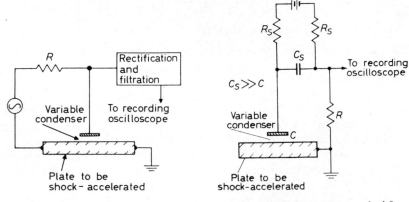

Figure 17. a.c. condenser method for
displacement measurement

Figure 18. d.c. condenser method for
velocity measurement

is executed by measurement with an analytical balance of the electrostatic force on the condenser plates, $F = (E^2/2)\, dC/dx$ as a function of spacing with a constant applied voltage.

The a.c. and d.c. condenser techniques, particularly in the application with high impedance loads across the condenser, are especially sensitive to electrical noise from detonating high explosive. This electrical noise may confuse or even prevent the measurement unless special care in electrical shielding is taken.

(iii) Resistance Wire

If a wire is attached to a surface and strung outward from that surface, the wire will begin to be shortened when surface motion begins. The resistance of the circuit from the unattached end of the metallic wire down through a conducting plate will decrease linearly with increase of distance travelled. An oscilloscope record of the voltage across a load resistor in series with the variable resistor and a voltage source is an interpretable distance versus time record for surface motion. Slope of this record gives free-surface velocity. Precision of the technique suffers because of uncertainties about the contact region between the plate and wire. It has been established, however, that superior results are obtained if the wire is inclined at an angle to the surface normal rather than mounted along the normal. This inclination assures a point of contact which travels across the plate.

(iv) Magnetic Method

The basis of the magnetic method is the voltage generated by a moving conductor in a magnetic field. If a shock-accelerated conducting surface is made one side of a conducting loop, the rate at which magnetic flux lines are intercepted determines the voltage generated in the loop. Knowledge of magnetic field distribution in the loop thus allows the voltage generated to be related directly to velocity. Other magnetic techniques may be devised, but are little used in dynamic high pressure studies of the type considered here.

(v) Piezoelectric and Ferroelectric Detectors

Thin piezoelectric crystals (such as quartz) mounted between conductors on a surface to be shock-accelerated can be used to generate a voltage which indicates when the crystal is shocked. When used in this manner, a piezoelectric detector is essentially a pin with its own built-in voltage source. The voltage output of a piezoelectric crystal disc as a plane shock traverses it depends upon the load impedance. If the impedance is large, the output as a function of time is a linearly rising voltage terminating at the time of complete transit. If the load is small, the output is a step function beginning when the shock enters the crystal and ending at the time of complete traversal. The output at intermediate loads is more complex. Over a substantial pressure range (depending on the crystal and the crystal axes orientations relative to the shock) the amplitude of the voltage output is linear with pressure of the shock wave in the crystal. With knowledge of the crystal Hugoniot and after calibration of voltage output with known shock intensities, such detectors can in principle also be used as shock pressure detectors. Reliable results of this sort have been difficult to obtain; however, some recent results[23] are impressive.

Polarized ferroelectric materials may be used in a similar manner. They differ in application from piezoelectric materials mainly in that the amplitude of signal is not proportional to pressure but is constant for all shocks stronger than those sufficient to depolarize the material.

(vi) Conductivity Measurements

As in static high-pressure work, some materials which are poor conductors or insulators at normal pressures can increase in conductivity when subjected to high-pressure shocks. The conductivity of good conductors as well may change under such conditions, particularly if phase changes occur at the higher pressures. Conducting probes placed in samples of such materials can be used to measure conductivity as the shock wave traverses them, though usually considerable questions exist both as to where the conducting path is located relative to the shock front and what the contact resistance at the probes may be. As in the resistance wire technique, some benefits may be gained by inclining the probe wires at an angle to the direction of shock propagation. One proposed method[23] employs conical probes to realize the advantage of inclination along with a four-electrode system. Two of the electrodes are used for supplying current and the other two intermediate ones are used for measurement of voltage; thus one obtains resistivity.

A recently reported[25] new technique employs the resistance variation with pressure of a thin sample of sulphur to determine unknown pressures. Calibration is accomplished by determining the resistance of similar samples when subjected to shocks of known amplitude. Unknown shock pressures in plates of known Hugoniots may then be determined by consideration of the interface interaction in the $P-U_p$ plane. It is doubtful whether this technique can be developed to give high precision.

(vii) *Microwave Velocity Determination*

Doppler radar techniques have been used to measure conducting surface motion, including the motion of detonation fronts in solid explosives. This technique involves the propagation of the microwaves (often in a wave guide) from the radiator to the moving conducting surface in a direction opposite to that of surface motion. The frequencies of the reflected and outgoing waves are compared at a detector near the source. The frequency difference is proportional to the moving conductor velocity.

VII. Radiography

The use of multiple-flash x-ray photographs at known time intervals (or records with other x-ray detectors) to measure directly both shock velocity and density behind strong shock waves is an appealing technique. These two variables enable determination of a Hugoniot point much as two velocity measurements do. Precision of the technique is, however, discouraging. The difficulty is caused primarily by peripheral rarefaction regions through which the x-ray beam must travel in order to reach uniform high-pressure regions near the axis of an explosive assembly. Unless high-energy x-rays are employed, small-diameter assemblies are required with consequent greater proportional curvature of the waves to be studied. In the face of this problem, it is remarkable that such reasonably good results have been obtained[26]. Flash radiography, however, like two-dimensional photography, can be extremely valuable for obtaining qualitative or semi-quantitative information about phenomena which otherwise may defy explanation.

VIII. Recovery

The technique of recovery of specimens after high pressure shock loading is, of course, one of the oldest techniques for the study of results of dynamic high pressures. Lack of control of firing and recovery conditions has in many instances led to considerable confusion, particularly where non-plane waves have been employed, or edge effects and severe recovery conditions have wiped out the more interesting plane-wave effects. Many interesting phenomena have been seen in recovered pieces in past years, but rarely has a reconstruction of wave shapes and reverberation histories been attempted, primarily because of the extreme difficulty. Plane wave systems developed and used in recent years eliminate some of these drawbacks. Samples may be mounted in plate centres where they can be isolated from important deleterious peripheral effects by making the plates of concentric rings. The outer ones of these split off when a tension is developed. Soft recovery is accomplished by slowing samples down, after some amount of free run, in some material such as foam plastic, wet or dry sawdust, vermiculite, or, in later stages of slower motion, by water.

Modern high-speed computers can be used to perform detailed plane-wave hydrodynamic calculations (employing Hugoniot data obtained by other techniques) for various high-pressure shock systems. Comparisons may then be made with recovered pieces. Particularly interesting deductions can be made concerning ultimate material strengths from recovery experiments involving spalling. In these experiments two plane rarefactions are allowed to interact to create a region of negative pressure or tension in the specimen which may break it along a plane. Nature and location of the spall plane or planes are the primary data obtained from the recovered pieces.

Considerable work has also been done recently in the metallographic examination of specimens recovered after a known shock history. One particularly notable piece of work[27] employing metallographic examination of recovered pieces has obtained Hugoniot data of reasonably good precision from such examination.

Acknowledgment

The author wishes to acknowledge the invaluable discussions of the subjects covered herein with his colleagues in group GMX-6 of the Los Alamos Scientific Laboratory.

References

[1]BRIDGMAN, P. W., *The Physics of High Pressure*, G. Bell and Sons, Ltd., London, 1949

[2]BRIDGMAN, P. W., *Rev. Mod. Phys.*. **18,** 1946, p. 1

[3]COURANT, R. and FRIEDRICHS, K. O., *Supersonic Flow and Shock Waves*, Interscience Publications, New York, N.Y., 1948, pp. 141–146

[4]*Ibid.*, pp. 80–88

[5]WALSH, J. M. and CHRISTIAN, R. H., *Phys. Rev.*, **97,** 1955, p. 1,544

[6]RICE, M. H., McQUEEN, R. G. and WALSH, J. M., 'Compression of Solids by Strong Shock Waves' in *Solid State Physics*, Vol. VI, Academic Press, Inc., New York, N.Y., 1957, pp. 47–60

[7]VON NEUMANN, J., *OSRD Report No. 549*, 1942

[8]TAYLOR, G. I., *Proc. Roy. Soc.*, London, **A200,** 1950, p. 235

[9]DUFF, R. E. and HOUSTON, E., *J. chem. Phys.*, **23,** 1955, p. 1,268

[10]DEAL, W. E., *J. chem. Phys.*, **27,** 1957, p. 796

[11]McQUEEN, R. G. and MARSH, S. P., *J. appl. Phys.*, **31,** 1960, p. 1,253

[12]AL'TSHULER, L. V., KRUPNIKOV, K. K., LEDENEV, B. N., ZUCHIKHIN, V. I. and BRAZHNIK, M. I., *J. exp. theor. Phys.*, Moscow, **34,** 1958, p. 606

[13]WALSH, J. M. and RICE, M. H., *J. chem. Phys.*, **4,** 1957, p. 815

[14]RICE, M. H. and WALSH, J. M., *J. chem. Phys.*, **4,** 1957, p. 824

[15]DAVIS, W. C. and CRAIG, B. G., *Rev. Sci. Instrum.*, **32,** 1961, p. 579

[16]ALLEN, W. A. and McCRARY, C. L., *Rev. Sci. Instrum.*, **24,** 1952, p. 165

[17]See reference 6, pp. 10–12

[18]MARSH, S. P. and McQUEEN, R. G., *Bull. Amer. Phys. Soc.*, Ser. II, **5,** 1960, p. 506

[19]MILLER, C. D., *J. Soc. Mot. Pict. Engrs.*, **43,** 1949, p. 479

[20]BRIXNER, B., *J. SMPTE* **59,** 1952, p. 503

REFERENCES

[21]HUGHES, D. S., *J. appl. Phys.* (to be submitted)

[22]RICE, M. H. (to be published)

[23]NEILSON, F. W. and BENEDICK, W. B., *Bull. Amer. Phys. Soc., Ser. II*, **5**, 1960, p. 511

[24]HUGHES, D. S., Private communication

[25]HAUVER, G. E., *Third ONR Symposium on Detonation, Report No. ACR-52*

[26]SCHALL, R., *Explosivestoffe*, **46**, 1958, p. 120

[27]FOWLER, C. M., MINSHALL, F. S. and ZUKAS, E. G., *Response of Metals to High-Velocity Deformation*, Interscience Publications, New York, 1961, pp. 275–308

APPENDIX A

Pressure Units

THERE are several units of pressure currently in use; the most important of these, each followed in parentheses by its abbreviation, are:

bar (bar)=10^6 dynes per square centimetre

kilobar (kb)=1,000 bars

atmosphere (atm)

kiloatmosphere (kat)=1,000 atm

kilograms per square centimetre (kg/cm²)

pounds per square inch (psi)

Their inter-relationships are given by the following table, in which each unit of pressure is followed on the right by its physical equivalent in pressure expressed in the other units.

	bar	atm	kg/cm²	psi
1 bar ..	1	0·98692	1·0197	14·504
1 atm ..	1·0133	1	1·0332	14·696
1 kg/cm²	0·980665	0·96784	1	14·223
1 psi ..	0·068947	0·068046	0·070307	1

Thus 1 atm represents a slightly higher physical pressure than 1 bar.

The bulk of current high pressure work is tending toward expression in terms of bars or kilobars.

APPENDIX B

Pressure Reference Phenomena

THE most probable pressures at which the various transitions frequently used for high pressure reference points occur at 25°C are given below in kilobars. The figures are subject to refinement or change. See Chapters 1, 2 and 5 for further details and references.

Substance	Phenomenon	Pressure, kb
KBr	Volume decrease 10·5 per cent	18·0
KCl	Volume decrease 11 per cent	20·2
Bismuth I→II ..	Volume decrease 5 per cent Resistance decrease 83 per cent	25·3
Bismuth II→III ..	Volume decrease 3 per cent Resistance increase 100 per cent	26·8
Thallium	Volume decrease 1 per cent Resistance decrease 30 per cent	37
Caesium	Volume decrease 9·2 per cent Resistance maximum	42
Barium	Volume decrease 1·9 per cent Resistance increase 25 per cent	59
AgBr	Volume decrease 1·1 per cent	84·5
AgCl	Volume decrease 1·6 per cent	88
Bismuth V→VII ..	Volume decrease 1·2 per cent Resistance decrease 250 per cent	89
Iron	Resistance increase 350 per cent Shock-wave velocity change	133 131
Barium	Resistance increase 40 per cent	144
Lead	Resistance increase 23 per cent	161
Rubidium	Resistance increase 150 per cent	193
Calcium	Resistance maximum	375
Rubidium	Resistance maximum	425

INDEX